IVAN PAVLOV
FROM FREEDOM TO FREEDOM

april 6, 2004

LaVaughn,

It has been wonderful
meeting you and having morning
exercise in the pool with you.
May the God of all the universe continue
to comfort, lift, and love you.

Love in Jesus,
Kathy Gronor :)

IVAN PAVLOV
FROM FREEDOM TO FREEDOM

BY

KATHY IVANOV

DORRANCE PUBLISHING CO., INC.
PITTSBURGH, PENNSYLVANIA 15222
1 - 800 - 788 - 7654
OR
amazon.com

ISBN # 0-8059-6288-3
Printed in the United States of America

First Printing

For information or to order additional books, please write:
Dorrance Publishing Co., Inc.
701 Smithfield Street
Pittsburgh, Pennsylvania 15222
U.S.A.
1-800-788-7654
Or visit our web site and on-line catalog at www.dorrancepublishing.com

I dedicate this book to Ivan, without whom, there would be no book, and to Pavel, Tony, Theresa, and Aleesa who encouraged me in its writing.

ACKNOWLEDGMENTS

Source of information and help with accuracy and revision: Ivan P. Ivanov.

Reading and help with revisions: Cynthia Soohoo Hui.

Advisors: printing; Brian Pautz, theology, Pastor Rick Elzinga.

Inspirational thoughts and prayer: Gladys Waldrep.

Prayers: Pat Kauffman, Mike and Carol Shepardson, Greg and Joanne Magarian, Diane and Rick Elzinga, Kerry and Rosalie Francetich, and most Southwest Hills Baptist Church members from 1997 to 2003.

Encouragement, Ruth and Burt Drexler, Pavel, Julie Ann, Jacob, Kristopher, Ivan, Zachary. And Faithann Ivanov, Tony and Debbie, Nic, Adrian, and Lilah Ivanov, Rachel and Becca Nickel, Marty, Theresa, Gary, Scott, and Ashley Denham, Aleesa Ivanov, Milco and Elena Moushmof, Gail Denham, Barbara Peskin, Carol Wilson, Loie Goff, Cecile Holthus, Kathy Kingma, Mira Matthews, Karen Pautz, Ron and Jennifer Anderson, Irl and Bea Clary, Bonnie Schmitt, Gary and Tyler Combs, Debi and Greg Leo, Mollie Woolf, Steve and Terri Beskow, and Bess Johnson.

Contents

1. FIRE

Dust clung to Vancho's[1] little sun-browned body as he sat, bony elbows on his wiry short legs, chin cradled in his hands, dark hazel eyes half closed in deep concentration.

Seeing him you would have likely assumed this five-year old to be nearly asleep. How far from the truth that assumption would have been. Beneath the surface thoughts were scurrying as quickly as field mice looking for kernels of wheat in late fall.

In the recesses of this child's mind, as in all humanity, only God knew the activity. People see only the surface and make assumptions.

Past the step on which he was perched, over the bit of lawn browned by the unrelenting summer's heat, into the hardened dirt of the outer yard he stared at the new mountain-stack of straw perhaps twenty feet high. It looked like an overgrown loaf of bread, rectangular with steep sides. The mound was about fifty feet from where he sat. A rutted dirt road passed by the right side of his house. In his village of Rogozen[2] eight miles from the Danube River, in the northwestern part of Bulgaria there was no other kind of road but rutted dirt, sometimes with gravel. The straw stack was about ten feet from this side street.

As Vancho sat idly his young thoughts drifted to the previous few days.

His father, a loyal soldier in the Bulgarian army, had been granted several days holiday for the annual wheat threshing. *Tatko*[3] had returned six days ago from his post in the Vratsa[4] region. Yesterday was the end-of-wheat-threshing festival.

Young Vancho loved having Tatko home for the full week of threshing. Normally his father was home for only one or two days every other month.

When Tatko had signed up for military service, His Majesty King Boris III, a Bulgarian Orthodox man, had been on the throne. He had been a good

1

king. He had cared about his subjects. Tatko had liked serving him in Kavalla, a northern Greek city. In those days Bulgaria protected their own land and adjacent regions from invading troops.

"Every year His Majesty gives us many days leave to be home. "Tatko had said. "He doesn't interfere with our way of life."

That way of life had changed suddenly.

Hitler had asked the Bulgarian king for support in World War II. His Majesty had agreed to send materials and weapons. He had refused, however, to dispatch his people.

Then King Boris III had been called to Germany in 1943. While he was there Hitler had demanded that the Bulgarian Jews be sent to Germany. His Majesty again refused to do as Hitler requested. Where people were concerned His Majesty would protect them at all cost.

Even with continued German pressure no Jews were forced from Bulgaria, not then or at anytime during or after the war.

Before the king could return to his land it was said, "King Boris III of Bulgaria developed a virus and has died in Germany."

Bulgarians suspected that poison had killed their king, since Hitler never allowed dissention from any of those aligned with him. To the Bulgarian mind poisoning was only part of the unspeakable horror that had taken place in those dark days.

Later the Bulgarian suspicions would prove to be close to the truth. Their king had been killed.

His Majesty's seven-year-old son Simeon II ascended to the throne under the guidance of his uncle, a Nazi sympathizer.

Most of the Bulgarian troops that were ordered to serve Hitler by the new acting king refused to leave their posts.

Vancho's father, loyal to Bulgaria and the king despite differing political views had been reassigned to a new post in Vratsa.

Being a soldier provided his family with money for desired things, which their traditional bartering didn't. In addition it supplied the funds to send *Chicho*[5], Tatko's younger brother, to the University in Oriahovo[6] where he studied to achieve his life-long dream of becoming a teacher.

It was not just money that had attracted Vancho's father to becoming a soldier. There was enough of everything in the village. What one family lacked the others willingly supplied: food and materials or hands to build structures, haul heavy equipment, and get a job done. In fact, that was how the stack of straw had come to be in the yard. Family had helped family and autumn tasks for each had been accomplished.

Work was the way of life in the village. If Tatko had not been a soldier and the Lord had willed, his brother would have worked harder himself to provide the money for his own teaching degree.

July 2001, Ivan at Rila Monastery—where Tsar Boris III lays at rest.

No, it had not been for money that Vancho's father was a soldier. He had simply answered God's call for this period of his life. He believed it a privilege as well as a duty. He fought to protect women and children, to maintain peace. He had fought in service to God and country. Tatko, the older brother, knew that his sacrifice of time in the army would not be wasted. He knew that God would use his faithfulness to glorify Himself and bring good to his family.

Now Vancho was resting in the sunshine thinking that in the short time that Tatko was home much work had been completed. Yesterday the neighbors had finished helping thresh Vancho's family's wheat. The grain had been stored in the scrubbed produce-room in the house. Indoors it was safe from destruction by weather and rodents. It would remain there for a few weeks until the village mill had an opening in its busy schedule to grind it into flour.

Everything was in order. When all the men were home from their posts at the same time a great celebration took place. This year it had been for wheat threshing. Sometimes the annual feast followed the wheat harvest, other years the sugar beet, sugar cane, corn, sunflowers, or dry bean harvests. Timing for the feast depended on when the acting king granted furloughs to his troops.

Because Tatko and Mama's wheat had been the last threshed it had been understood that the festival would be held on their property.

Tatko had fashioned tables from unpainted, ugly, dry wooden planks and wood supports. The feast had required a table twenty-feet long to hold all the soup pots, bread, and dishes.

Something had been needed to hide the grayed, warped, and splintered makeshift affair. Mama's hand-embroidered cloths with bright red, green, yellow, blue, and black thread worked into beautiful geometric patterns had made festive covers to highlight the wholesome food.

Looking into space, his mind no longer seeing the stack, Vancho was remembering that his mother had killed ten chickens. She had borrowed nine huge pots from friends. Adding her own she made ten steaming pots of soup, one chicken per pot. Mama and Sister had labored over those pots the day before yesterday. They had put every part of the chicken except the guts and feathers into them along with onions, carrots, parsley, salt, and large amounts of garlic. Sister was only three years older than Vancho but she had been helping their mother with domestic chores since she was his age.

Still daydreaming Vancho continued thinking about that village soup of Rogozen. He had been happy that all the people had been able to eat their fill.

He had a not-so-happy memory too. He would always remember what had happened when it was finally time to eat. There had been more soup than he could ever remember seeing, but he was disappointed with what was in his bowl.

His favorite cousin had received the prized chicken head out of the same pot from which Vancho was served. Chicken heads were sweet and the best of the best! Vancho loved to dislodge the eyes from their sockets with his tongue and spit them as far as he could. Last time he had eaten a chicken head he had been able to shoot an eye ten feet! Hoping to increase his record he had wanted the head again for another try. Who knew when chicken soup would be made again?

Since his cousin lived outside Rogozen, Vancho supposed it was okay for him to get that prized portion. He had, after all, been a guest of the village. A girl cousin who did live in his village had been served one bony foot and a neighbor he hardly knew the other. Those two had a great time pretending to "walk" on the table with their chicken feet while he had watched enviously. All the fun parts of the chicken had been dipped into every one's bowl. Because his mother had made the soup he had thought that he should have been given *one* of them at least but he had not been!

Vancho resigned himself to his dilemma and had eventually enjoyed eating a portion of the back. Sucking the sweet meat from the bones had made the meal last longer than getting a meaty part. He had partially recovered from not being given what he wanted, but he would remember and continue to hope for better fare next year.

As little Vancho pouted in remembrance trickles of sweat ran down his back tickling him, making him squirm. He became aware of the heat of the day and the stack in the distance.

Preferring to live in his memory of the celebration rather than with the discomfort of the heat, he could almost smell the soup with its pungent garlic overtones. He had smelled it as it cooked and again, yesterday, during the feast. Suddenly the aroma of the crusty bread baking in the outdoor oven rushed into his memory. It had tantalized him! He loved bread more than anything. Mama knew him well. She often pulled off chunks of bread dough and made *mekitzi* for him before forming loaves. She stretched the chunks so thin that he could see the light through them, then she gently lowered them into near boiling sunflower oil, which was deep enough to let them float. They would deep fry to a golden brown. He liked them best when bits of dough separated into bubbles, frying crisp, contrasting to the softer dough flanking the bubbles. Although he loved *mekitsi* young Vancho was never allowed to eat as much as he wanted.

Someday, he vowed, *I will sneak into a bakery and eat fresh bread of all kinds until I pop!*

On that feast day, like every other baking day when the aroma became a temptation, he dreamed of reaching into the brick oven before the bread was removed to snatch a handful. Even if he had been able to do so he knew that he would have been afraid of getting into trouble again. Trouble always seemed to be close, bringing him at least a scolding and usually a spanking.

It seemed to him that one reason he existed was to learn to resist being naughty. He realized with pride that lately he sometimes had thought before acting, which had resulted in fewer consequences.

Here I go again, he thought, *how my mind drifts. Oh, yes, the festival...*

There had been plenty of fresh *booza*,[8] Vancho's favorite festival drink, made by mixing fried millet or flour with water. When served cool it was thick, tasty, and satisfying. After sitting for a few hours in the heat of the day it fermented, which pleased the tastes of older folk.

A neighbor had brought the rest of last year's wine for this festivity. He had emptied his *buchva*[9] to make room for this year's grape juice, which would again come from his own vineyard. The resulting wine would be served at his daughter's already-planned wedding the following summer.

Someone else had supplied the traditional village plum *rakia*[10].

Later in the evening after the eating and drinking had slowed someone had started to play a lively tune on an *ocarina*[11]. Another had played the *balalaika*[12]. Folks from a few blocks away had even brought their *gayda*[13]. Vancho's young aunt's clear soprano voice had sung in accompaniment. Music had become the focus of the festival.

Soon young people had begun dancing the circle dances of the village. Older ones had joined them. He liked watching the *horo*[14] with their wide skirts swinging in large circles around the women. Later men in baggy pants had danced Cossack-style, raising dust with their acrobatics. Although Cossack dances were not the common dances of Bulgaria but of Russia, in this village the men enjoyed the flamboyant dances which required agility and strength. Their women's eyes danced as they laughed, clapping approval. The women's encouragement always demonstrated high respect and passionate loyalty to their men.

Vancho enjoyed watching the squatting men, arms crossed over their chests, jumping and alternately thrusting their legs forward, or swishing one leg around near the ground as they leapt over it with the other, still squatting, balancing themselves on the ground with alternating hands. As much as he tried he had not mastered those techniques, the high leaps the men executed in near-split position or the back flips which ended with high-pitched hoots as they landed squarely on their feet.

His private attempts at these gymnastics usually found him on his back gasping for breath, laughing as he spat dirt, or sitting unexpectedly hard hoping that his tailbone was still intact. If practice were the key he would someday be as proficient as those dancing young men.

Then Vancho's mind shifted back to the present and his eyes re-focused. He again saw that great heap of straw from the freshly threshed wheat.

"Just look at it," he mused aloud although he was alone. "All those short stick-like pieces piled together to make that huge stack."

Little by little the heap would be reduced to nothing until next year's wheat would again be gathered. The stack in front of him would be used for many household needs including re-stuffing the sleeping mattress, which accommodated his whole family at the same time.

Just thinking about the mattress, a large tightly woven straw-stuffed bag, brought embarrassment to the little boy. He knew that Mama usually had to re-stuff it only when he had wet the bed in his deep, fatigued sleep. How he tried to wake up dry! He usually did, but occasionally he woke to find that he had been dreaming. He would have dreamed that he had found his way outside in the darkest and coldest part of the night. In his dream he would have been safely outside next to the animal's dung heap, not quite to the outhouse before releasing the stream. In his dream he shivered from the cold. Then as he foggily regained awareness he would realize that everything felt warm, not cold. Dampness alerted him to the truth. After those accidents Sister wouldn't talk to him for a few days. She made it clear that she didn't like to change her clothing in the middle of the night as a result of her little brother wetting the bed. He felt like a baby, vulnerable and uncomfortable, although he was five. He hoped that by the time he was an adult those awful dreams would stop.

Most of the straw would be for their farm animals' bedding in the lower-back portion of the house. It was Vancho's job to throw out the old animal straw and replace it with new clean straw from the stack. He was often told that his good work kept the animals healthy because they didn't have to lie in their waste. He always did the best job he could but when complimented he worked even harder.

Other straw would be fuel for the outdoor oven, because straw produced baking's required high temperature.

Their dome-top oven was made from their homemade brick, except for the metal door, and was taller than Vancho. The door was wide-mouthed, about three feet above the ground. Straw for the fire was placed on the raised floor of the oven onto which the door opened. After the straw burned and the ashes were removed the floor was quickly swept with a damp mop leaving steam inside. Many large round loaves of bread were quickly slid onto the oven floor with a long-handled wooden paddle. The door was then closed and sealed with mud. The residual moist heat slowly baked the bread to crispy crust and soft interior. Vancho could almost taste it as he thought about its near perfection.

Besides regular bread Mama baked *banitsi*[15] in the oven. She made this tasty delicacy by using one ultra-thin sheet of flour pastry or *filo* at a time. Vancho liked to watch Mama's practiced hands as she rolled and stretched the *filo* on a table using a three-foot long stick until the pastry was thin.

"You must be able to see light through it," she told him. Each eighteen-inch diameter sheet would be placed on a cloth when ready and

Mama about age 40

spread with sunflower oil. She splattered half-teaspoon blobs of salty feta cheese and egg mixture sparsely onto the oiled filo. Then Mama lifted the underlying cloth and deftly rolled the sheet carefully around the filling trapping air. When completed each sheet looked like a long sausage. Mama coiled the first "sausage" to form the center of the *banitsa*. Then she placed another tightly against the end of the first, coiling it around the center. She continued that pattern to form a fifteen-inch circle about two inches tall, baking it until golden brown. When it was baked she drizzled the confection with a light honey or sugar syrup. Finished, the *banitsa* was crispy in spots and chewy in others. The saltiness of the feta contrasted perfectly with the sweetness of the syrup. There was nothing like it to excite young Vancho's tastebuds.

There were brooms, which required straw, too.

Enough thinking about how we use the straw, he thought bringing his mind abruptly to the present.

I wonder does each little straw burn individually or just a big bunch of it like the handfuls we throw into the oven?

He had to find out right that minute! Jumping up, his agile body dove to the task of building a trail from the stack.

One by one he carefully placed the short straws geometrically, almost artistically, one crossing slightly over the end of the one in front of it. He angled each stick in opposite directions, first right then left. Finished, it formed a twenty-foot feathery tail from the mammoth stack in the yard toward the animal dung heap. The ten minute task completed he stepped back to survey his work.

It looks good, he thought. *Let's see if it will burn!*

Forgetting that he was forbidden to play with matches, or perhaps not caring since this was an experiment, Vancho took a match from the match-jar on the porch.

Going into the yard he found a stone and carried it to the end of the 'tail'. Copying the dexterity of his father, which he had often seen, he struck the match on the stone. Springing to life a small flame flickered on the end of the match for a second. Almost without breathing, moving very slowly so that the flame would not go out, Vancho reached to the end straw lightly touching it with the tiny flame. Quickly, like a fuse, it ignited. The straws were consumed, first one, then the next and the next.

What joy! His plan was being executed precisely as his mind had seen. Little fits of flame were moving across the ground silently, ever closer to the stack, leaving an almost imperceptible trail of gray ash behind. His heart beat excitedly as he watched.

Then, too late, he realized what his plan meant. The fire would get to the stack. Would it ignite? Oh, how he hoped it wouldn't!

9

His backside still stung from the morning's spanking. He had carelessly kicked the soccer ball hard against the tomato basket filled with the day's crop. Tomatoes flew everywhere. His mother made him replace all of them in the basket while she had simply scowled at him, hands on hips, while he scurried here and there to retrieve them. She had not picked up one but had coldly instructed him until he completed the job to her satisfaction.

What will Mama do to me if the new stack catches fire? Waves of fear went up and down his spine.

Then more reasonably he thought, *Tatko is home! Maybe he'll talk to me. Maybe he'll know I didn't want to be bad.* He clung to that hope.

The flame didn't stop. It jumped into the stack almost gleefully. Quickly it began circling around and around like a wolf making her nest, increasing in size and heat. He tried to beat it out but it wouldn't be stopped.

Heat burned his hands and face as he lifted a discarded board from one of the makeshift tables he found lying nearby and repeatedly pounded the flames.

Tears were streaming down his anguished cheeks as Mama and Tatko came on the scene. When Tatko saw Vancho trying to fight the fire he lifted him and put him under the cherry tree near the house, far from the fire.

"Stay here!" he ordered, then ran to help Mama beat the flames.

Vancho couldn't determine what his father's reaction to him was. He knew that Tatko's immediate concern was to put out the blaze.

With the fire's crackling the neighbors were alerted.

People carrying shovels ran to help. Water wells were too far from the fire to be useful. The neighbors knew that the only way of stopping the flames was to smother them with dirt. Soil would prevent oxygen from feeding the fire. They tried to pry enough from the rock-hard ground stomping on their shovels, then jumping on them. The ground was too dry, too compact to yield. By then the flames were shooting up tens of feet into the still air.

It was an impossible task! There were more than enough people but there was not enough loose soil to stop the raging fire. It demonstrated a will of its own.

The heat intensified, driving people stumbling away. Everyone showed respect for the fire. They were resigned to letting it run its course. In their helplessness they stood watching, their faces smudged with soot.

It seemed like hours but finally they realized that their efforts were fruitless. Tatko strode purposefully toward Vancho.

Here he comes, Vancho thought, smiling up at his father, hoping to explain what had happened.

With one hand Vancho's father pulled the child to himself. With the other strong bare hand he paddled him until Vancho's backside seemed nearly as hot as the fire.

Mama tried unsuccessfully to shield him from the spanking. However, she herself would have administered the same discipline had her husband not been there.

Finally Vancho was released. He limped to the side of the house leaning his shoulder against it to protect the newly painful part of his body.

I thought he might understand, Vancho sobbed. He tried to be quiet, afraid of being heard and calling more negative attention to himself.

Through a blur of tears he saw one neighbor after another leave and come back slowly toward the fire. This time they were pushing wheelbarrows filled with pumpkins. Soon all around the burning stack there were piles of pumpkins on wheelbarrows waiting for the last of the flames to die. When only the red hot embers remained each of the neighbors slowly, carefully, placed their produce for cooking. His parents too, added their pumpkin harvest to the others making the best of the terrible situation.

Increasingly the chatter became friendlier and more cheerful.

As the first pumpkins were retrieved from the heat, then sliced and cubed for eating their aroma drifted onto the early evening air.

From the side of the house Vancho's nose picked up the smell and his tummy groaned with hunger.

What fun they are having! he thought. *Because of me they can have this wonderful unexpected meal. But here I am ...* and his heart broke, as did his resolve to not cry. Tears came as he thought self-pityingly, *I am soooo hungry. And I know Tatko will be mad at me again if I ask for some pumpkin. And my hands still sting from trying to put out the fire. And my bottom still hurts. I can't sit down. I'll probably never be able to sit or walk normally again or run or...or...or even play soccer. Oh, I feel awful! And I thought this was a free country! I don't feel free right now! And I want Tatko to be proud of me but I'm certain he isn't!*

After gorging themselves on the juicy golden fruit folks took their remaining produce home to prepare jars to preserve it to use in the months ahead. It was added work for the already tired people. They had thought that the last threshing meant a few days of rest. With this unforeseen occurrence their plans had taken an abrupt turn. Not ones to waste anything, especially food, these hard-working people had survived for centuries. There was no question that they would continue to work until this new and unexpected task would be completed. They hoped the work would not continue beyond dark but who could say?

That night Vancho slept very little, lying on his stomach on an old mattress. It was a mattress that wouldn't be re-stuffed that year unless the neighbors shared their straw with his family.

I have to stay dry all year, he resolved. *I hope I can.*

He wondered how someone so small could create such a big stir and end up feeling as miserable as he did. After all, he had just been acting on a curious thought. He had often heard his mother talking about how wonderful it was that he had an active, inquisitive mind but as he drifted in and out of sleep he was no longer certain that he believed what he had heard.

He knew that he would never be able to enjoy talking about the execution of his perfect plan with his parents. On top of that Tatko was leaving tomorrow.

2. THE RUSSIAN ARMY

Tatko returned to his station the next day. Life continued as it had before he came home, before harvest festivities, before the straw fire, and before the unexpected pumpkin feast.

Vancho's backside and pride healed. His feelings bounced back to being happy quickly as little boys' feelings often do.

After chores he spent time with the village boys on the soccer field. When they tired of play, or darkness forced a stop, they lay in a circle and talked until dinner.

That night the smell of sautéing onions found him. In the yard, on the soccer field, at a friend's home, that smell always found him. Why were cooked onions so appealing? Vancho not only smelled them today but he was certain he could taste them, but smelling and perhaps tasting did not appease his hunger. He felt as if he had not eaten in two days. He couldn't wait to be called home.

The darkening evening dulled his vision as the sun rapidly disappeared behind the houses. Cool air crept around him. He began to shake. Was he shivering from the cool September evening or from what Vladi[16], an older boy and the most vocal in the group, was saying? Something inside him was unsettled.

Suddenly Vancho realized that his small body ached from lying on his belly so long. The shivering alerted him and made him get up and leave.

Pushing against the dry bumpy ground where the brown grass struggled to grow, he jumped up feeling stiff between his thin shoulder blades. Bouncing around, arms loose and flapping like a galloping hound's ears helped to restore blood flow and warmth but he still felt uneasy.

These after soccer chats with the older boys are usually more fun than this evening, he thought with an attitude of disgust. *I bet that if I liked today's talk better I would not even feel the ache in my back... Funny how that works!*

Vaguely trying to make sense of what the boys were discussing he looked around for his jacket, pleased that he had remembered it this time.

Maybe Mama won't be angry with me tonight. It seems she always gets mad when I forget my jacket. 'Vanko, Zabravanko'[17] *she calls me without even smiling. I don't know why she gets so mad. No one ever takes it. It is always there the next morning. Maybe it gets a little wet but it dries. I don't understand grown-ups. Little things seem to bother them.*

One of the boys from the group called, "Vancho, *kade oteevash?*"[18]

"Ah, I've gotta get home. I heard Mama calling," he lied, hoping they believed him. "I'll be back tomorrow."

What had Vladi been saying? he wondered. He understood the words but the thoughts were strange to him. *The Russian army is coming. When? Why? Does the king know about the army coming? Are the Russians going to try to invade and hurt people like Tatko who protect us? Will they come into Bulgaria and hurt the rest of us? I've heard adults talk about Russians. They're our enemy. It sounds like they must be different from us but how? Don't people there love God and their country like we do? And doesn't God love them the same as He loves us? After all, 'God loves all people everywhere,' Mama says. What could make us be so against them?* His child's mind was filled with questions that gave way to fear.

A month ago the German army, with which Bulgaria was aligned as part of the Axis[19] during this Second World War, had come through Bulgaria. They had fought the Allies. The parade of equipment, animals, and people had passed for hours. The little boy had been occupied with watching for most of the afternoon.

I hope that if the Russian soldiers come they will be like the Germans.

I remember trying to hold my breath when the long column of dark-green trucks passed my house. It was impossible to see the end. When I finally had to breathe only a small part of the long line had gone by.

What a sight! I still don't know what was in those trucks. Most of them were covered with tarps and so dark inside that I couldn't see except for a few 'kitchens-on-wheels'. Other trucks pulled huge guns. Mama told me that those guns were called cannons. I never saw any weapon that powerful!

When I grow up I'll be in the army and drive a big truck like one of those. Or even shoot a cannon. Wow! That will be wonderful! Being stationed like Tatko would be fine but being responsible for the care and shooting of a cannon would be even better.

He had imagined himself looking through the sights of a gun and triggering the huge mechanism even though he didn't know anything about the working of a cannon. He had postured like a man with a rifle. "Pppchewwww! Pppchewwww! Pppchewwww!"

While he had been "shooting" a flank of horses and their riders walked by.

With all the trucks and jeeps it had seemed strange to see men on horseback. The animals were well cared for, none was sweaty or dirty. I love horses but I wonder why

14

they were in the army. There were plenty of jeeps and trucks. Why would they need horses? Aren't horses for farming?

And there were so many soldiers! Just like Tatko but not in Bulgarian uniforms. Each one carried a rifle. I remember that the first rifle I saw that day scared me. I thought the soldier would shoot me or someone I knew but he didn't.

Minding their own business, the men didn't seem to care that I was watching them. It was fun to see Mama walk up to them and five soldiers stop to drink water she offered before moving on. The soldiers were four or six abreast, not marching, just walking in columns.

His mind shifted. *I wonder when we will walk on holiday again like those soldiers to visit my aunts and cousins?* The three-kilometer[20] trip to his relatives took the best part of a day after the afternoon nap even when riding in the ox cart. Vancho preferred to walk while the cow pulled Mama and Sister. It made him feel as if he was grown-up. They always stayed three or four days, so the long trip wasn't tiring. They hadn't seen that part of the family in three months. He was ready to visit again.

He thought about the stuffed cabbage rolls Lelia[21] always made and the smell of fresh bread that greeted them as they neared her house.

Oh, I'm hungry! the five-year-old grumbled to himself.

What was I thinking? Oh, yes, another army coming to Bulgaria. I wish I wasn't so young. It scares me to think of another army coming, especially the enemy! Life is good just as it is.

He had much to learn. In three years he would start school. Then he might begin to understand adult concerns but now they were a mystery. He knew things, but not enough to bring him comfort or confidence in threatening situations.

Fear pricked his spine as he remembered the hushed way the older boys had talked; serious, urgent, and secretive.

He liked it better when they talked about girls. Maybe he couldn't understand that any better than this scary Russian army talk but at least *girls* were familiar. Having a sister to think about when they talked about girls helped him feel included. When girls were the subject of conversation the older boys laughed and whistled, making funny noises. He liked funny better than scary.

Finally Vancho got home. He washed the afternoon grime from his face and hands in the wash bowl at the entry door.

Later, sitting with Mama and Sister before eating he thought, *Mama makes good food. I think I can eat more food than she and Sister have made today.* They all sat silently eating cucumber, tomato, and parsley salad with salt sprinkled on it. Wonderful fresh homemade bread was cut into thick chunks that looked and smelled appealing. The smell of freshly boiled *Bop*[22], Vancho's favorite navy bean soup, teased his nose.

15

I'm really hungry, he thought after forcing a swallow of salad, *but it does-n't taste good.* His stomach felt unusually tight and would not accept what was put into it. Despite his hunger and the availability of food he went to bed with an empty stomach. He could find no way to coax food into it.

That night Vancho was restless and annoyed with himself for being so. He found none of his ways of going to sleep worked. Something was very wrong! He didn't know what it was. His mind was active but he couldn't focus his thinking. He felt as if an unseen giant was shaking him with little hope of being released.

When he awoke he was tired and had trouble functioning. He didn't remember falling asleep. He struggled to control his thoughts and when he spoke his words were garbled. He knew he had chores, but forgot them. Sitting on the front steps looking into space he let the summer warmth befriend him.

Mama, knowing of his near-sleepless night, allowed him to rest while she did his work herself.

As he sat in the still, summer morning he heard a low unusual rumble. He fought fatigue to concentrate on the strange sound. Cricket, grasshopper, frog, bird, and farm animal noises seemed to diminish as they were covered by the yet undefined mechanical hum.

He followed the sound to the street in front of the house. He looked left, certain the sounds were coming from the north.

After several minutes he saw dust rising behind his friend Mitco's[23] house a block away. The noise got louder.

Tripping up the stairs in his tiredness, going inside to the open bedroom window facing the main village road, Vancho leaned out trying to see what was making the increasing racket.

Soon he saw the first dark green trucks.

The army! he thought. They were coming down the eighteen-foot-wide strip of rutted dirt and gravel 'pavement' in front of his home. The gravel was now ground into the soil, no longer on the surface. This was the main street of Rogozen, which led to all other villages.

They're going to pass my house just like the German troops did!

The familiar scene moved before Vancho.

He wondered, *have I fallen asleep? Maybe I'm dreaming about the German army. But something is different,* and he knew he was wide-awake.

His mind went to the previous evening, to the conversation among the older boys. *Maybe these are the Russian troops. Maybe Bulgaria is being invaded! I guess there's nothing I can do,* he thought. *I'll stay here until Mama tells me to move.*

Trucks pulling strange-looking weapons came into view. They seemed bigger than the German cannons. They were certainly larger than the can-nons he saw today. Later he was to hear the adults call them Katuwshi[24].

16

Mentally he assessed what he could from where he watched. Each mechanism had two levels of rails guiding large rockets toward their firing position. As it rattled past, the machine's wheels protesting the ruts in the road, Vancho wondered if the rockets were secure.

They could bounce right off, he thought. *If they're armed the rough ride might explode them.* With these thoughts he gripped the windowsill with sweaty tension, seemingly too great for one so young. His heart pounded with fear and he dared not think any more nor even breathe until those awful weapons were out of sight.

He became engrossed in watching wonderful small-boy-sights. Most things were interesting and thought-provoking. His curious and tired mind tried to make sense of them with little success.

Foot soldiers came into view. Like the German infantry these Russian troops were walking behind the equipment but they weren't in formation. They walked casually in groups of six or eight talking among themselves as they passed. They seemed like a rag-tag group compared to the Germans.

Tatko never came home with a dirty and wrinkled uniform like these, Vancho thought.

One soldier noticed eight-year-old Sister in the garden hoeing weeds. He elbowed both comrades near him, jerking his head in her direction. Several young men looked. She tried to ignore them. As she put more effort into her work they knew that she was aware of their attention. They began to sneer with raucous laughter.

Watching these coarse young soldiers from atop the steps Vancho felt his cheeks warming with discomfort and muscles tighten. He didn't know these were natural protective responses toward his sister, toward any girl. His body was ready to fight if needed. He did know, however, that he did not like what he had just observed. As the soldiers continued down the road Vancho's eyes narrowed into slits. Inwardly he acknowledged his distrust and watched, fists clenched at his sides, until they disappeared. Finally his hands, face, and stomach relaxed.

After several hours of standing, watching instruments of war pass, Vancho left his lookout to find friends. He was anxious to talk about what was happening.

He checked all the boys' houses finding no one in the neighborhood able to spend time with him.

Reluctantly he headed home. Fatigued, the walk seemed longer than usual.

The stream of men was still passing his house when he shuffled inside. It was late afternoon. He found Sister and Mama quietly preparing dinner. When he greeted them they were silent.

I wonder if they heard me, Vancho thought.

When food was ready they sat and began eating.

Someone knocked. Both Mama and Sister quickly exchanged glances but did not move. Vancho sensed a new, unknown tension in his home.

Mama, with no man to protect her and her family, her husband still in Vratsa, moved slowly, opening the door cautiously. Seeing who was there she stretched herself to her full, not-quite five-foot height, her strong chin jutting upward as she looked directly into two young men's faces.

They waited for an invitation. Both men were as tall as Tatko, their uniforms like those Vancho had seen all day. They looked dirty, tired, and angry. They asked for a meal. It was customary in Bulgaria that anyone asking for food or shelter, whether civilian or soldier, friend or foe, would be given what was available. That was their Christian way. Inviting the two in she instructed Vancho to put more wooden bowls and spoons on the table.

He thought, *Mama is kind but her voice sounds scared.*

Haltingly Mama communicated with the Russian soldiers. Vancho realized that Russian was similar to Bulgarian. They were able to understand each other with some difficulty. While the "guests" were eating they spoke of parents and siblings waiting for them. Neither was married.

They seem old, Vancho thought, looking at their worn faces. They were probably not yet twenty.

One sat quietly after eating, expressionless, looking at the picture of Vancho's father hanging on the wall. Squinting he pursed his lips, rhythmic tension playing in his jaws.

Vancho knew that the King's army uniform in the picture was their enemy's.

Will they hurt us now? Vancho thought with apprehension. *What should I do to protect us if that soldier starts to shoot? We hid everything else that could bring us harm, even the animals so that 'the enemy' wouldn't kill them for food. Why didn't we remove Tatko's picture?*

Vancho saw his mother's face pale. Her eyes avoided the soldier's inquiring look as she focused on her dinner bowl. Nothing was said about the picture.

He got up from the table and went toward the door with his comrade close behind. They turned and thanked Mama for the meal. With a slight bow the two young men left.

The diminished parade in the street, though still passing, had slowed.

For several quiet minutes Vancho's family sat together allowing their fear to transform into relief. Mama anticipated Vancho's need and gave him comfort. With gratitude he allowed Mama to pull him to her side. Her knuckles, made rough and dry by relentless hard farm work, stroked his cheek. Her touch, scratchy as it was, spoke love. He absorbed what she provided like a sponge soaking up water, feeling his tension leave.

Later she crooned him a lullaby as he nestled his head against her hip on his way to sleep, while she sat in bed knitting next to him.

In spite of tension Vancho's sleep was deep, making up for its lack the previous night.

Thinking that it was earlier than usual he jumped out of bed the next morning. Because of his fatigue he had slept an extra two hours. He was the last one up again.

How does it always happen to me? Why can't I ever be up before the others? he thought.

With anticipation of more intrigue he flung open the door. It didn't seem possible! No one was in the street! There was no evidence of an army having gone through, not a sign of animal, person, or machine.

Is it over? Vancho wondered. *Is this what the boys were talking about the day before yesterday? Just this? If I had known what was going to happen I wouldn't have been so nervous! I wish I hadn't been. We're still okay.*

He was beginning to grow up but until he could get out of bed earlier he knew he was still 'the baby'.

3. HOMECOMING

Vancho heard no more about Russian troops.

Sometimes he listened while Mama talked quietly with friends about the new "rebel" government. He heard that for many years some people had been dissatisfied with the king. Now they wanted a democracy to replace the monarchy. King Simeon II was too young to influence his uncle's way of managing the country, which was not headed in the direction King Boris III would have wanted. Vancho heard that Mama still preferred the king to the new so-called democratic government. He heard with interest that the queen, Simeon II's mother, had taken the young king and his sister into exile in Spain.

I wonder where that is? He thought and never asked.

Those were heavy issues for five year old Vancho. He didn't understand government. He didn't care to learn. To the small boy the subject was simply talk. He didn't know that his life would change because of it. He chose to think about lighter things, not what was or was to be. Life was to be lived as it happened.

While King Boris III had reigned, Tatko had enjoyed army duty knowing that it was God's plan for him. When Tatko had been stationed away from home it seemed to Vancho that he would never come back. The last time Tatko was home he talked about why he had chosen to stay in the military after King Boris III had died

"I do what I can to serve God and my country. It makes me sad," Tatko had said, "to hear many of my friends getting upset and restless with our new monarch, King Simeon II's uncle, and the men he has chosen to be his advisors. Many people are talking in favor of a 'new democracy' but with God's help I believe that Bulgarians will stop this foolish fad and life will continue as it always has.

"Part of my job is to keep young rebel fighters from raiding the villages around Vratsa. That is why I am stationed there. If we can keep the rebels from advancing and gaining advantage we can stop this dangerous situation from becoming worse."

However, his efforts had not stopped change. The Bulgarian rebels had taken over and the army was dissolved. Tatko and the other soldiers of the king could no longer serve.

Early partisan leaders such as Georgi Dimitrov[25] had gone from Bulgaria to the USSR and learned from the Marxists there. Some older leaders had returned with their "new vision," which they planted in naive young Bulgarian minds.

Unhappy people struggling in life, seeing no future, were ripe for a new movement. The young people were not taught to believe the Bible. To anyone lacking faith in Christ Jesus, lies often appear to be truth. When young Bulgarians sought answers to problems they preferred to trust the hollow promises of the new man-led way, not God. They knew that the great world powers functioned as democracies, that democracy would work better in Bulgaria than monarchy. Democratic socialism, which they believed to be synonymous with democracy, was offered. Without much information or thought they embraced the new idea.

The rebel's thinking had been: "Democracies bring good to their people. Democracies are powerful. Power is good. We must become powerful."

So the young rebels had been fashioned into raiding gangs with the powerful physical strength of youth.

These gangs lived in the hills coming out unexpectedly from hiding to attack cities, towns, and villages taking food and whatever else they wanted from homes and businesses. They vandalized and terrorized because they could. They loved their new power. They believed they were right and were willing to kill for their cause. They were heedless. Youth is usually unaware of their own mortality.

Some good hard-working citizens of Bulgaria hated the gangs but feared them more.

The mottoes the rebel gangs lived by were: "From everyone according to his ability, to everyone according to his need." "The state is everything; the individual is nothing. The state provides everything for the individual; everyone works for the state."

Soon the rebel government began asking for voluntary relinquishment of privately owned guns, then confiscating those that remained. Some citizens feared a military state wherein they would have no protection against forceful government intrusion. People who still owned guns began hiding them. After Ivan's father left the service his military weapon was carefully wrapped for protection and buried in the dirt under the entry door of their home. Although the new rebels were certain that Tatko had a gun, having been in the king's army, and they searched the house several times, no one ever found it.

Bulgarian's would later find that the 'free world' called their form of government "communism," not "democracy" or "socialism." They found that it had not provided the people any thing good. Only those officials faithful to the Party were economically better off while the rest were impoverished by political corruption. By then, much damage had been done.

Vancho's father did what he could to keep the new government from taking over and de-throning the acting king. He helped maintain Bulgarian freedom as he had known it.

Vancho, as most children, was not aware that this change would drastically alter life in his country. For him all days were alike.

Mornings began crisp, warming to almost unbearable temperatures by mid-day that September of 1944. The nights threatened to freeze.

One morning Vancho woke, running outside after his bread and tea. He found Sister and Mama busy in the garden. The summer had yielded a bountiful supply of vegetables. Now the drying tomato vines, pepper plants, and various debris needed to be pulled up and worked back into the soil.

"Vancho, clean my row." Mama ordered handing him her hoe. "We want the garden cleaned for Tatko's homecoming. He will want to turn the soil for next year's garden before winter sets in."

"Is Tatko coming home?" Vancho excitedly questioned her, letting the tool fall to the ground without seeing it as he danced up and down.

He wanted immediate confirmation.

"When is he coming?

"Why is he coming home now?

"Did something happen?

"Will he be here today?

"How long will he stay?"

He left no time for her to answer one question before impulsively asking another.

Vancho had thought that there were several more months of service for Tatko. He didn't know that this homecoming would be forever, that the new government had made the king's military obsolete. Tatko would be a permanent husband and father, responsible for the family and farm. His new Divine call was to be with his family.

"When will he be here?

"Why didn't you tell me he was coming home?

"What can I do before he gets here?

"Will we go to meet him today?"

Vancho's thoughts tumbled into disorderly questions.

"*Teebo!*²⁶ You talk too much." His mother spoke harshly while her smiling eyes caressed him.

Shocked, Vancho stopped babbling, his mouth still open for more questions, eyes round with a strange almost-frightened look as he responded to his mother's harsh words.

Shaking her head and laughing Mama took his hands and spun him in a running circle around her. Then he knew that she had been teasing. He felt like they were dancing a new dance, faster and faster. What fun! How he loved his mother!

While she whirled him around she said, "Patience. Do your work. Tatko will be here when he gets here. It will likely not be today. We all have to wait until he returns. No one knows exactly when that will be."

Digging with new, never-known vigor little Vancho toiled. He willed that when he finished his work Father would be with them. He wondered how soon that would be.

His thoughts kept him persevering.

At noon a lunch of *kashkaval*,²⁷ bread, and an apple lulled him to sleep. After a two-hour nap he resumed his efforts.

Still no Tatko!

Day turned to dusk. He was still working. His arms ached. He feared they would fall off. However, before long Mama was telling him to wash for dinner.

"I made chicken for your effort today," Mama said.

Vancho was hungry and tired. *This chicken is the best I have ever eaten*, he thought. Maybe it was good because he had earned it.

Later he slept well, cozy between Mama and Sister.

He dreamed of Tatko as though he was already home. In his dream Tatko played and worked alongside him showing how things should be done. Whatever Tatko did Vancho copied. The dream stayed with him for many days. He told no one. It was a secret he believed he shared with Tatko and God.

One day led to another. Time began to drag. There were chores. There were meals. There were friends with whom to talk and to play.

As he was preparing for sleep one night Mama almost sang, "Tomorrow is the day! Tatko will finally be home!"

Vancho was up early. For the first time he hardly noticed what he ate, finishing breakfast quickly.

A homemade ceramic water jug with a drinking spout on the handle had been filled earlier from the well at a neighbor's house. Taking the jug Ivan began his first daily task. *Today Mama won't have to tell me to do my chores*, he thought, happy with himself. He lightly sprinkled the floor, which was built of rough wooden boards nailed to floor joists, shaking the bulbous container causing droplets of water to spurt from the openings on the handle and the filling-hole on top. Over the planks of the floor was a three-inch layer of soil mixed with wheat chaff for substance. Dirt was a vapor barrier between floors and provided a safe walking surface. It effectively covered old wooden splinters. It was Vancho's job to clean and examine the dirt floor so that no feet would suffer.

Vancho put the jug back onto the table. He had been careful to use only what was essential, not wasting their drinking water.

He swept with the broom Mama had made recently and stepped back to evaluate his work. The small amount of water had dampened the floor just enough to keep dust from rising. To his eye it was perfect. There were no crumbs of food or pieces of straw. Slight depressions were acceptable. Nothing looked gouged. Work always made him feel good.

Mama will be pleased, he thought. *So will Tatko when he gets here and sees that I help the family now.*

Mama was outside feeding the farm animals.

Vancho heard her happily singing voice. Following the sound he found her quickly. Her song of joy was loud and clear, music to his heart as well as his ears. Her beautiful voice always sent little shivers down his back. He loved her singing and was glad that he too was musically gifted.

Lifting his voice he joined the melody he knew well. The woman's rich full sound balanced the high-pitched clarity of his childish addition. He followed her from chickens to sheep to cattle, helping her as she fed them, blending his voice to hers as they sang. They were united in the joy of living in this place, at this time. They sang with shared anticipation for the homecoming.

God is great and awesome, Vancho's heart sang. *He's making Himself real by filling me with this happiness of knowing Tatko will be home today.*

With chores done Sister joined them. They began walking arm in arm to the village square.

As they neared the village's artesian well Vancho heard the water coming from the beautifully curved brick wall long before he could see it.

He knew that he was more than halfway to the square when he heard that sound.

Unending streams of artesian-well water came from four pipes approximately six feet apart. The pipes were mortared through the brick wall, extending four inches from its concave face two feet above the ground. The water splashed from the pipes into an open ended cement trough dug into the soil. The trough was a few inches off level to aid the water to drain to a graveled area at the lower end.

This morning two teen-aged girls were filling their families' water jugs at the well.

Since most of the villagers knew one another they visited when meeting. The family of three told the girls of the wondrous homecoming they were about to experience. Laughter rang from all five.

It seemed to Vancho that everyone and everything; the trees, the birds, and the blue sky were in unified good humor because of his family.

Turning from the girls Mama hurried her children toward the court-house. Vancho saw his young father coming toward them. He was handsome, his face stretched to a smile. He began to run and laugh.

"My wife, my daughter, my son!" he called. Reaching down he put strong hands under Vancho's little arms and swung the boy onto his shoulders in one effortless move.

Scooping his wife and daughter to himself he hugged them hard as they all buried their heads in each other's shoulders, talking and laughing together with no one listening but everyone hearing. They all spoke the same universal language of love and joy. If there had ever been a day as happy as this one Vancho could not remember it.

Somehow in spite of repeatedly stumbling over one another like a group of circus clowns with Vancho holding Tatko's ears to stay on, they got home.

Tatko was home to stay.

That evening Vancho's father spoke with his family about his work in the Bulgarian army.

"His Majesty King Boris III is no longer head of state," he said restating what he was aware they knew, "things are different, people think differently. We had a different goal when I joined the army. We had a well-defined purpose for good. Now..." his voice trailed.

"With Boris III's brother as acting king, while His Majesty King Simeon II was still so young and the national mood changing…," again Tatko silently reflected on the many changes he had observed.

The family sat quietly waiting through the silences, listening intently to his narrative. Hearing Tatko again was wonderful for the young boy. Vancho had almost forgotten the strength and depth of his father's voice.

He heard wisdom as he listened to not only the words and the content but also to his father's tone.

"I am glad, as I think all soldiers are, to have served away from home. As a peasant I have no better way to see my country and other parts of the world. Where could I have found time or money for such luxury as travel? I was honored to serve so kind a man as His Majesty King Boris III ... but, as I said, things have changed."

He sighed, "The uneducated rebel government believes that in time everyone will have all the material things that they need including food, never wanting more than is available. Then everyone will be content. Money will not be necessary. Somehow they neglect to examine their own hearts to realize that in healthy human beings there is always a desire for better and for more of all that life has to offer. In well-balanced humans there is the willingness to work hard if necessary to obtain those extras. Self-centered

Tatko about age 30

mankind always wants to be 'in charge' or have the 'best' or 'more' than others. It is the natural state of mankind, who will never be content being a like, or having the same as everyone else. Only Jesus can bring a state of peace and contentment out of greediness. Rewarded hard work is the key to satisfaction."

He paused a few moments, and reflected, then said, "I believe the most important reason I joined the army was, as I have told you before, that I felt God's call to serve. I had no doubt that I was to be a soldier.

"Now," Tatko said, "I'm back to farming. This is my life's work inherited from my father, his father, and generations back as far as anyone can remember. The Rykinski[28] clan has always been known for excellent farming, good crop management, and production.

"I love working the earth and taking care of farm animals. When I walk behind the water buffalo holding the plow steady as it turns the soft soil of spring," he told them, "I draw in the mixed smells of raw earth, sweaty animal, and fresh spring air. Some city folk might say animal smell is a stench, but to me it is the sweetest of smells. Farming is God's work using tools He's given us, therefore, everything about it is sweet. He is the one who told us to maintain the earth, to work it. From Him comes every good and necessary thing.

"I love the muscle-work of harvest, using my hands, arms, back, and legs while swinging the scythe and throwing the bundled hay.

"I like the sweat cleansing my body from the inside out. There is no bathing, either with well water or soaking in the river, that cleanses like sweating.

"I love the itchiness as harvest particles cling to my skin in August and September because it makes me acutely aware of my choice to sacrifice my own comfort to take care of you, my family, in the time-honored way that I know.

"When a puff of cool breeze comes to refresh me it is an unexpected reward for my hard work. Then I stop and thank the Lord Jesus.

"There is nothing as refreshing as the well water that cools my parched throat when I stop to catch my breath and take a drink after long hours of farm work. The water is sweetest when one of you hands it to me with a smile.

"In the army there aren't these rewards."

Tatko expressed his acute pleasure at simply being home to concentrate on those people whom God had given into his immediate care. When he finished his workday now he would relax in their presence as they gathered together before retiring for the night. He would be able to watch them, touch them, hear them, smell them, play with them, talk with them, and love them.

"Being far from all of you has not been easy." Tatko smiled into Sister's eyes then Vancho's, his contentment evidenced by holding his wife's gaze. "It has been as difficult for me to be gone from you as it has been for you, my sweet wife, to be without me. No man is pleased having his wife care for their farm alone. Besides the farm I left you with two young children. Although I trusted God to give you what you needed these past three years of duty I am very glad to be home."

Vancho listened to his father talk. To him life hadn't seemed troublesome.

Mama takes care of everything just fine, he thought, *but I will like having Tatko home. He will teach me men's jobs. He will show me how to become a man. It will be fun to play with him when we have time. Like today when he made me feel tall carrying me on his shoulders. I wonder if I will be that tall when I'm a man.*

Much later Vancho stirred in his sleep when Mama shifted in bed. He wondered why he was almost crushed between her and Sister. Then, remembering that his father was home leaving less space for him, he drifted contentedly back to sleep. Tomorrow they would still be a complete family. That completeness would continue forever.

Even as Vancho delighted in the wholeness of his family, Bulgaria was facing the awful results of its political division.

4. TRAGEDY

To five-year-old Vancho life seemed better than ever.

What did he care if Bulgarians were feuding? Politics? Democracy versus monarchy? Nothing requiring mature thinking mattered to Vancho.

The change he didn't like was they didn't attend church anymore. No one did. Criss-crossed boards were nailed over all churches' doors and windows.

Under King Boris III people in Bulgaria had been free to worship the One True God. Christianity had been the country's stabilizing factor since sometime between A.D. 852-889 when Khan Boris ruled and united the country, not allowing paganism to continue.[29] Bulgarian Orthodoxy was established in the tenth century. Turkish oppression in Bulgaria from 1360 to 1878 attempted to destroy Christianity but did not succeed.

In the center of each village was the church. A priest, or pope as he was called in Bulgaria, led the Christian believers. The married pope had children as an example to families of how to live as God intended domestically. The pope demonstrated how God reaches through man to treat others with love and respect. The pope taught those who attended Sunday services how to love Jesus. He taught Biblical truth according to the Nicene Creed.[30] Jesus was God before time and still is. We all sin by turning from God to our own way. On the cross Jesus took man's sin in exchange for His own righteousness. Jesus became human to bring sinful man back to God the Father in faith. Therefore, we must confess our sin and turn from sin to God. The pope taught that all who believe this truth, who repent, who allow the Holy Spirit to reign in their lives and are obedient to God according to His word will receive eternal life in His presence. By trusting this good news anyone can receive the life-changing salvation of Jesus Christ.

The pope always wore a black flowing robe and a tall black hat. His long beard also identified him as a man of God. His hair was long, always neatly trimmed. Vancho recognized the pope of any village by his distinctive appearance.

Rogozen's pope was a gentle intelligent man with grace and dignity. Whenever he saw Vancho he smiled, bending to look directly at the child, greeting him by name. His long, curly, bushy beard intrigued the youngster. It looked soft. Vancho wondered what it felt like but he would never have attempted to touch it. He and all the village children had been taught utmost respect for their elders, especially for the pope. Touching any part of him, even out of curiosity, would have shamed the child and his family.

When Tatko had been home the family had walked to church together. They sat side-by-side on the hard pew. Vancho enjoyed feeling his father's warmth next to him. He anticipated Sunday mornings when Tatko was home.

I can't wait till I'm old enough to take Communion, he thought. *Even Sister, who is three years older than me, is still too young. She has to stay in the pew while our parents go forward to take the sacrament. It represents the broken body and shed redemptive blood of Jesus, the final required blood sacrifice that atoned for sin.*

"Tatko, where did the pope go?" Vancho asked one day after his father had come home to stay.

"He still lives in Rogozen, Vancho. He must work as the rest of us do now. He cannot be our church leader. He was made to 'conform,' to shave his honored beard, and cut his hair. He can no longer wear his priestly robe or hat. He has been disgraced by this new government."

"But why?"

"That is a difficult question to answer. We must trust God even though we are not permitted to speak about Him anymore. It is against state policy. The new leaders do not believe in Jesus Christ and think no one should," his father had patiently answered.

Vancho tried to understand what Tatko had said. He couldn't understand why a good man would be disgraced. *It doesn't make any sense,* he finally thought.

Tatko had been home for almost three months. 1944 with all its change was ending and there still was work to be done for next year's crops. Very few people were tilling so late in the year.

Vancho had been waking early. Every day was filled with new things to learn. He rarely noticed early morning tiredness.

"What a beautiful day!" Vancho sang raking the side garden with his father. Warm sun was breaking through the cold. It was not quite seven o'clock in the morning. They rose at dawn to complete tasks before the early dark chased them inside.

Soil melted like butter under Tatko's spade as he turned the dark, rich earth in huge bites. Vancho beat the big chunks of dirt until they broke, then raked them smooth.

Next summer there would be peppers, tomatoes, beans, peas, onions, cabbages, *sini domati*,[31] pumpkins, garlic, dill, parsley, mint, oregano, and basil in their garden. He knew those plants by their wonderful summer aromas and flavors. Like every good thing in life one has to work and wait for them. He knew that he would wait and while waiting be content.

Tatko and Mama grew grapes in their separate vineyard a mile outside the village. The vineyard was a special place for the young boy when his parents let him join them. Vancho played in the boy-sized hut his father had built for overnight stays. Adults, even Sister, had to stoop to enter the door but not he. Inside he was the head of his playhouse. He always pretended to act, as he knew Tatko acted. Outside, standing high above the supported vines, was the crow "watchtower." Vancho had made that his "fort." Perhaps his parents suspected his pretense but they never spoke of it. They treated his child-play with indifference and left him alone unless it became destructive or dangerous. So far he was careful and demonstrated respect for the grapevines. He didn't need correcting.

Every year Vancho's parents planted acres of crops in their farmland near the vineyard. They sowed navy beans, sugar cane, sunflower, corn, and wheat. With these crops, watered from the nearby stream, their produce from the garden next to their home, their livestock raised for food, and free fresh water from the village artesian well or the neighbor's well, they were basically self-sustained. It was their way of life.

Some families raised hemp for rope and fabric and sugar beets in addition to the other necessities.

If Vancho's family had a need for something they didn't grow or raise they bartered.

On the first day of field planting last spring Sister and Vancho had joined their mother early in the morning. They had ridden in the ox cart to the fields long before the eastern sky brightened into peach and pink with the rising sun. Chilly, damp, early morning air had not daunted them. Vancho was cozy as he huddled under heavy woolen blankets. Whether it was his or his sister's body heat that kept him warm he hadn't known. He had simply relaxed and enjoyed himself.

He hadn't known what to expect that morning, never having been "old enough" to "go to the fields" before. He hadn't realized how far the cow had to plod to get there. He could hardly contain himself because of excitement. After the first several minutes of quietly bouncing on the wooden floorboards of the cart he impatiently asked, "Are we there yet?" Thereafter, he asked the same question repeatedly, perhaps every two minutes. Needless to say, no one bothered to answer but he didn't notice. He was simply a little boy in a hurry to get to a new adventure. They arrived twenty minutes later.

Unloading the equipment and seed took almost two hours. Vancho joyfully participated in the process. The activity warmed him and he was invigorated. Each trip to the edge of the field with a small bag of seed produced more energy.

By mid-morning he became restless with disappointment. There was nothing more for him to do after dragging seed bags. Everyone else began planting but he was not allowed. They said he would get in the way.

"Keep the cow in the grazing area away from the planting," Mama told him. Taking the cow's halter he led the animal into the young grass growing nearby and watched her. He saw that she was content to stay where she was. *Soon she'll lie down to chew her cud*, he thought. *Now what can I do?* The stone wall at the edge of the field beckoned to him and he climbed up. *So, he figured, by sitting on this wall I can watch the cow and the planting. At least I can learn how the work is done. Maybe next year I will know enough to not get in the way and they might let me help.*

Later as he sat and watched, little songs ran through his head. He started swaying to his music. Soon he began bouncing on the stone wall like a soccer ball on the playing pitch across the street from his house. He was dancing sitting down and he liked it! At one particularly "moving" part of his song, Vancho lost his balance, falling backwards. He banged his head soundly on a large sharp stone before landing on his stomach, filling his mouth no longer with sweet melody, but with gritty dirt.

"*Buk-luk!*"³² He spat and his spit was black with soil.

Glancing at his shoulder he saw that it was bright red and wet. Blood was splattering from somewhere. Instinctively he knew it was his own. Quickly he shifted from a happy singer to a frightened little boy. He hadn't yet felt pain but his siren-like scream brought Sister running. She pressed her hand hard against the wound shouting at him, "You are a trouble-maker!" She was angrier than he had ever seen her. His crying did not gain sympathy, so he quieted and let her do what was necessary.

"Now I can't plant until this bleeding stops!" she yelled. "Mama needs me to help ... And you were *supposed* to be watching the cow!" As soon as the bleeding had abated she headed back into the field.

"Get into any more trouble," she yelled over her shoulder emphatically stomping back to work, "and you'll be sorry!"

The rest of the week he elected to stay home while Mama and Sister went to the field.

Spring became summer.

Summer threatened to be long and lazy for Vancho. It was hot. There was always work to do and then it was *sabor*³³. Unlike other *sabory*, this time Vancho had been successful in convincing his mother to barter for a toy. Usually he was only permitted to look with longing at the rows of tables covered with exciting things like rings, leather belts, hats, and small toys, items that always enticed the boy. He hadn't expected his mother to actually *purchase* something.

Sabor was the annual day of village celebration. The feast's meat was always mutton.

Quickly Chicho slaughtered the sheep letting the blood drain onto the soil. He skillfully skinned and gutted it. Lelia, Mama, and Sister painstakingly turned the stomach inside out and cleaned it, to make *shkembe chorba*[34] later. They prepared the intestines to use as *lukanka*[35] casings.

The highly valued kidneys were left attached to the sheep during baking, which flavored the meat. The head with its succulent brain was also left in place.

To prevent fouling by dirt the whole prepared animal was wrapped carefully in burlap, placed over red and white hot coals in the deep fire pit, covered with loose soil and left to bake for hours.

Throughout the village *Sabor* food was the same. If Vancho visited a friend's family when the meal was ready it was expected that he eat with them. It would be identical to what he had eaten at home or with his relatives.

Tatko had come home in the fall after *Sabor*.

Vancho remembered the painful incident of last spring's planting as he worked with his father during this relatively warm December morning and he was glad that today Tatko wanted his help in the vegetable garden next to the house. He believed it a sign that his parents thought he was growing up.

Vancho's contribution to the job was small but his growing body gave all it could to the task. He liked working as a man rather than doing women's chores. Tatko was teaching him dangerous and heavy man's work. Working hard kept him warm. He felt good.

His expectation of having his father home to teach him manly arts was being met. Growing into a man with his father's continual presence, encouragement, and correction was going to be wonderful! Life couldn't be better.

He had been shown how to hold and swing the long-handled harvester's scythe. He had cut tall grass and weeds to prepare for harvesting wheat with the other men. His lesson with a knife had come with decapitating a chicken for dinner while standing on its wings. He let the blood run onto the ground as he had been told to do and when the bleeding stopped he scooped soil over the pool of blood to keep insects away. Without realizing it Vancho was learning what chores were necessary for him to be a good steward of land and animals. He knew that his parents were pleased with each new step of growth.

These past two and a half months had been vastly different from life the way it had been. Now he was one of two men who balanced the two women in his family.

Soon after Tatko came home Vancho had discovered that Tatko understood him better than Mama seemed to. When necessary his father disciplined him. Vancho thought that spankings seemed to be less than when his mother had been the sole disciplinarian. Sometimes his father had gently stopped Mama when she intended to correct him. Then he would overhear Tatko talking calmly to her about Vancho being, "still a boy." The tight lines of anger would melt from Mama's mouth and eyes. She would smile lovingly first at her husband and then at Vancho. That would be the end of the tension caused by his childish behavior. He would know from his parent's conversation that his actions had been unacceptable. He would make the necessary corrections without having to be spanked. He liked this way of learning better than physical discomfort.

How he loved his father! He felt special because of those interventions. He worked to meet his father's expectations. One day he was pleasantly surprised to realize that since Tatko had been home his embarrassing problem of wetting the bed in his sleep had stopped.

Vancho worked happily on the clumps of dirt his father had turned.

As they worked side by side, sometimes humming or talking to one another, two village men, friends of the family came to the fence and called for Tatko. As usual, when neighbors stopped Tatko went to the group and listened as they spoke to him.

People seemed to stop often, chat for a moment and move on. Tatko was always happy to spend time with his neighbors. Those were pleasant moments taking rest from the task at hand. They were also opportunities for Vancho to learn how to communicate with neighbors unhurriedly without irritation. Tatko was a good example for Vancho.

"There is always work," he would tell his son. "It never gets done, but a break from time to time, especially with 'folks,' is healthy."

Vancho believed his father to be a good man. He took care of his own family and helped others when they needed help. He commanded respect from everyone just by his own respectful attitude.

Vancho's mother had often said, "Live with respect for others and you will be respected." Indeed their family was respected in their village and in others. Whenever they went to Malorad three kilometers away to visit a family member villagers came to eat and talk with them. People liked Vancho's family.

Planks balanced on braces made a typical Bulgarian knee-high table to accommodate everyone. Dry warped wood hid under brightly embroidered tablecloths. The mood was always festive and there was music. Bulgarian backless three-legged stools were pulled up. The stools were also short, about table height, with places cut out for adult legs to fit. Vancho's short legs barely touched the ground when seated. He often felt the need to get up and run around. He remembered the only time he sat there fighting that need and letting his legs tickle, then tingle. He sat quietly wondering why his legs felt strange, until all feeling left. When he tried to stand he couldn't. The experience had scared him and it had hurt while he waited through the awful stinging for his legs to recover.

Since then eating tasty food from his wooden bowl had made him forget that time and the roughness against his legs. Thinking about the food that his aunt made in Malorad he could almost taste the hot peppers filled with soft navy beans, the roasted corn, the crusty bread. Thoughts of food only made his stomach ache with hunger and he had to wait for lunch.

Vancho forced his mind from thinking about food to his present work with Tatko.

As he watched the two men interact with his father at the fence he thought, *Something is different today from the other visits with neighbors.* He couldn't pinpoint the difference but he felt uneasy.

They are acting strangely, he analyzed. *Tatko is holding his head too stiffly. He quickly jerks it as he looks from one man to the other. He doesn't look as relaxed as usual. No one is laughing. They are talking too long.*

Vancho couldn't hear what the men said. He caught snatches of his father's voice, "I'll ... tonight ... to the ... tomorrow ...see..."

Then Tatko rejoined his son working to prepare the soil for its rest during the remainder of winter in anticipation of spring planting.

Nothing was said to the boy about the visit.

Vancho didn't expect to be told. Children were not excluded from adult talk but neither were they intentionally informed about adult affairs.

He became aware that his father had stopped talking and humming.

He wanted to ask why his father's mood had changed, what the men had been talking about. He couldn't formulate a question that made sense to his child-mind so, wondering, he finished his work in silence.

That night as Vancho slept he was unaware that his parents talked.

The sun had been ready to break through the dark when Mama tearfully begged Tatko, "Leave the village before dawn! Run! Get away while you can!"

Tatko insisted, "Everything is in order. It will be fine. I have done nothing wrong." He kissed his wife's tear-streaked cheeks. "There will certainly be questions to answer and then I will return home. Go to sleep, my sweet one," he told her.

There was to be no sleep for Mama. Nothing could settle her anxiety.

She prayed to Almighty God to give her comfort but would not accept it. God had given her a wonderful man as her life partner. She had a foreboding that he would be taken from her.

She couldn't understand why this horrible thing was happening.

The rest of that night, which wasn't long, she lay awake holding the hand of the man who had brought her happiness by making her his bride, by giving her sweet children.

Less than two hours later Tatko left his bride's side in the dark of pre-dawn. He moved quietly to prevent waking the children. He bent, gently kissing his precious daughter and son while they slept.

Turning to Mama, Tatko embraced her tenderly. Mama held him, reluctant to let him leave her. She kissed him good-bye, her cheeks wet, her eyes reddened and swollen from crying. When she kissed her beloved she tasted the salt of her own tears. Her sorrow was too great to bear but she had no choice. She must bear it.

Vancho woke in their one-room home, much earlier than usual; the sun was barely making the room bright.

Being unaware of the night's events he watched Mama, surprised that he did not hear her familiar humming while she sliced cheese and bread onto a plate for his breakfast.

"Where's Tatko?" Vancho sleepily asked yawning and stretching his arms over his head to wakefulness.

Mama turned toward him. She put the knife down and slowly, like an old woman although she was in fact only thirty-one years old, walked to where he lay. He stretched first this way and then that in the family bed. How he luxuriated in its expanse when he was alone!

Sitting by Vancho's side Mama brushed the hair from his forehead. Her roughened fingers felt scratchy but her touch was light and loving. It made him shiver as he lay quietly enjoying her caress. Mama's eyes looked tired. He had never known her to seem as sad as now. Barely breathing he looked hard at her willing her to tell him why she was unhappy. She remained silent. His question about Tatko's whereabouts was left unanswered.

He watched as she pushed her tiredness to her feet and, almost stumbling, returned to her work. It appeared that she had forgotten how to walk.

Chores filled their day and the next and the next.

"Mamo![36]" Ivan said one evening during dinner, "Tell me about Tatko. Why is he gone? Where is he?"

"He has gone to Oriahovo, Vancho," she said in resignation, not looking at her son. "He was taken into custody. There will be a trial. Then he will be home." She showed no emotion, no voice inflection.

"What did he do?" the child asked.

"He has done nothing wrong. He served in King Boris III's army. We have a new government, which believes men like your father are traitors to Bulgaria. I will not speak more of this. Now everything we do, we must do with respect for Tatko. He must always be proud of us."

While in bed, before sleeping, Vancho wondered about his father. He knew that his questions about Tatko would not be answered so he left them unasked.

Snow fell and melted several times.

Mama's newly knit scarf, hat, and gloves kept Vancho warm as he fed the animals and changed their straw.

February was biting cold with icy snow a few inches deep.

One frozen morning Sister left the bed to do chores sometime before Vancho's eyes opened. Vancho was not aware that she had hitched the cow to the cart for a drive as soon as they were ready.

Mama greeted him as he woke and said, "Today we will see your father, Little One. Get dressed. We must eat and then go."

When Sister returned from work the three of them sat at the table and silently spooned honey onto their bread and ate, sipping tea.

Vancho looked first at Mama and then at Sister and back again. Neither seemed aware of his stare. Sister cleaned the dishes in the wash basin. Vancho noticed that even at eight she looked 'old'.

What is happening? He wondered. *They don't seem to be aware of anything.*

Without looking at him Sister took his left hand and lifted it as a signal to stand. Mama eased hers into his right hand. The three of them walked quickly into the crisp air to the waiting cart.

Climbing into it and covering themselves snugly with woolen blankets the three left their home heading toward the county courthouse square about twenty-one miles away. With the pace of the cow the journey would take eight to ten hours.

Mama held the reins and stared between the cow's ears as though she didn't see or hear anything. Her jaws were locked, setting her chin at a strange angle of determination.

Turning his head to look at Sister as they lay in the cart Vancho saw her lips tightly pressed together with the normally smiling corners of her mouth turned decisively downward.

He saw other people he knew driving from home. By the silence in their carts early this morning, all heading in the same direction, he assumed they were going to the same place. He believed that was Oriahovo. He sensed that, wherever their destination, he must behave in a quiet serious manner. When he saw his friends he did not try to speak to them. His threesome did not stop to acknowledge anyone.

Silently they drove. He became sleepy.

Vancho fell asleep shortly after leaving the village while Mama guided the cow slowly.

He woke when the cart stopped in the county square in Oriahovo outside the county courthouse. The daylight had slipped away.

Sister tied the animal and cart to a tree behind the large gathering. The three quietly stood there, near the back of the crowd, waiting. Being small, Vancho couldn't see much. Many were in front of him.

After they stood on the frozen lawn a long time an unsmiling man walked onto one of the lighted balconies outside a narrow second story door of the courthouse. Vancho could clearly see the man elevated above the heads of the people. The man sat behind a pile of papers on a table. A brick paperweight kept gusts of winter wind from whisking the papers away.

The building was beautiful. Vancho loved the red tiled roofs of Bulgaria. This large community building had a massive roof. The building itself was balanced architecturally. Exquisite, heavy, double wooden doors were centered at the top of exterior stairs. Three-foot long rounded balconies were spaced about twenty feet apart on both sides of the door the length of the building.

Vancho observed everything: the beautiful building, the large crowd and the man on the balcony. No one was speaking and he wondered what he, Mama, Sister, and the others were doing there, that winter day.

The proceedings began.

The seated man called a name in his commanding voice. Another man presumably bearing that name walked onto the closest balcony facing the gathering below. He stood tall with confidence smiling to those watching.

The seated man, the "judge," as it became apparent, read, "Before you stands a man accused of tyranny against the people of Bulgaria. I sentence him to five years at hard labor."

"No," some people near the front of the crowd shouted, "we want more."

"Ten years!"

"Not enough!" The cry became louder as more voices joined in.

"Fif!...Teen!"

"No!...More!...More!" Much of the crowd was screaming now. Fisted arms were raised and waving.

"I sentence him...to...death!"

Vancho heard the words and saw people in front of him beat the air rhythmically with their fists yelling their approval of the sentence. A high-pitched woman's voice pierced through the crowd's noise screaming in anguish. Then it softened to wailing sobs eventually drowned by the cacophony of the frenzied crowd.

Raising his hand of authority the judge quieted the crowd momentarily to ask the prisoner, "Do you have anything to say?"

The sentenced man gave a shocked look in response.

The yelling resumed. Some people laughed hysterically.

One by one more men were called onto the second balcony. Progressively confidence and smiles faded as each went through his own 'trial.' Most men received the same sentence. Each left the balcony like a wooden soldier entering the dark building having responded nothing to the judge.

Then Vancho heard his father's name called. Although it was late and inky dark outside the lighted balcony allowed Vancho to see that there was no smile on Tatko's face only a look of deep emotional pain, his head and shoulders slumped forward, his eyes downcast. Never had Vancho seen his father so emptied of strength or joy.

Quickly he looked up at Mama for comfort. He needed her stability. She always smiled down to him when he needed her but today was different. There was no smile to help him through this new, terrible trouble. Today there were tears on her face. Her eyes were fixed straight ahead toward the man she loved. She did not, could not, look at her son. Vancho grabbed her hand and held it tightly in both his small ones. He pressed it against his shaking chest. He could hardly breathe.

Then he heard the judge like a gunshot, "Death!"

The crowd cheered.

Vancho's ears heard. His mind died.

Had he known the Bible, he might have thought about the One who had similarly been falsely accused and sentenced to death, even to death on a cross. He might have thought of Jesus and in a supernatural way been comforted but he didn't. There was no comfort.

They waited while many more were called. He heard nothing, saw nothing. How much time elapsed he didn't know.

Somewhere within that time the "trials" ended. People dispersed, leaving behind only the loved ones of those sentenced.

They waited like statues. Minds numb from the barbaric proceedings could not fathom that people, even some friends and relatives who were in the crowd, could be so cruel. Would the sentences be carried out? Would the men indeed be killed?

All that was left was to see the prisoners being led away. Hours dragged. It became very late. How long had they been standing? There was no awareness of time, hunger, or anything. Weary legs were not acknowledged. The icy cold of February seemed to not touch them. They waited eyes straining to see.

Then Vancho saw them; the long silent mass of accused men walking away; rather, being led away. There were perhaps a couple of dozen rows of men, five in a row, appearing identical in their prison clothing, chained together by their wrists.

On both sides of this group were armed soldiers prepared, it appeared, to shoot if deemed necessary. Vanko recognized one of the soldiers, his cousin who had joined the Communist *militsia*.[37]

Mama touched Vancho's shoulder and pointed to a man shuffling close to them. Through his rainbow of tears Vancho saw him. It was Tatko, looking at Mama.

39

As he watched, his father lifted both shackled hands toward his face and leaned forward to wipe tears from his eyes with the backs of his thumbs. He would never see his loved ones again.

How could he handle his sadness?

In his time of need the little boy recognized that Mama could not comfort him. Instead with a heavy heart, older by far than his five years, he embraced Mama to comfort her. Sister joined him. He didn't know how long they embraced in their common misery.

When they dropped their arms very few people were still in the courthouse yard. What had been a crush of people earlier was now an empty field except for a few like Vancho, Sister, and their mother.

Together the broken family began their long journey back to their home. The home which no longer held joy nor song for them.

5. SILK

Winter finished with difficulty and spring followed suit.

It's different now from when Tatko was in the army, Vancho thought. *I hope our family will someday get back to "normal."*

Since the "trials" everyone was quiet. Mama didn't sing or even smile much. Sister seemed to grow busier and tougher. Vancho knew he had to continue his chores but they weren't enjoyable anymore without Tatko.

One summer morning well after sunrise Vancho was still in bed, waking, dozing, being lazy, feeling tired. He had just begun dreaming again when Sister came into the bedroom.

"Vancho, wake up!" Sister said roughly rocking the little boy from sleep, pushing his shoulder. "Wake up! Baba[38] wants us at her house. Vancho! Wake up!"

Sleepily he opened his eyes. Late last night he had been playing soccer, running hard outside. He wasn't ready to get up. He moaned when he saw his sister and rolled over impudently turning his back to her. "I don't want to wake up!"

Shaking him again she dragged him out of bed.

"You listen to me! Mama told me to get you up. The silk worms have hatched. Baba doesn't want them on her belly anymore. Do you want her to lose them? They'll crawl all over her...." His sister's walking fingers found his ribs as she playfully taunted, *"Buba lazi, buba lazi."*[39]

He doubled over giggling, *"Neday! Kako, Neday!"*[40]

"Well then," she said with one last tickle, "get dressed and eat something. We have work to do. I'm going now. Come as soon as you can! We don't want them to starve and Baba says it's your job to feed them."

Sleep gone, Vancho threw the bedclothes back to air the bed and put on his green shirt and short pants. He washed sleep from his eyes and face, even washing his ears at the basin, pouring water into it from the jug Sister had filled at the neighbor's well.

41

Baba will check behind my ears, he thought as his fingers scrubbed. *I'd better make sure my fingernails aren't dirty. She is like Mama when it comes to cleanliness.*

Going back inside he found the bread and cheese Mama had left for breakfast. He ate quickly and ran the three blocks to his grandmother's house, looking for her, hardly noticing the distance.

"Hello, *Rasboynik*,"[41] she called to him. "How's my sleepy helper this morning?"

"Babo, where are the worms? Sister said the eggs hatched. Can I see them?"

Laughing, Baba lifted the blouse she wore loosely over her skirt. She lifted it just high enough for him to see the linen wrap that was around her middle. She untied the bandage-like ribbon exposing the small card stock box he remembered having seen frequently; the last time when little black specks were in it and Baba had wrapped it within the fabric around herself. Gently she held the box in her hands. It was about four by three inches and a half-inch tall.

"This is as much as you can see now, Vancho. First we must have everything ready. Your mama and sister are busy making sure the 'crawlers' can't get out of the clean room upstairs. Then you must provide them with food before I release them.

Earlier that morning Baba had opened the box to discover that the eggs had become larvae. They were dark and small, about the same size and appearance as the eggs but now, unlike eggs, they were visibly moving around the box. They had tiny suction cups on tiny legs that couldn't be seen by the naked eye.

Knowing that her curious grandson would be arriving soon she had rewound the fabric, securing the box to her body again in its "hatching" position. She loved educating him.

"Your job now, Vancho, is to pick mulberry leaves for them to eat. We don't want any to die from starvation. Go! Gather leaves. The sack is over there." Baba pointed to a brown loosely woven bag. It seemed she had thought of everything.

Vancho scurried away. Even though there were leaves that he could reach from the ground he grabbed the nearest branch of the closest mulberry tree on Diado[42] and Baba's property. He swung his leg over a branch and in no time pulled himself up. Reaching for a higher limb he climbed as high as he dared. He was soon stuffing his gunnysack with the necessary food for the silkworms.

Picking mulberry leaves is the best job for me. I'm good at climbing and I like it! He thought.

After stuffing the bag Vancho carried it into the room in which Diado had built a three foot high wooden table, a platform. The structure sat in the middle of the clean room covered with a white cloth. To Vancho it looked like a King's banquet table instead of an eating place for a box of worms.

He dumped the contents of the bulging sack onto the table in the otherwise empty room made ready to receive the living creatures. Quickly he rearranged the pile of leaves on the table distributing them evenly before going for more.

Stepping back he looked at his work. Surprised to see how much food he had already gathered, he let out a whistle of satisfaction. He was anxious to heap the table with fresh leaves to insure a healthy start for the 'babies'. He left the room and house quickly, climbed the tree and resumed his work.

After he had gathered the second bagful he found Baba before going back into the silkworm room. She was busy in the garden weeding between rows of tomatoes. His grandmother had carefully placed straw under each plant to keep the fruit from rotting on the ground. Now in mid-summer the plants were getting heavy with green tomatoes and dotted with bright yellow flowers, promises of more fruit.

"Babo, come with me. This is my second bag. We can release the silkworms as soon as I put these leaves with the others."

Together they went up the stairs of the house into the hall. They turned to their right into the silkworm room.

When Baba saw the mound of mulberry leaves already on the platform she stopped, surprised.

"Why, Vancho!" she exclaimed, "You have been very busy! If this is the contents of one bag, you won't need two bags until the caterpillars grow much bigger."

His little chest puffed with pride as a smile stretched his cheeks. Shyly he simply said, "Thank you, Babo."

Slightly embarrassed because he had already picked the second bag he arranged the new load, watching his grandmother. She put the small box gently on the table among the greenery. Her care made him think that the box contained a rare treasure, which in a sense it did. Slowly she opened the lid.

Spellbound, Vancho couldn't speak as he watched. He looked up at her, his eyes dancing, and laughed. His child's mirth rang like music and seemed to fill the entire home.

Finding his speech he asked, "When, Babo, when did they hatch?"

She laughed with him at his wide-eyed wonder.

"Do you remember when I put the eggs into this box and wrapped it around me ten days ago? The eggs were tiny only as big as a period at the end of a sentence in a newspaper."

Without waiting for his answer she asked? "Do you remember what you said?"

"No, Babo. What did I say?"

You said, "They look like poppy seeds."

"Yes, I remember...They did. The bottom of the box was covered with them."

"Well, after I put them on, my body gave them the heat they needed to hatch. These past two mornings I've checked them and sure enough today they were hatched and crawling. They are hungry and want their freedom and food."

Baba and Vancho saw the moving specks clamber up the short walls of the box down the outside and seemingly become lost in the leaves. Vancho's sharp eyes located one little silkworm slowly munching at the edge of a leaf. Although he was able to watch the slow progress the child soon tired, becoming bored and impatient.

He left the room with a sense of satisfaction at having helped begin an important process of his village.

As he began to run toward home he heard his grandmother's voice.

"Vancho, You still have work to do. Go now and gather an armload of small sticks from the mulberry trees. Add them to the table."

"Do I have to take the leaves off first?" he asked.

"No. The worms may or may not eat the leaves, it doesn't matter. But they will need the branches."

"What for?"

"You'll see," she said her eyes smiling at him.

He knew she would not tell him no matter how much he wanted to know. He went to the tree and broke off twenty or thirty long sticks no thicker than a third of an inch in diameter, as instructed, and put them on the table heaped with greens.

He again found Baba busy in the garden.

"Babo, the branches are on the table with the silkworms and leaves. Now what do you want me to do?"

"Come. I have some instructions."

Inside the room she said, "You've done a good job, Vancho. There is nothing more for today. However when you clean the table of veins and wilted leaves every day, be sure to leave these sticks on the table." As she spoke she arranged them in a structure to act as a support for the loose leaves. "Their leaves will be wilting, but keep them here anyway. I'll see you tomorrow."

Vancho saw the teasing smile playing in the corners of his grandmother's mouth again. He was intrigued but said nothing. He liked surprises and suspected that she was really playing a trick on him.

It's to make the daily cleanup harder, he thought. *There is no need for them. She is having fun with me but I'll do as she says. No one is going to call me lazy or disrespectful.*

Every day Vancho ran to Baba's to clean up waste, searching carefully for little-black-speck-creatures so that none inadvertently got thrown out. He replaced the wilted leaves with fresh ones without removing any of the sticks. When one fell to the floor as he took away old leaves nearby, he quickly retrieved it.

It was marvelous watching the larvae grow bigger and lighter in color. It was as though they increased in size before his gaze.

Into the fourth week of their larval stage they had become voracious eaters and large enough for him to see easily how they used their suction cups and heads to eat the leaves systematically. He enjoyed watching their activity. At this stage the table was filled with one-inch-long creeping things. They were awkward looking worms but they had an important job in the village.

Picking fresh leaves required an hour or two each day. There was no place to put them except on top of the caterpillars. They didn't seem to mind, simply, patiently taking another leaf from above and eating it.

Each one always found a leaf. There were enough leaves for every worm to have one for itself. Sometimes, however, several caterpillars ate from the same leaf. Each larva methodically chomped along the edge of its chosen spot. Little semicircles became big semicircles as Vancho watched. Soon all but the vein of the leaf was gone. Seemingly unconcerned, the caterpillar bumped along until it found another leaf or another section of the same one and the process continued. One after another the tender portion of the leaves disappeared, consumed by hungry silkworms.

It seemed to the small boy that these worms might eat the whole village's supply of mulberries and that his athletic and social life would be eradicated by his job. However, his grandparents had planted enough mulberry trees for twice the number of silkworms they had decided to raise. Every year that they raised silkworms there were always enough leaves.

Sometimes the morning check revealed that the larvae were nearly out of food. In those rare cases Vancho rushed to re-supply without first stopping to clean the table. He basically hand fed the hungry caterpillars when they raised their bodies looking for more food. Working that into the process of removing the old leaves became a challenging game.

Day after day he faithfully checked on 'his' silkworms and maintained their lives with the leaves that would allow them to become cocoons. From when they were period-on-a-page-size to ready-to-pupate-size they had grown ten thousand times as big.

Finally the day came when Vancho opened the door and found a surprise in addition to the hungry creepy-crawlies.

"Wow!" he exclaimed. "Now I get it! Baba wasn't tricking me after all."

About a dozen fuzzy-looking white packages were hanging by sturdy thin silk cords, onto the almost forgotten but preserved sticks. The little packages were longer than they were wide, shaped somewhat like a peanut. His job of leaf collecting was coming to an end. Those few silkworms had metamorphosed into cocoons wrapped in their own silk threads. Soon the others would do the same.

God really makes some strange and wonderful creatures, Vancho thought as he reflected on all that had happened since the eggs were placed in their little container.

Calling Baba into the room he watched as she carefully gathered the sticks with their precious cargo and placed them upright in a box. She treated them gently, knowing that they were still living and could be harmed by rough handling.

Every day Vancho found new cocoons when he went to clean. He called his grandmother who removed the branches with their precious cargo, allowing him to finish his work.

Without being prompted Vancho brought more branches to which the worms could attach, as he saw the need for them.

Several days after his surprise there were no more 'creepers'.

Baba collected all the tight bundles.

Vancho was left with his final task of cleaning the table and the surrounding floor. After sweeping and adding the dried materials that had fallen from the table he put the collected debris onto the cloth. This time cleaning was easy. He lifted the corners of the cloth collecting the refuse into a tidy bundle. Outdoors he opened the cloth and dumped its contents onto the soil between rows of cucumbers and raked it in.

This will help keep the soil healthy, he thought.

Baba wasn't far away. He went to her and asked, "Now what is done to make silk, Babo?"

"We must soak the cocoons in hot water to kill the worms. There are two weeks after pupating before they emerge as adults, breaking the strands of the silk as they do. We don't want that to happen.

"The first worms have been cocoons for six days so it is best to boil the water today to kill them while I have time. I never know when something else might come along. I could miss the hatching date.

"After the worm dies the silk floats off the cocoon into the water. We will work it in our hands until it separates. Then it is ready to spin onto spindles. We must spin the silk several times to make it fine and usable for our *naro-dne*[43] clothing."

"Babo, how much silk do we get from one cocoon?" Vancho asked.

"It is enough," she answered. "Since you watched them so closely you know that each worm makes one cocoon. The silk of each cocoon is one continuous filament. I would say that each filament is on average six hundred meters or two thousand feet long.[44] That is about six soccer-field lengths."

"Wow! We will have enough silk for many clothes, won't we?" he asked.

"Oh, yes," she answered. "Your mama, Lelia, Sister. and I will be busy this winter. The silk will be spun. Then Diado will set up my loom in the room where the worms have been. Your mother and aunt will also assemble their looms. We will weave the silk into fabric, cut it, sew it into clothing and then ornament it with embroidery. It will be beautiful. You have done a good job, Little One." She bent and kissed his forehead.

Vancho was learning essentials of village life at the normal pace of a seven-year-old. He had been pleased to have worked so hard for so long. Now he was thankful to be finished with the task that had seemed endless for the past two weeks.

It was time for him to go to the soccer field and kick the ball awhile. Maybe other boys would be there and they could begin the evening game a little earlier than usual.

6. BURNED

It had been many months since the silk worms had provided silk for shirts, pants, dresses, and table covers. The women had worked all winter making necessities. The cycle continued, one season after another.

This autumn was not new with its cool nights, yellow and brown leaves, and most staple crops gathered from the fields.

Vancho was part of another harvest with Mama, Sister, *Diado*, *Baba*, *Lelia*, and *Chicho*. It seemed to him that all his neighbors had joined them. In reality only five families were together. Three were neighbors. Two were family. Without help from the others none would have been able to complete his task.

Mama, Sister, and Vancho were free to harvest their own crops. Certainly it was sad and more difficult not having Tatko to help, but Vancho had not had a long-lived luxury of expecting him to be there. Only three months after he had returned from the army the socialist leaders, with common people backing the new order, had sentenced him to death. Mama kept telling Vancho that she was sure he would come home again.

"How can he come home if they killed him?" the boy asked in his confusion.

"People have seen others who were sentenced at those trials. They were sent to work camps, not killed. I can't believe that your father is dead!" she had told him.

Mama was nervous about farming these days. Many families were joining the Colhose.[45] The process was the same for the Colhose as for the previous village harvest but the Colhose' Central Government's control replaced individual family's organizing and working together.

This year there were still families who had not joined the Colhose, and family and friends helped bring in the crops.

When one family's wheat crop was done they moved to the next until all were in. Usually a crop was cut, rolled, and brought into the village in two or three days. Today Vancho's friends and family were starting *Diado* and *Baba's* wheat, the fourth crop of the group. The day before yesterday the group had finished Mama's. This and one more family's and they could then thresh the grain, preparing it for grinding into flour at the mill.

Of course, Vancho thought, *there would be no grinding of wheat kernels until the annual in-gathering feast is over. My friends whose families belong to the collective no longer have a feast when threshing is done. I don't like that about the Colhose.*

During harvest families develop close relationships as they work together. Not working side-by-side was the major change the Colhose introduced. Large government machines did almost everything so that fewer people were needed. More time was available for pursuing other interests than deepening relationships among family and friends, only one of many things that turned socializing into socialism.

Last week several women in Vancho's family's group, (all those over twelve years of age and his hard working sister) had met before sun-up at the wheat field. It was earlier than Vancho had ever gotten out of bed but he had felt honored to be invited to join the women for the first part of harvest. He would not have missed that opportunity!

At eight years old he was too young to help. He loved watching his elders work, nonetheless, usually learning something new. He remembered a boring trip to watch his family plant crops several years ago. He remembered what his boredom had led to. His head still bore the scar although his emotions had healed. The harvest held more interesting activity than did planting. This time he had not been bored or restless as he observed the women from his stonewall perch.

They had begun work at dawn. While the dew still glistened on the grain each woman gathered a handful of stems. Swish! The short hand-held sickle sliced cleanly through the dozen stems low to the ground leaving a two-inch stubble. Dividing the handful into two bundles she artfully twisted them together, tying the grain heads in the middle, leaving the stems to the outside. From end to end the bundle measured three to four feet in length. She tossed it to the side of the standing grain. These long small bundles would later serve to tie the wheat sheaves. Continuing down the rows the women working together had made enough "ties" to complete the process of making sheaves for the day's work.

How quickly they work, Vancho thought. *I wonder how they know how many bundles of 'ties' to make.*

Of course, the women with years of experience as to how to correctly estimate what would be needed for the day's work taught the younger ones. Vancho would also learn how to estimate through his own experience at later harvests.

The women had nearly finished their task about an hour or two later when men began to join them.

"Ah, look at what busy hands have done," *Chicho* called out in compliment, loud enough for the women to hear. "Our women have prepared hard work for us this morning. Come, *Tate*[46], let's drop this wheat and be done for another day."

Two strong armed men, Vancho's *Diado* and *Chicho*, began to slice through wheat with their sharpened and honed, two-yard long, curved scythes used for cutting through large stands of grain. The rhythm of bodies and sounds of metal on wheat seemed like a dance performance to Vancho.

I want to look like that when I cut weeds, he thought.

As he watched, more men pulled up in their wagons and entered the wheat field beginning their workday.

He loved the harvest songs the farmers were singing. They had a strong exciting beat that kept rhythm with their bodies.

Do the songs help the work or does the work help the songs? He wondered.

Standing and moving as needed, the farmers swung their scythes expertly, slicing the stems horizontally, skimming the ground. Wheat fell into orderly rows as though placed there. One man or woman closely following each cutter quickly laid one pliable tie on the ground from the many which the women had prepared earlier. He or she then scooped and laid an armful of the freshly cut wheat onto the tie, condensing its middle into a twelve or eighteen-inch diameter sheaf with the sheer strength of muscular hands and arms. He deftly secured it tightly so that it would stay together and threw the prepared sheaf to the side of the cut wheat. Those making sheaves found 'tying bundles' when needed lying conveniently nearby where experienced women had left them. Each worker continued in a rhythm that Vancho thought was choreographed.

From where he sat he could see several people making sheaves.

Others followed behind the 'sheaf makers', gathering and stacking sheaves with the grain heads in the middle, stems outward, until the circular stack held perhaps ten to twenty sheaves. In that way the grain was protected in the center with the stems sloping downward to the outside. If it rained before threshing and storage the rainwater would run off the slippery stems to the outside of the stack. The grain itself would not remain wet, therefore, it would not become moldy. It would be safe.

Those working at their various tasks moved as one unit down the rows.

By mid-morning there were mini-wheat-stacks where standing wheat had been. Only a small portion of the field had been harvested but the heat of the day was beginning to tire the workers. It was time to stop.

Baba called, "Vancho, it's time for breakfast and rest. Come."

After he ate his portion of bread, cheese, onions, and tomatoes he lay in the shade of the old tree at the side of the field. Although he hadn't helped, the early hour of wakening and his 'mental work' had taken its toll on his young body and mind. Rest had been welcome. Within minutes he fell asleep.

Although the scorching heat of the day was past when Vancho woke he saw the workers sweating and straining hard at their tasks. *Diado* and *Chicho* were now helping to stack sheaves. He figured it must be mid-afternoon. Work must have resumed about two hours earlier, from the number of new stacks punctuating the field.

Vancho was more alert than he had been for the past few days but he didn't like sleeping longer than everyone else. His family, knowing that he needed rest, hadn't awakened him when it was time to restart work.

Don't they understand me? Don't they realize that I want to be part of every-thing? With the amount of work still left to do, he didn't bother anyone with his concerns. He knew better than to get Mama or Sister angry with him. A swift hand to his backside always stung.

Work continued until early evening. When it was time to stop, sweaty bodies with scythes thrown over shoulders headed to their carts. Putting the tools in the back, *Diado* sat in the driver's seat and guided the cows slowly toward home. It would be another day or two before this field was completely cut and the sheaves bundled.

Finally that day of completion came. *Baba, Diado, Chicho*, his aunts, and Mama praised God silently for the dry weather, which had aided them in their efforts. It was time to bring the wheat home.

Black water buffaloes rather than cows, gentle and docile but rippling with strength, were hitched to large carts with tall wood-slat sides. Pitchforks were thrown into the carts.

What fun Vancho had as he rode bouncing in the cart, being careful around the pitchforks, so he would avoid a serious accident! It didn't matter to him that he would have bruises on his arms and legs tomorrow. In fact it would be unusual if he even felt them when they showed themselves. Life was too full of wonder for him to be concerned with mundane things like discomfort.

At the field bodies strengthened from years of manual labor pitched the golden yellow harvest onto the carts with measured swings of the pitchforks. To Vancho there was a natural rhythm in all the work his family did. It was, again, a well-performed dance.

Baba and *Diado's* home was the wheat's destination.

It was unloaded and stacked there. Again the heads of grain were placed carefully in the center with the stems outside. Workers flung each sheaf onto the growing stack while others stood on the pile arranging each sheaf as it was tossed up.

Wheat stacks were at least eighteen feet, and often over twenty-five feet, high and fifteen or so feet in diameter at the base. Their conical shape gave them stability.

The village's threshing machine was in heavy use during this part of fall. Sometimes it was shut down for repairs. Each farmer must wait until the machine was available for separating the wheat from the chaff and stems. During the wait it was imperative to protect the grain from molding due to unexpected rain. Always the harvested wheat, no matter the size of the stack, was in the same configuration; grain in the center, stalks on the outside. When his turn came the farmer would pull the thresher with his tractor from the previous location into position for his job.

The whole village prayed, no longer openly as they had in earlier years, for clear skies until the last of the threshing was over. There had been lean years due to God's releasing rain in the middle of their work. Sometimes the harvesters could not get the wheat cut before the rains fell. Other times unexpected downpours during threshing ruined much of the grain. During those years supplies had to be shared with the neighbors whose harvest had beaten the weather odds.

Because of sharing no one ever starved. There wasn't a villager who wouldn't share if his neighbor needed something. Sometimes there wasn't enough flour from the wheat to have bread all year. At other times the straw ran out. Chaff, too, would be shared on occasion. Every villager would gladly share what he had with someone in need. Wasn't that, after all, right? Wasn't that the will of God?

A successful harvest brought a full year's supply of wheat, new straw, and chaff, the brittle bracts around the kernels.

Chaff was stored in stacked gunnysacks outside. One of Vancho's weekly chores, weather permitting, was to take a sack of chaff into the cattle pasture and sprinkle each new, soft 'cow pie' with a handful or two from the sack. Chaff absorbed much of the moisture. Later, when the sun had finished drying the cow pie, he returned with another sack and gathered the dry, solid circles that would furnish heat in the pot-bellied stove for keeping the house warm in winter while boiling *bop*. It amazed him that after adding chaff and the sun had worked, the strong smell of the cow pie disappeared. In addition to diminishing the stench of the manure, chaff added more combustible substance. Chaff when mixed with clay also hardened the bricks.

Next to wheat for flour, straw was the most important product of the crop.

Straw was the main heat source for baking bread in the outdoor brick oven. It filled the family's mattress while the farm animals, too, slept on straw. Skilled hands would manufacture brooms from new straw.

Vancho wondered *will I be allowed to make our household brooms this year? I enjoy stuffing our mattress, but I think I've also earned the right to make brooms. Last year I sat at Mother's side watching and learning as she gathered the straw, folding it precisely in half and securing it around a sturdy straight-branch which became its handle. Spinning the handle and straw quickly she had wrapped hemp twine around the straw carefully placing each round snugly against the one before. She had pulled mightily on the twine to prevent the handle from wiggling free and had finished the broom by tucking the loose end of the twine through the previous rows, pulling it taut.*

I remember how she did it. She should let me make some of them this year.

He seemed to enjoy making things more than doing anything else except maybe eating.

He looked forward to eating after the fields were harvested, the wheat stacked and waiting. Feasting lasted for almost a full day. Vancho enjoyed it but the big feast was yet to come.

The skies remained clear. In three weeks threshing began.

Everyone worked. Even the smallest children were given tasks. Children worked hard and were praised for helping. No one forced them to do more than they could easily do. When they tired, they left the work area and watched, day-dreamed, or slept.

As threshing started adult singing could be heard throughout the area. Children joined them. Some sang without being aware of singing.

The monster thresher was at Diado's neighbor's house positioned between the new stacks of wheat built after harvest.

The hopper to accept sheaves was near the middle, at the top of the machine. Two exit chutes for chaff and grain were at one side near the front with the straw chute higher and on the other side. A tractor was positioned behind the thresher. A twisted-into-figure-eight rotating belt connected the two machines. The tractor's engine supplied power to turn the thresher's mechanisms and to separate the components by weight through their respective chutes.

The "stack men" were on top of the stacks tossing sheaves to the 'thresher man'.

He cut the ties and fed the released sheaves grain first into the hopper of the machine.

The "thresher man" had the most dangerous job. He invariably stood on slippery wheat in a well around the machine's mouth. In the blink of an eye an unexpected move could cause the 'thresher man's' hand or arm to be mercilessly mangled. Villagers with missing fingers or even hands were recognized as threshers.

The team worked quickly but never glutted the massive machine. Had they, they might have caused a feeding problem, which would have shut the machine down requiring mechanical repair. Who knew how long that would delay the job?

Vancho thought, *This has to be the tallest machine made. It's way taller than any of the men. It's even taller than the trucks and weapons that went through here a long time ago.*

53

Those three chutes pump out everything. There's no waste!

When a basket filled with grain two men hauled it into the house, storing the grain in a room. Some, however, was bagged and set aside for next year's seed, which was stored in small sacks in the basement.

Later, when the mill was free to take their grain the large sacks planned for flour would be taken to the mill in the ox cart. The grain would be ground and put into clean sacks, which would then also be stored in the basement.

Chaff, never a food source, was stored in bags outside the house.

Vancho saw straw being belched from the large chute across from where the chaff and grain was collected. It didn't stay on the ground long enough to pile up.

Bodies seemed to fly as people pushed as much straw as they could efficiently take in front of a wooden hayfork to a growing straw-stack nearby. The stack, growing by the moment, was a safe distance from the house. The straw would stay there until it was diminished by use or, as Vancho remembered unhappily, it was accidentally burned.

Watching the forks pushing dimples into ample midsections Vancho thought with alarm, *The forks will poke right through them.* That, of course, would never happen.

When someone returned from the straw stack they pushed another pile using the same torturous technique.

To Vancho it seemed that the line of adults was endless as people continued walking in circles pushing their loads from thresher to stack.

All the time voices sang like nightingales through moistened handkerchiefs tied across their mouths and noses. Dark eyebrows faded with a coating of fine particles. Dust glittered in the fading sunlight around the threshing scene. If Vancho had known the story, *Peter Pan*, he would have thought that it looked like "pixie dust."

He and the other children under twelve had grown weary of the hard work hours earlier. Vancho had struggled for a few hours working with the adults. He had outworked most of the other children his age but now he too was resting.

Most of the youngest children were sleeping on old hand-woven wool blankets, their bright colors long since faded. They slept within their parent's eyesight in the last sunshine, soaking in what warmth was left. The chill of autumn was increasing.

The children would rise later with their 'work' smudged hands, faces, and feet proving their earlier industry. Parents, although exhausted from the daylong labor, would take time to lovingly clean their precious ones without waking them before they themselves would bathe for retiring. By then all the grain from the fields would be safely stored in the house, the chaff bags next to the house, and the straw stacked.

Inside the lower level of the house down a few stairs, was the kitchen. A pot-bellied stove was heating wash water in one pot and boiling navy beans to stuff baked sweet peppers in another. All the workers were looking forward to that special addition to the meal. A feast would be served when the threshing was over. If all went as anticipated that would be the next day. The feast would have all the hearty foods of harvest time. There would be cabbage-dill salad, tomato-cucumber-onion salad, home preserved dill pickles, stuffed bell peppers topped with tomato sauce and bread crumbs or cheese, breaded fried eggplant, and most likely creme caramel[47], the favorite dessert for many Bulgarians with its delicate flavor and smooth consistency.

Around the cooking stove the older children gathered to talk. A few of the boys had sticks or pieces of discarded utensils with which they dawdled. Some drew in the dust as they sat cross-legged on the dirt floor. Others held their particular prizes in the fire of the open stove to watch the ends of sticks or metal glow bright red and eventually white as it got hotter.

They respected fire, knowing its potential. Each made certain he was far from the flames and away from the searing heat, his hand protected with old rags while he held his 'toy' in the fire. Occasionally one of them yelped suddenly and shot, like a bullet, from the stove when he accidentally touched its hot side.

Next to the stove was a rickety ladder made of branches lashed together with hemp rope and nailed to the wall. The ladder would allow a diligent climber access to the small storage area at the top.

"If we get done with threshing today we'll be bringing chicken to the feast tomorrow," one of the boys said.

Vancho knew that several people would bring chicken, the staple of the village. *I wish it were winter when the pigs are killed,* Vancho thought. *Instead of chicken we might have pork. I like pork rind. I can't wait for it, scraped and baked 'till its hard and scratches the roof of my mouth if I'm not careful. If I try to eat it too soon it sizzles and burns my mouth!* He knew from last year. *But its wonderful snap and crunch is worth the risk of a minor burn. Nothing beats baked pork skin for flavor! If only I could have it all year long but once a year is better than never,* he figured.

Then he heard the others talking.

"Mama is making corn bread," one of Vancho's friend's said. "I heard her say we have to use up last year's corn meal to make room for the new crop."

"We've got lots of *sirene*[48] from our sheep. She keeps giving milk and we don't drink it all, so Mama made too much *sirene* this year. Even though its brine keeps it forever Mama wants to bring some."

Someone else offered, "Our tomatoes are still growing. I heard Mama say that she canned all we and *vuenah's*[49] family need until next year's crop, so she's making tomato/parsley salad for the feast. She said she might bring *lutika*[50] too. I have to pick the hot peppers and my sister has to dig the onions and then chop them with the hot peppers. I guess it depends on when we get home to sleep before the feast. I have to be able to get up early enough to pick them. If the feast is tomorrow I hope we don't stay too late tonight."

Silence reigned for a long time.

Talking about sleep seemed to impose it on Vancho as he watched the fire flicker but he fought to keep his eyes open. Blinking didn't help anymore, so he dug his fists into his eye sockets and rubbed to win the battle against fatigue. He noticed some of the other boys getting restless and yawning. He hated it when someone else yawned because he had to follow suit. Admitting to sleepiness in front of friends bothered him. He felt as if he were not growing up. He never saw the adults look sleepy.

Vancho's friend spoke of his brother's wedding next summer, but to the other children that was grown-up talk. They cared nothing for the wedding itself. What did interest them was the fun and festivity they all knew would follow.

Vancho lost his sleepiness temporarily as they talked about the *mekitzi* that some villagers offered children at weddings. He loved the taste of bread fried in fresh sunflower oil pressed from the village's own sunflowers. Sometimes *mekitzi* were even dusted with refined sugar from their sugar cane. Then not only was it greasy, warm, soft, and wonderful but it was also sweet, never too sweet. He could always taste the delicacy of the bread and oil no matter how much sugar was on it.

Next to *Bop*, Rogozen's Chicken Soup, or pork rind he loved *mekitzi* best!

He heard the children talk about dancing, running, and laughing in the warm summer weather.

Unable to continue his fight against sleep, he dozed, sounds of quiet talk fading.

How long he slept he didn't know.

Then suddenly, shrieking in pain, Vancho jumped up and ran, no longer asleep but awakened by a painful stabbing in his back. Was he awake? He only reacted! Where could he go? How could he get away? It hurt! He couldn't think. He ran straight ahead. In front of him was the wall next to the stove. The rungs made of sticks were almost flat against the wall. He grabbed one with his small hand.

I've got to get up! he thought, clambering up one or two rungs screaming as he climbed.

I've got to get away from it! He could hardly feel his feet. He didn't know everyone was looking at him.

Some of the small children were now awake. Babies' screams added to the horror-filled sounds coming from Vancho. Some adults ran into the room.

They were confused.

When he had gone up six rungs he felt his legs being pulled. He tried to hold on with his hands, his hip burning as though on fire. He knew that he was almost horizontal. How could that be?

People go up and down, not sideways! My legs should be down; his mind somehow managed to tell him. His screaming never stopped. His red distorted face was wet with tears.

Then he felt himself falling.

Expressing intolerable anguish, his screams continued. What was happening to him? When would the awfulness end?

He landed across someone's arms. One arm was under the front of his legs and another under his chest. He saw the legs, below the knees, of the one holding him. He knew it was Mama.

Turning his head as best he could, he saw her face.

Her eyes looked angry. Her mouth was opening and closing. She must be saying something. He couldn't hear anything. His siren voice blocked all other sound.

His mother was shaking her head, ordering him to silence. He would not be silent. Nothing could quiet him.

Wrenching from her arms he tried in vain to climb the ladder again. She restrained him. Then she saw a spoon handle, still glowing from the heat, slip from his short pant leg to the ground where he was jumping, struggling to climb again.

Holding him firmly with one hand she stooped to pick up the handle, dropping it quickly at first touch. It had burned her thumb and finger. Then she understood.

Quickly Mama scooped him into her arms and began to run, Mariana at her side, both of them crying as they rushed toward home.

Vancho's screams turned hoarse, still very alarming.

Hours earlier the sunset had tinted the sky with a glowing peach color, now the earth was barely illuminated by the millions of stars overhead. There must have been a new moon because the night was as black as the horrid deed done to Vancho.

Mother and Sister prayed to not trip in the inky night during their dash to get Vancho safely home and treated.

Vancho was still wailing as his mother quietly set him on his feet inside the door of their home and gently, with eyes now filled with tears of compassion, removed his pants.

There beneath his clothing were two four-inch circles of seeping flesh, burned raw by the red-hot spoon. One spot was burned more deeply than the other was. The fabric of his pants had apparently held the spoon against his tender skin while he was sitting. The other wound was on the outside of his upper thigh, burned when the spoon slipped from its resting-place, touching him again before dropping to the dirt.

The child's cries were no longer audible but still wrenching his small body into spasms of contortion.

Mama and Sister carefully put fresh well water, from the jug by the door, on the open wounds.

"Perhaps if we can keep them from infection he will live through this," his mother reasoned. "Only God knows for sure."

If only the churches were not closed, she thought. *I would take my child for prayer and healing but now they are boarded up. I fear what the neighbors would do to us if I sought the pope's help.*

Either from exhaustion or from the added pain of bathing the raw flesh, Vancho's terror-filled eyes closed, finally ending his screams.

Whether in restful sleep or the sleep of unconsciousness his mother didn't know, but for Vancho it was welcome.

He awoke two days later with the sun barely up. Being on his stomach he was uncomfortable. His back from the waist down felt stiff and numb. Mercifully, he had forgotten what had happened. If someone were to ask he would have said he felt a strange, numb-like pain, all over his backside and legs. When he tried to move the pain increased. He elected to lie still.

Slowly turning his head to see where he was, he realized he was not in bed. He was off the floor, directly under the open front window. Mama had fashioned a long cot wide enough for him to lie on. It was comfortably padded with blankets. He felt the cool morning breeze brush over his back side, stinging the open wound and comforting it, both at the same time. Trying to swallow he noticed that his throat was also sore. He couldn't figure why it should hurt so badly.

I remember having a nightmare in which I was screaming. Can my throat be sore from that? He thought. Nothing was clear to him and he fell back asleep.

All day and all night he lay on his stomach. How he slept! A deep, healing sleep, a sleep of confusing and often alarming dreams. Sometimes as he came into wakefulness he felt as if he was burning with fever. At other times he was cold. Either Sister or Mama, it seemed, were constantly waking him and insisting he drink a few sips of water. He could not raise himself enough to see outside. He continued to sleep. He had never slept so much in his life. Occasionally he drank a little soup or ate a bite of bread. Mostly he slept.

One day, several days later, he opened his eyes. Above his waist on his back he felt an unusual warmth and heaviness. He opened his eyes and realized that he was across his mother's lap, face down.

The warmth was his mother's hands resting on his back.

She was not fully awake, sitting on the bed with her back against the wall.

Vancho's feet were on the bed and so was his face, with his stomach across his mother's legs. Never before had he awakened in this position. He was puzzled.

When he tried to pull his legs under himself to get up, agonizing, shooting pain went down his legs and up his back.

What happened to me? He wondered. As he continued to awaken he halfway remembered the terrible night.

"Vancho," his mother said.

"Yes, Mamo?" he replied.

"You were badly hurt. We thought you might die, but I think you will get well. Don't try to move. I'll help you get up."

He let her move him, mainly because his own effort hurt. Little by little, very slowly they worked their way to the edge of the bed where his mother could get her feet onto the floor, easing him off her lap.

"You cannot wear any clothing below your waist. I'll put an old dress and sweater of Sister's on you. I'll sew the backside of the dress so that the fabric won't rub on your sores. From the front you'll be modestly covered, so don't worry about that. When you rest you must rest on your stomach. I have put a white paste on your burns. That should help them heal. While we both are awake instead of sitting you can lie on my lap. I do not know how long it will take to heal but until it does, you cannot play. If you get dirt onto the wound it may become infected and then you might die. We won't let that happen. You must be very careful to do everything I tell you. This is very serious! Do you understand me?"

"Yes, Mamo," Vancho committed.

Last winter a classmate had been showing off. He had scooped snow into his cap before laughingly putting it on. As the snow melted, dripping down his face, the children, including Vancho, had also laughed. Shortly afterward there was no laughter when the boy was buried in the village cemetery, having died of spinal meningitis. The chilling snow was suspected of increasing his susceptibility.

There was no coming back to life from death. Vancho had seen that first hand. Although frightened, he was calmed by his mother's firm voice. He knew that he would obey her.

He wondered how he had been injured.

As days went by, and then weeks, he pieced together what he heard from a variety of sources.

It was said that when Vancho's father had been accused of treason some villagers began to hate him, believing that he had jeopardized their very lives. With Vancho's father gone those villagers' hatred had turned toward the family, impelling a half-witted youngster to act. When the boy had seen his opportunity to punish Vancho and perhaps to feel good about acting out his own hatred, he took it. Heating a spoon in the fire meant to comfort the children, he had dropped the white-hot metal down Vancho's shirt. He had had enough 'self-protective' wits about him to wait until Vancho's eyes had closed in near-sleep, so that he wouldn't be seen. He had not, of course, considered that there would be many others who would see what he did.

A few of those were pleased that someone in the 'traitor's' family was hurt.

Most thought it a cruel child's prank and dismissed it.

Vancho's mother considered it an act so hideous that she remembered it with other offenses, leading her to the major decision she would soon make.

7. DECISION

Vancho's wounds healed into nasty two-inch diameter red scars. The deeper wound left a sunken place in his flesh but he was alive. Recovery to this point had taken ten months. Now the scars needed to fade in color.

He busied himself in the side garden hoeing weeds.

At Sister's cry Vancho ran to the back of the house to join her. He found her with Mama staring at a disturbing sight, a small dying fire.

Mama stood quietly, lips pressed together. Sister was saying, "No! No!" repeatedly. Tears spilled from her eyes.

Smoke puffed impotently at the base of the brick structure, which served as both their home and their draft animals' shelter.

Vancho stood next to Mama looking toward the smoke when he felt her hardened, rough hands on his shoulder and head. He felt himself drawn close into his mother's warmth. Standing soundlessly he felt her body tremble.

After several minutes she asked barely audibly to no one in particular, "How could they do this? They have known me all my life. How can they be so hateful? I praise God that there isn't any damage but the message is clear. I must give everything to the Colhose and maybe even leave. Next time their hateful act might end differently."

The *Colhose* was the new government's method of collective farming. Each family that joined contributed its land and most of its farm equipment to the collective. Large plots were farmed with modern government-bought machinery. The machinery was built to do much work at one time. The biggest weapons Vancho had seen passing his home seemed small by comparison to those monsters. There were machines to prepare the soil, to plant it, and to harvest the crops. The threshing machine was almost twice the size of the village's thresher which those who were not in the Colhose continued to use each harvest. With such large and diverse equipment fewer people were needed to raise the same quantity of crops. Farming in the Colhose became an eight to five job.

Many of the villagers who had already abandoned farming turned to the city for their livelihood.

The Colhose, the government, would stop at nothing until all the village's land was under its control.

The socialist government had been responsible for the execution of Vancho's father. Mama wanted nothing to do with the bureaucracy that treated human life, especially her husband's, so cheaply. However, she knew that without the help of others she could not work her land. Like a few others in the village she had continued to stay in Rogozen and do the best she could using the old system.

Against her desires Vancho's mother had tried for two consecutive years to join the Colhose in order to have help when it was needed. Both times, entrance was refused her. The officials had 'read between the lines' and had known that she had no true intention of 'joining' them in their atheistic ways; her faith in God was too strong. Baba, Diado, and most of the other relatives were already in the Colhose.

Now, what was she to do? Without totally 'giving in' to them she and her two children might starve. The village had changed. People didn't help each other as they used to ... unless they were members of the Colhose working in the collective. There were not enough people outside the Colhose to complete the work needed to maintain life.

Together the three continued to stare at the spot where the feeble attempt to destroy their home or their composure had taken place. Perhaps the one(s) who had done this wanted only to frighten them away knowing that the brick and mortar structure would not burn. Perhaps it was no more than a threat. Or was it a practical joke? Mama could not believe it was a joke, cruel or otherwise.

Whatever the motive Mama made a decision. Drawing upon her inner strength supplied by Christ Jesus, her life companion, she announced in a clear, steady voice, "I will go to city hall and talk to them ... again.

"Farming is my life. Whatever I must do, with the help of God I will do!"

A brief word of conviction and their gloom lifted. Sister wiped her face and stared at her mother realizing that she was indeed serious. She smiled her relief. Vancho turned away and began his chores. Mama turned her back on the catalyst of her decision and sought a hand trowel to cultivate the flowers. The anger, the fear, the indecision were gone. Her strength had returned.

Later that morning the family hitched the cow to her cart and they climbed in. Sister sat on the seat with Mama, Vancho in the bed of the cart looking back at his home as they moved toward City Hall. He was thankful that they were not being driven out, never to return. When they got to their destination Vancho walked with his hand firmly in Mama's. She walked quickly, determined.

"When we get to the office you children sit on the bench and wait for me." Mama instructed.

They walked toward the old brick building with the twelve-foot-tall wooden double doors having two balconies on either side of the entrance. There were about six tall narrow windows on both the first and second floors. They marched up the wide stairs to a long hall.

Down to the right Vancho saw an office with a closed door directly across from a long, rough but sturdy-looking bench. Mama walked decisively to that door, which opened into the controller's office.

Being obedient the children remembered their mother's instructions. Without hesitation Sister backed into the bench, jumped slightly and was on board. Vancho literally had to climb up to sit. The bench was uncomfortable for him. The hard flat seat was designed for an adult. He had either to push himself to the uncompromising straight back with his legs in front of him in a rigid ninety-degree angle or sit near the edge with his feet dangling above the floor by at least fourteen inches. He chose the latter of the two positions. Hanging his legs threatened them with numbness as the back of his thighs rested on the seat, cutting off blood circulation. He hoped Mama would hurry. He thought about the time in Malorad[51] when his legs went numb and hurt from sitting too long on the village chairs.

To occupy his time he looked at the empty wall facing him next to the controller's door, nothing of interest there. Turning his eyes to the other side of the door he saw a larger than life picture of Giorgi Dimitrov smiling at him. He knew that as a "hero" of Bulgaria Dimitrov lived and worked in Sofia, the country's capital.

Will I ever see Sofia? It doesn't seem likely without an army. I'll probably never go farther from Rogozen than Malorad. How can a peasant boy like me dream of going to Sofia? It is so far and we don't have a way to get there.

His puzzled thoughts brought him back to reality where he continued to evaluate his surroundings.

There was nothing else on the wall.

Although the ceiling had two, lighted, bare electric bulbs it was almost as dark indoors as outdoors after sunset. It was still relatively light outside and it seemed to him that it should also be light inside but there were no exterior windows to bring that light into the hall.

I wonder if there are windows in the rooms behind those closed doors, he thought as he looked at the solid wooden doors every twenty feet along the hallway. Then he remembered, *Of course there are. I like the way they look from outside. It's just so dark in here that I forgot.* He felt foolish reasoning with himself although he knew no one was aware of what he was thinking.

He looked to the far end of the corridor on his left. There was a wall without doorways or windows. To the far right was an opening for the descending stairway. Hands and equipment moving the length of the hall had left grime about three feet above the floor. Above and below that foot-wide smudge, the dull off-white paint was chipped and cracked. In places there were actual gouges in the plaster.

Obediently, the children sat and waited.

Vancho heard voices. His eyes leapt toward the door from where they came. He tried to hear the words but couldn't until Mama's familiar voice was raised to its fullest, "You have what you wanted. Why can't you be decent to us?"

It always frightened him to hear Mama shout. Today was no exception. He sat waiting uneasily. His eyes were now riveted on the door through which Mama had gone. When it was flung open, banging against the dirty wall and resounding in the cavernous hallway like a bomb exploding, he was not caught off guard. He did not expect what he saw. Mama's set jaw and narrowed eyes made the adrenaline flow into his system and he was ready for anything.

The door hit the wall so loudly that he had instinctively covered his ears as his eyes held the image of Mama's anger coming into the hallway. Never had he known her more agitated than at that moment.

Mama didn't pause at their seats but roughly grabbed his hand, jerking him along with her. He stumbled until his shorter legs could match her momentum. He fell into stride, two steps for her one. Mama grabbed Sister's hand. Sister started breathing fast. She had not expected to be quickly pulled away.

They were all puffing from the near-run they made from that bench in the city hall building to their wagon. Nothing was said during the short ride home.

When Mama returned to normal she told them, "They will not accept us in the Colhose. They tell me that as enemies of the people our kind has no place here. I have given them our land and our animals. The only thing left is our home. We can no longer stay in Rogozen."

Did Vancho hear correctly?

Did Mama say we have to leave our home? He questioned in his mind. He had known this home, this house, this village, these people all of his nine years.

Where would we go? Most of Mama and Tatko's family lives in Rogozen. The others live three kilometers away in Malorad but they have a Colhose too. I know Mama wouldn't try to live in Malorad without land. There is someone related to us in Sofia but that is too far away. What does she mean?

As though she could read his mind she said, "I don't know where we will go or what we will do, but we cannot stay here!"

After a few days Mama said to Vancho, "I am taking you to Baba and Diado's home. I must talk with them for several hours. You will spend the night there while we talk. Then I will go home and return for you in the morning."

That night at Baba and Diado's Vancho heard Mama begin to pour out the story after they thought that he was asleep. He heard her express her concern for her family and her conviction that they must leave. He was numb. What was he supposed to feel? He couldn't imagine going away. He couldn't imagine living anywhere but in Rogozen. It was even hard staying with his grandparents, not knowing for certain when he would go home.

"Petra," said Diado, "You go to Sofia. Find work. It is a big impersonal city. They won't persecute you there. We will be happy to raise our grandchildren. We love them. Besides, with our son dead perhaps the children will help fill the void of loneliness we feel."

In spite of Vancho's desire to listen sleep deadened his hearing.

In his dreams he was with Mama. They were hoeing the vegetable garden together.

"I will never leave you," she said as she wrapped her arms around him. In his dream he felt safe. He had heard those words from her when awake many times. He believed them to be true.

Perhaps in his dream Vancho subconsciously recalled what Mama had often read to him from the Bible before socialism took over the country. God had spoken through Moses to Joshua within the hearing of Israel, "I will never leave you nor forsake you."[52]

Even though Vancho loved Baba and Diado, Mama was the one with whom he had spent his life. She was always there when he needed her. She had nursed him after he had been burned. Without her perseverance and strictness with him he would not have survived. He knew that and loved her for it.

When Tatko had been taken away Vancho had become the man of the household. He would always take care of Mama and Sister no matter where they went. Mama needed him just as surely as he needed her. He wanted to prove he could be trusted. *When I become a man no one will come between Mama and me*, he often thought.

Waking to a new day Vancho was uneasy. *Am I still thinking about my dream?* He wondered. *No, my dream was a good one. It must be something else. Where is Sister?*

Oh, last night Mama, Baba, and Diado were talking. Now I remember. Sister wasn't with us. I don't know where she is.

A shiver ran itself the length of his spine. *Mama won't leave me with Baba and Diado. She can't*, he thought.

After rising, he found Mama having tea with Baba in the outdoor 'dining room' waiting for him to awaken.

Mother and son walked silently home together.

Several days of normalcy followed. Vancho's apprehension faded.

Going to school, practicing his singing after school hours and studying after dinner kept Vancho busy.

He was featured as soloist in the school choir. Everyone loved to listen to his sweet soprano voice when he sang. The whole village knew he was gifted. Once he had overheard the adults talking about the wisdom of his being trained as a professional singer. When the village had parades he was always asked to lead, like a drum major. He liked the prestigious position.

Schoolwork was always enjoyable for Vancho. He liked the mental challenge of math and science. He worked diligently until he could successfully do every math problem without cheating. Because of his tenacity, whenever he was called to the board to work out a problem he was quick and accurate. He pressed himself to understand each principle of science and the math surrounding it before moving ahead to new concepts. Although political history was not among his interests he knew that he had to work to earn an A or B in that class as in all others, or take the whole year over. Unlike some of the village children he had never had to re-take a school year.

Sometimes lately he had had time for an hour or so of soccer before bed.

Mama was proud of him for working hard and being serious about his schoolwork. He rarely got into trouble or neglected his responsibilities. Only twice did his teacher call Mama into school for Vancho's lack of homework or for disciplinary measures. After school on those occasions Mama administered a swift decisive swat with a sturdy spoon to where he sat and his behavior changed.

Mama, Sister, and he continued doing the chores, preparing food, and enjoying life in Rogozen.

One late afternoon in spring Vancho came home from school after choir practice. Mama was not home from planting the fields. Sister was busy somewhere outside. He hadn't seen her since school let out.

Maybe she went to help Mama finish planting today, he thought. *I'll surprise them and have dinner waiting. I'm getting hungry myself. That way we can eat sooner.*

He set about his self-imposed task of making *bop*. He loved to watch the pot's volatile activity as the beans played leapfrog with each other but today he couldn't waste time watching. He must dice onions and dried tomatoes. Sautéing the onions until soft, he combined the boiled beans, caramelized onions, and tomatoes, keeping the soup simmering.

Then he waited for Mama and Sister to arrive home. He knew they would be dirty, tired, and hungry.

What a surprise awaited them!

With smiles of appreciation Mama and Sister ate their soup, praising him for his thoughtfulness. With their kind words Vancho felt like an accomplished chef until he took his first mouthful.

How can they smile and eat, much less enjoy, such tasteless soup? The burned onions and beans are awful! Next time, he promised himself, *I will remember to add salt and to stir it while it is boiling so it won't burn.*

66

His sister and mother ate silently and hungrily. They were apparently grateful. They refilled their bowls several times. Vancho ate more bread than usual with the original small portion of soup. His appetite diminished he hoped that he could last until breakfast.

When dinner was over the soup pot was empty.

8. Abandoned

Throughout spring and summer young Vancho was sad. Having little control over his emotions when he thought about his sister, he tried to think of other things. She had left by train to live with relatives in Sofia. Mama had said, "She will get better schooling there". Vancho knew that because food was scarce Sister had been chosen, as the older child, to go elsewhere to live until things stabilized for Mama.

Fall's fresh air helped keep his mind free from problems. Sweet fragrance in the wind whirling in wild undisciplined gusts down the road buoyed his spirits. Leaves jumped from where they lay into mini-cyclones and danced as though to music.

Vancho liked walking home in the flurry of fall. Sometimes he raced the leaves, twirling with them and laughing with the joy of being alive.

Jumping up two steps at a time he found Mama inside their home packing some of his things in a cloth bag.

"I'm taking you to Diado and Baba's," she said simply.

Along the way he chattered about his day.

Mama seemed to listen, but unlike herself on their usual walks together she was silent. Vancho didn't notice. He was too busy with his happy life. His hair was tussled by the unruly wind and he liked it.

"I was the first student called to work math homework on the board today," he said. "It took me only a few minutes to do five problems. The teacher told the class that everyone should study like I do! Mamo, that made me proud! You should be proud too. You make me do the work. Some of the students' parents don't insist that their children finish their assignments like you make me. I think that is why they don't do well in school. Someday I will do something with my mathematics, just wait, Mamo. You'll see. I like solving problems especially with numbers. Maybe I will be an engineer."

When they got to his father's parents' home his mother went inside to talk and to help prepare dinner. Vancho joined the neighboring boys playing soccer for an hour before everyone had to go inside. Vancho was hungry when called to dinner.

His grandmother's cooking met his expectations as he had hoped it would. From experience he knew that she prepared the foods he best enjoyed, communicating her love for him. She always provided more than enough and he, in turn, ate enough to please her, often leaving the table feeling as though he wouldn't be able to eat for a week.

That night for dinner Baba had made stuffed red peppers preparing beans as she did for soup, for *bop*. When they were soup-ready she allowed them to continue boiling until the liquid was almost gone. Then she added flour for additional thickening. Seasoned just right, the peppers almost melted in Vancho's mouth. He loved eating Baba's food. She served food far tastier than he could make.

After their meal Mama said, "You are sleeping here tonight."

Vancho usually enjoyed staying at his grandparents. It was wonderfully cozy nestled between them in the dark, feeling protected.

Sometimes he wondered what it would have been like to still have Tatko living at home. *Would I feel more secure than I do now?* He wondered. Then he invariably came to the same conclusion. *I don't think that would be possible. I have everything with Mama.*

"It is time for bed now, Vancho," His mother said when he didn't move from the table.

"Where are you going?"

"I will be here." she responded sternly. Vancho didn't understand why she spoke sharply to him but he feared to ask.

When he awoke Mama was there, true to her word.

Mid-morning came and Mama said good-bye.

"Where are you going?" Vancho asked. He seemed to be asking that question a lot.

"I have to go to the capital, to Sofia, Little One," she said matter-of-factly. The tautness of her chin was no longer new to Vancho. The look on her face as she turned and walked away puzzled him.

"I'm going with you!" Vancho called and tried to follow. His grandfather's firm hold on his upper arms prevented his leaving. He tried to pull away. Diado's grip tightened. Vancho couldn't move.

"I want to be with you and Sister!" he yelled to his retreating mother.

Not able to join her he cried out, kicking to connect with his captor, to inflict pain and thus be released. He became a little boy fury. He had never displayed such temper. In fact neither he nor his grandfather knew that he was capable of such behavior. Without a word Diado held him. There was no getting away.

His mother's stiff back ignored him. She did not turn. He could do nothing but scream and cry and flail.

"Maaa maa!"

When her small figure was out of sight Vancho was released. He turned, running to the comfort of the quiet bedroom, flinging himself upon the bed. He buried his head in the bed coverings to muffle his sobs. Never had he felt so rejected and so completely alone. Baba and Diado were there but they did not fill this new deep emptiness.

No one had hinted that his mother would leave him.

Why did she do this? I don't want to stay with Diado and Baba! I want to live with Mama and Sister. Will I ever see them again? When she told me many months ago that we couldn't live in Rogozen any longer that meant me going with her. She wouldn't leave me and go alone. What is happening?

Vancho was abandoned. His hurt went to the core. There was no comforting him. He seemed consumed. Not even the burn that had threatened his life had been as devastating as this. A little boy's needs had been totally dismissed and with them he himself might as well have been dismissed.

Why not just push me off a cliff? He thought.

Only time and perhaps, someday, God's grace would restore his sense of balance. He could not begin to think of forgiving. He would certainly never forget!

Although it was only noon two hours of crying and shaking as though chilled had made him very tired. He fell easily into the arms of sleep.

When he woke it was dark, the middle of the night.

He was dressed in his nightclothes under the bed coverings, warm between his grandparents. If he got up he would wake them. Crying softly because there was nothing else he knew to do, he fell asleep again.

The next day and the next he went through the motions of living. Sometimes he forgot that Mama was gone. He would remember and feel guilty that he had forgotten. Most of the time he felt hollow as if someone had pulled out an important part from inside him and had not replaced it.

After a couple of weeks he found that he could still do well at school if he did his homework the evening it was assigned. Studies became more important to him than they had ever been. *Maybe,* he thought, *they are the reason for my being alive.*

Playing soccer regularly no longer interested him. Sometimes, maybe twice a week, he would want to kick the ball around. Someone was always willing to play but it was no longer his daily focus.

For two or three months Vancho existed with his grandparents. Somehow he endured.

No one spoke of Sister. He didn't know where she was. Sometimes he thought she must be with Mama in Sofia. *Mama loves her as much as she loves me. She has to be somewhere safe.* At other times he thought she was with other relatives or family friends in another village. *After all, she too is a child. At thirteen there is much time before finishing her education. After that there will be work or marriage but that is at least seven years away.*

Sometimes after waking he remembered dreaming of Mother and Sister. He lay still, focusing on his dream, willing it to be true and could hear their voices. Sometimes they sang, usually there was laughter and he did not want his sense of wellbeing to leave, even though it was dream-based.

Often his face would still be wet with tears upon waking. At those times he rarely remembered what he had been dreaming. *It is just as well*, he figured.

Long ago he had stopped asking Baba or Diado about Mama and Sister. They didn't answer his questions, seeming to act as if there were no mother or sister. They became his only family. He did not see any of his other relatives while he was with them.

Life had changed drastically. Sometimes he wondered if he had ever lived differently. When he thought about it nothing made sense except school, so he studied.

Ivan eleven years old in school uniform

9. City

In late summer of 1950 Vanko[53] was becoming a serious, quiet youngster. He did what he was told. He tried to choose what was right. He rarely caused problems for his grandparents in school or out.

Then one day, unannounced, Mama was there!

Was he awake? Was he really seeing Mama? He couldn't move. He couldn't talk. He could hardly breathe. In fact all he heard was the rhythmic thumping coming from somewhere inside him as he watched the most-beautiful, tired-looking woman he had ever seen reaching toward him.

As though hurled by an explosive Vanko was in Mama's arms. Hugging her tightly to himself he felt her smooth his hair and caress his cheeks with hands softer than he remembered.

"Where have you been, Mamo?" he asked. "No one told me anything about you after you left. I was afraid you were never coming back to me!" A soft sob left Vanko's mouth. He had trouble regaining his composure.

"*Teeho, deteto me.*[54] I am here now. We will not be separated again."

Feeling and smelling her clothing, contentment washed over him in waves. Such happiness! When Tatko had returned from the army the pleasure was not the same, not so...complete.

"Where is Sister? Did she come home with you? Are we going to live here with Diado and Baba? Will we go home to live?" Hope for the latter was evident in his voice.

Gently Mama pried him away from her. She took his hands in hers and looking into his eyes, smiled at his impatience.

"Let's find the others," she said. "You will know everything before long."

As usual his grandparents were working, tending the animals in the yard.

After the surprise reunion the four sat together on short, three-legged stools on the packed earth serving as the porch outside the back door of the house. There in the shade of an old tree they began talking. Roses releasing their aroma surrounded them with sweet fragrance.

Baba went indoors to prepare snacks and sok[55] while Diado asked questions of Mama.

"So where is our precious little girl?" was his first question.

As Diado carefully listened to Mama's response an expression of immense sorrow replaced cheerfulness on his face. His age and weariness showed.

Vanko listened and learned.

"Sister is living with some of my new friends in Sofia. As an acting daughter in that family she is in no danger of being sent away by the authorities. She was admitted to an art school in the city. She seems to be doing well. I have had little direct contact with her. I have been busy with my primary job of finding work...." Mama paused before talking again.

"Because I am not a citizen of Sofia I have been staying there illegally. If I am discovered by the housing authorities I will be sent out of the city and will never be allowed to work or live there. Becoming a citizen requires work and a place to live."

Vanko learned that with the socialist government and the collective farm many farmers had emigrated to Sofia.

"There is a shortage of housing. Good jobs are scarce. Many people are left on the streets and are forced to go back to their villages with only the hope of working in the Colhose. It is not easy. I am extremely tired but I will succeed. No one will ever need to take care of my children or of me."

Allowing Sister to stay with friends for a time did not seem to her to be incongruous with her last statement.

"I have been helped by kind people who feel compassion for me. They were all Orthodox Christians. They have not renounced Jesus Christ in order to join the Communist Party.

"For two weeks I stayed with the family that has taken Sister. They found three other families with whom I could rotate approximately every two weeks. I would move with little or no advance notice whenever they told me. I would go from one family to another in no particular order. They did not need to tell me why I had to leave. I knew that fear drove them. I would leave with a heavy heart and also with appreciation for the time of hiding that they had provided.

"All those who helped me had risked being caught in 'subversive activity' by hiding me. If caught they would suffer. Either there would be heavy fines, imprisonment, or perhaps both."

She talked with deep love and respect for these people whom she had not met before leaving Rogozen. The people who were willing to help her in her life or death situation had become her new family.

"Last week I finally found work. It is hard work." she told them. "The war destroyed much of the city. Workers are needed to rebuild it. I have been trying to find suitable work for months. I had to realize finally that I am qualified to work in the city only in construction. The government has hired me to begin learning the trade of bricklaying this week."

She stopped.

There was silence.

Vanko watched Diado focus attention on his sock. Baba was slowly eating a piece of *lukanka* as she looked unsmilingly into the distance.

Mama's chest moved noticeably as she dragged air into her lungs in a tired, forced way. He saw her hand move slowly to her eye as she wiped away a tear, preventing it from falling.

Quickly he averted his eyes. He didn't understand what made grown ups cry. He felt uncomfortable and helpless. He knew there wasn't much he could say or do to make Mama feel better and that made him unhappy. Mama had always been strong except when Tatko had been sentenced. Vanko had nothing to give her now in her weakness.

He bit into the crunchy crust of his bread. It was good but not as good as it would have been under different circumstances. He sat chewing and waited.

Still no one spoke. He knew better than to break the silence. He did not want to look at his family again. He sat hunched over studying the ground between his feet.

Finally Mama began again. He had to listen hard to hear what she was saying. Her soft voice had become shaky.

"It is time for Vanko to join me. I must take him with me on the train to Sofia tomorrow. Moving around can be slow while I am avoiding the authorities. I must be at work early in two days and we must settle ourselves in Sofia tomorrow evening."

"Do you have a place to stay?" Diado asked. Vanko thought his hoarse voice sounded mean and gruff.

"School will start in the fall. By then I will have found a permanent place to stay. Tomorrow I will show Vanko the city and where we are living. No one will question him about his home. In a week or two we will find our own place. This is not what I would have chosen for my child but I must have my son with me! It has almost killed me not having either of my children."

Vanko was uneasy not knowing what lay ahead. He wanted to trust his mother because he knew that he had no choice in the matter but found it difficult. She had betrayed him in abandonment. Now she spoke of dangerous situations in Sofia, in a strange and distant place.

I will not know anyone. I will be away from all the familiar places. I know Sofia is big but it has to be okay. I will be strong for Mama, he thought.

He raised his eyes to see Baba standing. Now she was wiping her tears as she turned toward the garden.

Looking at Mama he saw the set of her jaw. Before she had abandoned him he had learned to understand that expression. He now knew it was determination. He knew that no one would succeed in changing her resolve.

Diado continued staring at his feet. His eyes were wide open but Vanko could tell he was seeing nothing.

"Petra," he finally said without looking at her. "We know you have to do what you believe is right. We want to keep Vanko with us. He is a bright boy and no trouble but he is your son. What more needs to be said? You are strong. Even though you have been alone you have raised our grandchildren well. We appreciate what you have done. It will be sad for us to have our grandchildren far away but so be it. Let them come to visit us when they aren't in school. We will continue to help them learn to farm. Please don't keep them from us, at least not for long."

Mama thought for awhile before answering.

"Both you and I love Pavel, even though he has been taken from us. Whether they actually executed him or not doesn't matter now. We may never know what happened to him. I know that he may never come back but I also know that he wants his children with me. You, his parents, have suffered as I have as a result of his sentence. Now I must be both mother and father to my children if God gives me strength for that. As far as the children coming back to Rogozen in the summers, I can only say, 'What will be, will be.' I will make no promises. I do not know what the future holds."

Diado lifted his glass wearily and drank slowly. It appeared to Vanko that his grandfather's shoulders leaned forward as his body shrunk. Diado's eyes became moist, blinking rapidly as he tried to swallow the mouthful of *sok*. His chin trembled.

The talking ended. Vanko felt an unrecognizable heaviness around him that made him uncomfortable.

Sitting there became difficult for the almost eleven-year old child. He got up. His body needed activity to rid itself of the anxiety he was feeling. When he walked into the garden Baba told him where to hoe. *How does she know what I need?* He thought. Finding the tool and focusing his energy on doing something useful helped him regain his composure.

Before long Baba was telling him, "Wash for dinner. We are having your favorite today, baked chicken. I cooked it mostly for you. I fixed beans and vegetables to go with it and we have a salad and fresh bread." Rarely did anyone eat chicken anymore except for a special meal. They were celebrating with a dinner having a festival appearance. The mood, however, was anything but festive.

Somehow the night was over and morning came.

Together the family of four walked five miles to the train stop.

'Good-byes' were said amongst hard hugs, tears, and trembling voices.

Vanko and Mama's train started toward Sofia. Turning in his seat Vanko looked out of the yellowing window. He saw Diado's hand waving and his grandmother waving her handkerchief in farewell. He waved back, watching them as long as possible, then sat back in his seat next to Mama trying to relax.

He gazed out of the window of the fast-moving vehicle transporting him to strange and unknown places. Fields moved past with people bent over working in them. He wondered if the people knew that a little boy was leaving home. He wondered if they cared or would care if they knew.

Nothing visible happened to Vanko on that relatively easy train trip but something inside him changed. Had he lost or gained something? He was too inexperienced at life to notice anything. It was quiet and subtle. He would have said that nothing happened. For all purposes Vanko seemed to be the same boy.

As they neared the train stop in Sofia, however, Vanko felt the muscles under his eyes and around his mouth tighten. He was losing his tender childhood.

There are so many buildings here, he thought. *Look at all those people. Nobody talking to anybody. They look unfriendly and busy. They run around like the ants I watch at home. It looks like they don't know where they're going but they are going fast. I don't like it here. I hope that after Mama works awhile we can go back home.* He withdrew into himself and became quieter although he had said nothing on the trip.

"Vanko, we are here. Let's get off," his mother said breaking into his brooding thoughts.

They left the train, Mama carrying their small bag with a few items of clothing; an extra pair of underpants and socks for each, one shirt, and two pairs of pants for Vanko and two dresses for Mama. They had eaten the lunch Baba had insisted on packing. They planned to keep the bottle which had carried their water. Such bottles were common in Bulgaria. For generations Bulgarian men had been using the art of weaving willow twigs to cover them in beautiful patterns. Forming handles out of the weaving material made the bottles portable. Each family used its preferred pattern. This bottle was their only tie to Rogozen and the people that still lived there. It had been a gift from Mama's closest friend on Mama's return trip to the village to get Vanko.

Upon leaving the train they went to the first of many places they were to stay.

Vanko was grateful for a place but he was not comfortable there.

The family that took them in was helpful, giving what they could, and more. The apartment itself was small. It had a kitchen/living room, a bath and two eight by ten feet rooms for sleeping. Six unrelated people living in such tight quarters was difficult.

Vanko slept on the floor in a corner with two blankets and no pillow. Mama slept on the daybed/sofa in the small living room area.

The other people didn't talk much. They rarely spoke to Mama. Sometimes when Vanko tried to sleep he heard tense or angry voices coming from their hosts' room.

Every day Mama bought two loaves of fresh bakery bread on her way from work. One of those was her thank you for her friends' help.

Although Vanko saw that Mama was dirty and fatigued after work she always prepared a meal for the two of them. Sometimes it wasn't enough to fill the boy's stomach but it had to do. He knew better than to complain.

Vanko learned where his school was, the quickest way there and how long it took. He didn't like leaving his shelter earlier than necessary.

Sometimes it doesn't seem right that Chicho taught me to ride a bike in Rogozen, Vanko thought. *I don't have one here. I wish there were something I could do here besides go to school and wait around afterwards for Mama to get off work.*

Every morning Mama gave Vanko a few *stutinki*[56] to buy yogurt on his walk to school. There was always a line of people waiting, sometimes a few but often there were many.

At school he had observed other children getting into their seats late. The teacher put their names on the chalkboard at the front of the room. During the principal's daily rounds he wrote the information in his notebook and immediately dismissed the child from class. The next day a parent was required to be at school, missing much needed work, to reinstate his child.

Vanko knew he couldn't be late. Mama had to work every day or risk losing her job.

On the days he chose to have breakfast when the line for yogurt was long he had to run at top speed to get to school on time. Sometimes he chose to miss breakfast.

The school served a snack of biscuit and jam at morning break. At lunch he was served a portion of bean soup or vegetables, a glass of milk, and an apple. Each school day lunch was different but somehow it all tasted the same. In mid-afternoon there was another serving of bread and jam.

The other students at school weren't like his friends in Rogozen. He had trouble getting to know them. He found no one with whom to play chess. He was a beginner and knew that if he played with anyone at his new school they would beat him. He would learn to play better and his opponents would enjoy the games because they would probably be easy wins but no one was willing to play.

He began walking with an overconfident air after school. He strutted when he saw other children around. He talked tough and scrunched his face to look mean. He didn't continue to try and make friends with his classmates, figuring that they didn't like him anyway.

Many afternoons before Mama's work finished he roamed the streets of Sofia looking for mischief. He usually found it. Sometimes he would sneak through the back door of the movie theater to see the latest 'Mickey Mouse' cartoon without paying. Sometimes he would sit outside and watch the backside of the screen seeing the *keno*[57] backwards.

Later in the evening he would often climb fruit trees in the yards near where he was living and eat the fruit he picked and sometimes store it inside his shirt to eat at his convenience. Mama never questioned him about the fruit stains.

One day he climbed a cherry tree intending to eat his fill. While he was perched twenty feet up the door of the house opened. Then he heard a man's voice calling, "Who's there? Where are you?" *If my foot slips from the branch, against which it is braced*, he thought, *I'll be caught and taken to the police station.* Just as he felt his leg losing sensation from being in one position for so long the man went inside. Vanko scurried down the tree and took note of the house. *I'll never steal from that house again*, he thought but it didn't dissuade him from thefts at other locations. Fruit was food.

When a group of boys younger than he was playing marbles he strode to their circle, "Give me those!" he'd bully in his newly learned voice. If the boys refused he might fight them. Usually they would run and he would gather up the six or so marbles lying on the ground where the boys had left them in their flight. In time he had his 'own' sack of marbles and the younger boys feared him. In spite of his 'success' he was unhappy. He had no friends with whom to play. Worst of all, he didn't seem to like himself anymore.

Back in Rogozen he could play his *harmonica*[58] to comfort himself when needed and to entertain friends or develop new ones through music. Vanko had learned to play in the last year of living in the village. He and everyone who heard him enjoyed what he played.

Sometimes Vanko took his soccer ball to a nearby empty lot in Sofia and begin kicking it. At those times other boys would gather and a spontaneous game would start. Those were the best times, but the games lasted only a short while until the boys had to go home and he didn't get to know the players.

Vanko had no home. He was tired of moving from apartment to apartment, from family to family. He knew Mama was thankful for a place to stay but he became angry. He couldn't tell her of his feelings. She no longer had patience with him.

Mama's life was difficult. Each day she mixed mortar and carried mortar or bricks in a hod on her shoulder up an inclined plank to the bricklayers. For eight or nine hours she worked, carrying her heavy load up the plank, balancing on the narrow board. If she fell she might fall only a few feet to a platform but she might also fall to the ground tens of feet below. Hers was a difficult job. Physically it was taxing but emotionally it was almost unbearable. She fought her fear of falling each time she began her ascent.

Every day she hoped the job supervisor would allow her to try laying brick. Although that job was tedious and would hurt her hands and back she would no longer have to think about her balance or falling.

Every week she also hoped to find a place for herself and her son to stay. Neither of her hopes was soon realized. One week, two, three, then she began counting months.

After a few months of life in Sofia Vanko's mama took him for a walk after dinner.

"We are no longer welcome in any of the places we have been," she told him. "Our friends are concerned that the authorities are becoming curious as to the amount of 'company' they seem to have. No one will continue to risk sheltering us.

"At the job site I learned of an old abandoned hospital that will be demolished and replaced by a new structure in a year or two. The building company for which I work has planned the project. They told me that we would be able to stay in a hospital room until it is gone without paying rent.

"However, we must live somewhere else until a room is ready for us. They told me we can stay at my job's architectural office building. I was told we could sleep on the stairs leading into the building. At night the surrounding fence is locked. It will be safe for us. It may take a few days but soon, my son; we will have a home again. I wish I could provide you a more comfortable place but I can't." Her voice was heavy and during her talk she sighed often.

Vanko could not believe his ears. *What has Mama done to deserve this?* He thought. *It was hard to live with people...but this? How can we sleep on stairs? I'm still small but Mama can't rest there. She is a good, hard-working woman. I am a good student. No one knows what trouble I get into after school, so how can this be happening to us? How can we be left outside with little shelter and no bed?*

He looked at his mother. She seemed...well...used up. He didn't see any humor playing around her mouth or her eyes. She was tired. Bone tired. Too tired to fight.

He too was tired. He was tired being a young boy, tired not having a place to live and tired of no one giving him any consideration. His form of tiredness made him angry. Now he was so angry he didn't care what he said.

He had scarcely seen his sister since he came to Sofia almost a year ago. He had been afraid to ask Mama about her. His anger dictated that it was time to ask.

"Mamo, where is Sister? Why don't we see her often? She is my sister! She is *your* daughter! What has happened to us?"

Mama heard him. With what seemed like great effort she said, "Vanko, your sister is in a family and is safe. She doesn't live far from here but I have no time to see her. I work six days a week when you are in school. There is no time for myself. You have more time than I do because school is over before my quitting time. Now that you are eleven years old and she is fourteen perhaps it is time for you to be together after school and on weekends. She needs you to help her stay out of trouble. I hear she is beginning to spend time with boys. She's not old enough for that. I will tell you where she is if you promise to protect her. Believe me, I want to see her too...but...."

This is the first responsible job Mama has given me, thought Vanko. *She doesn't seem to know that I need my sister to keep me out of trouble. I hope that I can help her to be safe. I don't know what problems Mama is talking about, but if I can stay with Sister between school and dinnertime maybe that will help. At least I won't be getting into more mischief.*

"Okay, Mamo," he said. "I'd like to be with her. Where is she?"

Carefully Mama told him how to find Sister. He listened, having no difficulty locating her the next day.

His days passed quickly. On most of them he saw his sister and enjoyed being with her and her boyfriend. They played with him and treated him like an equal even though he was three years younger than she was and thirteen years younger than he was. The boyfriend was a nice man but too old for his sister.

Vanko became concerned for her when he discovered that her friend was a member of the Communist Party. He hoped Mama wouldn't be angry when she found out. He didn't tell his mother even though his loyalties were stronger to her than to his sister. He didn't want to risk hurting his mother with the difficult news. *That is for Sister or her boyfriend to tell her anyway*, he rationalized.

One Saturday during summer break the three young people were together as usual.

Sister asked, "Vanko, do you want some ice cream?" That was a treat to which no eleven-year-old would say, "No". He happily took the money from her boyfriend and went into the *sladkarnitsa*[59] for his dish of ice cream. When he came out his sister and her friend were gone. The rest of the day Vanko was alone. Too late he knew he had been tricked. *At least the ice cream was good*, he thought.

That evening Mama came from work.

"The bread lines were too long again for me to wait," she said. "We still have some onions left. We can eat them tonight."

Together they sat, each peeling his onion. When Vanko's was peeled to the juicy inner portion he placed it between the butts of his hands with fingers laced. In a well-practiced manner he squeezed until the juice no longer ran freely from it. Then he took small bites, trying to make it last. He was hungry. *One onion won't fill my stomach*, he thought. *At least I had ice cream earlier...Mama had nothing.*

As they ate their only food they talked about life on the stairs. Days had become long and the nights longer. They had believed that by now they would have a roof over their heads. The possibility of being in shelter was becoming remote.

Mama told Vanko, "Soon we will move to the hospital room."

"Mamo!" Vanko almost shouted in his anger. "You tell me that every day. How long have we been here? Think about it. When is soon?"

Weariness showed in her eyes when she responded.

"I am not the one to ask. We must wait. We will wait. You will wait."

Once again, she had the last word.

Vanko felt sad for his mother, sad that the fight was leaving her. He was angry that his life had become so unbearable. He had little control over anything. He knew that now he was losing control over his outbursts of anger, his last area of any control.

When he finished eating his onion he said, trying to control his voice, "Mamo, I'm going out for awhile. I'll be back before dark."

He left, hoping that taking his mind off food would stop his hunger. He climbed the fence and began walking in the early evening's cooling air.

As he walked he whistled and dragged a stick along the fences next to the sidewalks listening to the "ratta ta tat" and improvising songs.

After several blocks of aimless walking he noticed an old oil drum standing on end down a service lane behind a large and beautiful building. His mother had told him that the building was used for 'official' government dinner meetings once a month. He thought he saw something on the upturned drum. His curiosity was aroused. Upon inspection he found chunks of bread and other food on a piece of clean paper. It looked fresh, as if it had been placed there within the last hour. There were teeth marks on almost everything, but his stomach didn't care. He picked up a four-inch-long chunk of bread. Carefully he pulled off the bitten part and tossed it for the birds to find the next day. He savored the taste of good bread. This was special! It was white and soft whereas the bread his mother could afford was the rough, tough, dark "people's" bread. It seemed an eternity since he had eaten bread. In truth it had been only several days. Saving most of the bread and all of the other food he gathered it carefully in the paper and took it to his mother.

Holding the wrapped food bundle between his teeth he climbed back over the fence into the protected yard.

His heart was heavy when he saw his mother's small body lying crunched upon a stair, her head resting as on a pillow on the step above her body.

He said with genuine excitement, "Look, Mamo. We have food."

His conscience hoped that the food would be an apology for his angry outburst directed toward her earlier that evening.

Quietly they finished the bread, cheese, bits of meat, and the fresh sliced cucumbers and tomatoes.

They prepared for another stressful night of partial sleep. It was not only difficult sleeping on the wooden stairs but also there is little sleep when the body is starving and the stomach unfilled. That night they slept better than they had the previous few days. No doubt the food was a godsend. It blessed them both.

Finally, in October of 1951, many days later, the hospital was ready for occupancy and they moved indoors. The building's central hall was fifty meters[60] long. The hallway had a cement floor, as did their room, with white ceramic tile halfway up the walls. Theirs was one of numerous rooms off both sides of the hall. Other workers were moving into many of the other rooms.

Their room was next to the bathroom, which was modern and clean. There was indoor plumbing with running water, something Vanko had seen for the first time when he had come to Sofia. The closest thing to running water in Rogozen was the artesian well. The water in the "new" bathroom he considered to be his, in his own home. Everyone on the floor shared that bathroom. Having "his own" water and sharing it with the others made him feel good. After his hard life he was beginning to lose his self-centeredness.

With the home came two twin-sized beds whose mattresses had been previously claimed by bedbugs. Neither Vanko nor Mama chose to share them with the bugs. The construction site's fire marshal gave Mama a can of kerosene to eradicate them. He taught her how to use it safely so that she wouldn't start a fire.

This hospital building took an entire city block. It had a brick wall completely surrounding it. Armed guards stood at the gate protecting the building, and they protected the newly started construction site. As inhabitants Vanko and Mama became benefactors of that protection.

During that summer of 1952 a fifteen-year-old boy came to the field to play soccer with Vanko, who was then twelve. The boys had much in common. Both were refugees from villages and now living in Sofia. Socialism had not been kind to either of them. The new acquaintance's father was a communist sympathizer but he wasn't convinced that the Communist Party was the best one for Bulgaria, coming into agreement with Vanko. The boys both loved soccer and electricity.

"I made a radio without using city electricity," the friend said.

"That's not possible, is it?" Vanko asked. Bulgaria was fifty years behind the western world in technology. There was no electricity in the villages. Vanko wanted to change that.

"Yes. In fact let's go to the foothills of Vitosha[61] next Sunday. We'll get crystals and I'll show you."

Together the boys walked to the foothills and found crystals, which they used to fashion a radio. Although they wound the coil and did all they knew how to do, the radio would not produce a sound. Had it, the boys might have gotten into trouble with the authorities.

God had intervened in Vanko's life to keep him safe but because of the communist's atheistic teaching in school he had long forgotten about God.

In their hospital room mother and son felt secure and 'at home' for the first time since arriving in Sofia.

For a year and a half they lived there and grew close again. Then it was time to move on. Their "home" was to come down in the name of progress sometime around March, 1953.

In the north yard of the hospital, barracks were constructed for the workers of the new building. Mama and Vanko were given a room there in spite of the fact that her work site was several blocks away.

Soldiers' barracks were along the East Side. Vanko had all the friends he could want during the summer when school was out. He was the men's honored "mascot," wearing the heavy wool uniform when he "visited" them, which was almost daily. The men laughed with him and at him prancing around in the hat they had given him which was much too large. They laughed the loudest when he pretended to march, stop, and execute an about-face. He turned. His hat didn't. He'd laugh and quickly twist the hat forward. Status came along with that hat. He loved wearing it.

Although he was considered the soldiers' mascot, the officers did not approve of his being there. Several times they escorted him out in an unfriendly manner, but he always returned to the delight of the men. Soon he became expert in escaping the notice of the superiors. Finally, after catching him again the officers discovered and repaired the hole in the fence through which Vanko had been entering.

In late summer of 1954 Vanko was fourteen years old. The new building was nearing completion and the workers began to leave. The barracks were being demolished and his mother said, "Once again we must move. This time an old but kind and compassionate communist man and his wife who live just outside the city limits were ordered to share their extra space with someone and they have taken pity on us. We will live in a small, vacant one-room shop, which they are willing to rent us. Of course we will pay the rent to the government, who in turn will give a small portion to the owners. Because there is no 'private business' any more it is vacant. It is adjacent to the sidewalk. Steps go down from the sidewalk into the room."

Mama said, "I'll raise the floor to be level with the sidewalk. The ceiling will be low. We're not tall. It will be fine. When It's finished we will need to duck our heads to enter, but we'll be able to stand up once we're inside. This will be our 'home' and once again we will have our privacy."

It didn't take Mama long to raise the floor, using scrap wood from her work site leaving a loose floorboard, creating their "storage" space. She

Ivan, age 13, and Mama in Central Sofia, Bulgaria

sewed window coverings. Somewhere she found a desk and a cot and brought them "home."

"I'll sleep on the desk and the desk drawers will hold our food; bread, onions, a pepper or two and when I'm able, a tomato, some apples, and occasionally some cheese or sausage." Mama said. "You will sleep on the cot."

They placed the desk against the right wall as they entered the room. Vanko's cot, which served as a sofa during the day, was against the wall facing the door.

There were many vacant lots nearby, good for soccer and the evening chats around the fires as Vanko remembered from Rogozen summers.

In one way it was good that Sister had married her boyfriend. There was certainly no room for her in their new home. The bad side was Sister's husband's affiliation with the Party. Mama, being anti-Communist, made Sister's situation with her husband and his family tense. When he was not drinking, her husband was kind and loving but violence seemed to come out of the bottle and Sister became its frequent recipient.

Mama had been working as a builder for about three and a half years. Her hard work had paid off in promotions. She gained respect, position, and income. The two of them were able to eat in a restaurant once every three months or so.

"Even if we don't eat well for the rest of the week," Mama told Vanko when they ate out, "We will have a whole chicken tonight for just the two of us."

Mama had been promoted to bricklayer. Her work was hard but she no longer got dizzy going up the hod carrier ramps. For that she was thankful.

Vanko and his close friend spent most of their spare time together while their parents worked.

"Why do you study so much just to go to college? Don't you know that you will have to work even harder when you get there?" Vanko's friend had asked one day. "There are many jobs you can do without a degree."

"I want my education. Every year the company issues Mama one pair of leather gloves. The bricks rub and cut through them during the first three months, so her hands aren't protected after that She can't buy gloves because they are too expensive but the quota of bricks per day remains the same. She works fast to meet her quota. There are no excuses, only hard work. During the winter is the worst. Mama shows me her bleeding hands when she gets home from work. Her fingers are cracked and the blood drips. She has said, 'If you want to be like this, come, I will teach you but...if you want to be like the architect...you have to do well in school.' By showing me and explaining she has taught me what it means to accept adult responsibilities. She also taught me the result of limited education and not correctly planning for life's terrible turns.

"She never expected to have to leave Rogozen. She is a great farmer and loves to work the soil and care for animals. Even though she is a farmer she is also a survivor. Because she knew how to build she was able to care for Sister and me when we came to Sofia by working in construction. I wish she had some other way. This is a hard life for Mama but it doesn't stop her. She's the best mother anyone could have."

Vanko finished secondary school by the time he was thirteen as was the custom in the Bulgarian school system. His dream was to become an electrical engineer and to provide light to villages, especially his "own" Rogozen.

He and five hundred and forty other applicants had taken the tests for post-high-school study. They learned that only the top thirty scores were accepted into the electrical engineering school. His was not one of them.

Because his test scores were within the top ninety and he was capable, he chose a placement in the mechanical engineering school. He found that the government's vision was to build better steam engines and steam systems. The propaganda was that with nuclear energy the up-and-coming technology, the students entering mechanical engineering would learn to harness that much needed energy.

Vanko didn't accept their sales pitch. He would have preferred to learn electrical engineering.

Why am I going to study hard to work on something we already have? He thought. Making the most of his situation, he decided, *I will become an electrical engineer someday! What I learn now I will apply then.* He had his mother's resolve. In fact, if she had not regularly shown him her bleeding hands after work he might not have realized the importance of getting an education to free him from a life of physical labor. He worked hard at school and made top grades. He became a mentor for other students, finding that teaching made him learn more quickly.

"I bought you a present," Mama said one evening.

"What is it?"

"Look. They told me at the store that this is what you need." She showed him a radio vacuum tube.

"Mamo, this is the best thing you could have bought me. Can we really afford it?"

"If we couldn't I would not have bought it," she said.

Now when Vanko's friend came over the two spent their time building a short wave radio. Then they listened to the radio together. It was diversion from a difficult life. Most of the stations broadcast communist propaganda, which annoyed Vanko. He knew that much of what he heard had to be untrue.

Amidst much static the boys accidentally discovered a different station. It was the "Voice of America." They listened to that station with guardedness. Not even Vanko's mother was aware of her son's learning about things in the 'free world.'

When there was no school Vanko's friend made a practice of spending time with Vanko at Vanko's 'home' while their parents worked. They talked about their interests, about their futures, and in general became close friends.

Listening to the radio became of major importance to the young men. Their newly found station fascinated them. If Vanko's mother knew that they listened to "Voice of America" she said nothing. Certainly if the local officials knew, the two friends would have been arrested and possibly imprisoned for breaking the law.

One day in June, 1955 before Vanko's mother came home from work the two were again listening to the "Voice of America."

"Do you think the West is really free?" Vanko's friend asked.

"There's only one way to find out," was Vanko's reply.

Never did the friends speak openly of trying to leave Bulgaria. There was too much risk in doing so. However, each knew that the other had that plan in mind.

During that early summer of Vanko's sixteenth year he asked, "Mamo, do you think I could get a job this summer?"

"I shall ask."

Mama's supervisor liked her clean work. She always laid her quota of bricks for the day, often exceeding it. When an upright stone face was needed she was the first to be asked to design and produce it. Her artistic eye created some of the most beautiful walls in Sofia. Mama asked her supervisor if Vanko could try his hand at the work.

After a two-week trial her boss accepted his work. Vanko was allowed to work as many hours as he wanted.

That and his friend's job were to be their financial means to test the truth of the western world's claims. The "Plan" was understood, not spoken.

Vanko became known at work as one of the fast-working, young nail reclaimers. When the crew dismantled wooden cement forms they threw them aside. As one of the hired youngsters Vanko scurried through the debris to find the used nails lying among the boards. Others had to be extracted from the wooden frames. Using a hammer, with a brick as an anvil he pounded whatever nails he found straight for re-use. Sometimes nails could be used eight or ten times before they finally broke. Vanko was paid for each nail he turned in. He often earned enough money in a day to buy bread and cheese for dinner and still to save for his plan. Usually he worked fewer hours than his mother did. He worked for most of the summer.

After their unspoken decision, when escape finally seemed financially possible, the boys learned what they needed to know about the border.

Sitting at an outdoor social fire one night at about ten o'clock Vanko turned the conversation to the army. He had observed the men getting more and more lax in their talk. As drink flowed tongues wagged.

"How much training is needed before being assigned duty?" he asked.

Conversation followed. They talked freely about how men were trained for duty, where they were stationed, how long they stayed in the army. They seemed pleased that Vanko was growing up and was interested in his required army service two years away.

After several minutes of general conversation among the men Vanko asked a retired border guard, "Is there much action at the border? That would be an exciting place to be stationed."

"Exciting? No, I didn't see much action. It can be real boring. I usually read a book or something. Maybe whittle."

After the retired guard had had more drink and there was more talk Vanko spoke to him again.

"I don't see how anyone could escape anyway." Vanko risked stating. It sounded as if the wine and *rakia* had dulled the older man's mind enough to get the information he wanted.

"The border guards are only fifty meters[62] apart, aren't they?' Vanko queried.

"Naw, shilly!" the man responded, slurring and stumbling in his drunken speech. "There wooden be 'nuff peopo to guar' tha' way. They' at leasht a coupa hun're' metersh apar'. We shtay in shmall guar' hutsh. Wha' a innoshent you ah!" and he laughed again.

"Yeah, maybe." Vanko retorted laughingly along with him and the other men who liked to poke fun at the youth. He was pleased to be getting useful information, while no one seemed to suspect his motive!

"But what about the dogs? They must really patrol the area pretty tightly, right?"

Now his informant couldn't contain himself. He laughed harder at this youngster's questions, slapping his leg. In his drunkenness and with slurred speech he said, "Dogsh on'y wor' a' nigh'. Dury th' day 'ey shtay wi' thei' mashtersh i' th' hutsh. Beshidsh no' ev'ry guar' hash a dog. You plannin' to ashk...for a patro' poshition...when i'sh time fo' you'...mi'itar'...shervishe?"

"I don't know. I've thought about it." Vanko hoped that he sounded convincing enough to quiet anyone's curiosity about his questions.

Information gathering was only part of their preparation. The two boys purchased items that they would need. They stored them under the loose floorboard of Vanko's 'home'. They didn't think they needed much but they believed certain items were essential. No one but they knew that the hiding place was being used.

"In August there is a big soccer game in Plovdiv," Ivan told his friend. "Maybe we could go by train to see it." He winked at his friend and nodded smiling. "We can really support *Dinamo Sofia*[63] if we go."

His friend smiled back recognizing a cover for their escape.

"Sounds good to me. We can both take a day off work, see the game and get back before dark."

Monday morning August 12, 1955, at six o'clock in the morning Vanko was slow getting ready for work. It was the day of the game in Plovdiv but not even Mama had been told.

Purposely he did not put on his shoes.

"Mamo," he asked nervously, "uh, do you have a hundred *leva*[62] you could give me...uh...without asking questions?"

She searched his eyes for a long time before getting the money out of its place under her mattress on the desk and placing it into his hand.

With both her hands she held his as she said, "You be careful! Remember your father. Let's go to work now, Vanko."

"You go ahead of me." he answered. "I'm not ready. I'll put on my shoes and catch up with you."

There weren't many mornings that they did not leave for work together, but she seemed to accept his ruse. She nodded and opening the door, left.

Watching her walk away a lump rose into Vanko's throat as he fought tears. Soon her back was blurred to his sight and he knew that he had lost the battle to keep back the evidence of his sadness.

How can I do this to her, he thought. *I will never see her again and she doesn't know it. She thinks I'm working as a member of the underground. She thinks the money will be used for some publication or to fight the cause. I can feel it. She is afraid I'll end up like Tatko, tried and executed.*

His heart was breaking. She had given him everything she had. How would she know that he was grateful?

"*Dovijdene,*[65] Mamo," he whispered through his tears, knowing she couldn't hear.

Collecting his stash of prepared items he hid them in his clothing. Binoculars were strung around his neck under his loose sweater. Chocolate, chunks of sausage, and his pocketknife were in a net also out of sight under his sweater. Carrying a loaf of bread and a water bottle he looked as he did everyday as he went to work.

Stepping out of the house for the last time, he did not look back.

10. GAME

Vanko met his friend as planned. Their eyes locked. Excitement with a tinge of fear passed from one to the other. Silently they walked to the station, bought tickets and boarded a train to Plovdiv, about eighty-seven miles southeast of Sofia.

Exiting, they saw most of the train's riders heading toward the soccer stadium.

"What a crowd," Ivan yelled above the heads of small children pushing between the two of them. "If we get separated I'll see you inside." The two fans inched toward the gate. They were increasingly divided by the crush of people oblivious to anything but their own desire to get seats.

This is really great, thought Ivan. *I haven't ever been to an away game. What an awesome stadium. The fans here are as noisy as the ones in Sofia. I remember how not too long ago I'd wait, sometimes for half an hour, until a man with no kids would show up. I'd ask if I could be his boy for the game to get in free. Not many said, 'No'.* Ivan enjoyed reliving episodes in his life in the privacy of his mind. *However, I do remember a big guy who stumbled when he walked. He pushed me away when I asked him to get me in with him. I fell and cut my leg on a stone. He never even looked to see what happened to me when he shoved. I guess he was just mean. I still got in with someone else that day. I remember that my team, Dinamo Sofia, lost on a penalty kick. The teams were evenly matched. We still won the championship that year though, like we usually did. I wonder what Dinamo Sofia will do against Lokomotif Plovdiv today.*

Still thinking about past games, he saw his friend waving his arms. He had found seats. Vanko joined him to watch the pre-game match between two local youth teams. *This brings back memories,* Ivan thought, *of when I played on Dinamo's youth team and we played pre-game matches for experience while the fans found seats.*

The game was going pretty well. The youngsters had great passing skills and seemed to be anticipating the ball defensively.

Ivan wanted to talk to his friend about their escape but with so many people nearby he believed that he couldn't.

We have to stay with our plan, he thought. *At five-fifty this afternoon the train leaves. It won't wait for us if we're late. Thirty-two leva[66] was a large sum to spend for two tickets but that will get us close to the border today. Now we're down to thirty-eight leva and seventy stutinki.[67] That should be enough money for what we need. If we cross the border tomorrow we'll be fine. We still have our voda[68], hleb[69], lukanka, and mlechen shocolad[70], to eat until we are able to get work in Greece.*

Silently he worked through their plan.

I'm glad my cousin in the Corps of Engineers works in Zlatograd[71] near the border. We can use going to visit him as our excuse to travel south. Kurdzhali[72] is the closest train station to the border that does not require special permits. Once we get to Kurdzhali no one will be suspicious of us. After a bus from there to Zlatograd it will only be a short walk to the border and freedom!

It didn't seem strange to Ivan that he was doing something which would drastically change his life.

When Ivan re-focused on the field the young soccer pre-professionals were leaving. It was time for the featured game to begin. Fans stood, waving their arms, screaming noisily.

Soon the two friends from Sofia were shouting encouragement to *Dinamo Sofia* along with many other *Dinamo* fans that had come by train. They inadvertently had sat in the "away" team's seats. They no longer felt like outsiders. Blending in, they lost the fear of being discovered.

By the end of the first half the score had become close. Neither of the youths was concerned about the time. It was only four-fifteen. There was plenty of time for the game to finish and to catch their 'getaway' train.

The two friends were pleased with *Dinamo Sofia's* win, 3:2.

Gathering their diminished supplies, the half-full water bottle, some sausage, and half of the chocolate they stood up to leave. Their bread had been absentmindedly eaten, as they were engrossed in the game. At least, now there wasn't much to carry.

Ivan patted his shoulder to make sure that the binocular with its built-in compass was still there. Everything in order, the friends turned to leave the packed stadium.

"Not a bad game. We have some decent defenders."

"Yes," Ivan replied. "Did you see our left fullback's save in the second half? He was just inside the line when *Lokomotif's* left forward shot to the upper right corner. Our fullback sprinted to intercept, trapping the shot. Great anticipation! Then to pass it to our mid-fielder for the goal! Some play! Someday I want to play again."

"Keep working at it, Ivan." his friend said. "You've got a good start on a great soccer career if you want one. I wish I could play like you but I can't push myself past the point of being winded. Sometimes I even wonder if I have a second wind. I think I've accepted the fact that I'm not an athlete."

"You know," Ivan said, "I've noticed that you do many things well but you don't always follow-through. I'm glad you're staying *this* course of action with me." He winked and grinned at his friend who understood the message.

"When you get to be nineteen, Ivane,[71] you'll realize you can't do what *you* want. Others have their agendas for you. If it isn't teachers or parents then it's the government. I can't even think ahead to plan what I want. It's like the radio. If they caught us listening to anything but their propaganda, prison! We are a link in a chain, and we do what others tell us to do. Just when I was becoming confident about where my life was heading something came along and knocked the confidence out of me. There are many things I have not had control over. You're younger than I and seem better able to deal with life. I used to be like you. But, believe me, you'll learn, unless the West is miraculously different and *is* free like 'Voice of America' says."

By then the boys were walking close together, crushed by the crowd leaving the stadium. They were able to talk quietly without being overheard. In this second biggest city in Bulgaria there was anonymity, as in all big cities. No one paid attention to two young men talking after the game. If anyone had heard something unusual from them they didn't seem to notice. Everyone was hurrying somewhere, to wait in line to board the train going home, or to buy milk, bread, or vegetables for dinner that night.

"I don't understand what you're saying," Ivan replied. "My only option was mechanical engineering. Our plans have changed that. *I* changed that. If anyone, I don't care who it is, tells me that I can't do something I do what I have to until I can do it! I wouldn't be leaving if they had let me study electrical engineering. I sure didn't want to learn about steam engines. They said it would lead to a new kind of energy, nuclear, which we would work on. Who knows if and when that will happen in Bulgaria? I can't imagine inventing something new in that field. When we're in the West I'll go to electrical engineering school. I'll be the best engineer I can be. That's my dream, my goal. I'll do it! Maybe I'll play non-professional soccer too. But to accept things without hope and not drive for what I think can be...

"I don't want to live the way Mama does, to work at whatever comes along until her fingers bleed. Although she loves me and shows it, she wouldn't be supportive of our plan now. She'd rather have me jailed than risk being shot at the border but I do what is necessary to get the job done.

"I cried this morning when she went to work without me. Now I'll never see her again. She doesn't know that I'm escaping. I didn't know it would affect me like this." Ivan became quiet as his thoughts took over.

He remembered what seemed a lifetime earlier, his feeling of being abandoned by Mama after she went to Sofia. It had almost driven him crazy. He was older now and didn't rage outwardly, but he mused about being alone again, this time of his own choosing. Did his act of leaving cause Mama to feel as he had? Would this loneliness and other experiences cause similar heartache? He hoped not. He would do whatever was in his ability to prevent it.

"I wonder what I'll do," his friend said, responding to Ivan's talk. "I will be happy to just get away from having to serve the two year mandatory military service. Electrical engineering sounds good to me too. Do you remember the crystal radio we built together? We had a good time hiking into the foothills to find the crystal. And then wrapping the coil. Do you remember?"

"Remember!" Ivan echoed. "Of course!" he laughed. "We never got that one to work! But Mama's tube gave us the ability to make one that did. I liked listening to 'Voice of America' with you last summer. It really changed our lives didn't it? You know a lot about electricity. I think you should study it wherever we go—you have taught me many things. I'm glad we're friends— this risk is better shared with you. You help me feel safe—let's hurry. The train should be here soon."

As they approached the station many other people were already waiting and more were headed there.

Over the public address system they heard, "Ivan Pavlov, come to the railroad ticket office."

Ivan and his friend stopped in their rush to the platform.

A chill ran down Ivan's spine.

Who told the officials we are here? This is a strange town. Who even knows us? They looked into one another's eyes. They each saw fear, felt its claws.

Someone must have overheard us talking. He didn't stop to think that his name was never mentioned. Raw nerves consumed him.

His friend said, "Go! I'll wait for you."

"No," Ivan replied. "If I don't come out before the train comes, you've got to leave. Just because they stop me doesn't mean you need to stay. I will be happy when you make it." Melodramatically he added, "Remember, write to me when you can."

He turned and ran to the ticket office. Glancing at the wall clock inside the office he saw that their train was due in less than five minutes. *How could we have been so foolish as to get caught? How could we have thought that the game was so important that we had to stay to see the end? This, after all, is our only chance to leave Bulgaria.*

Inside the ticket house a railroad official was leaning his chair back on two legs against the wall, his hat pushed off his forehead in the heat of the small office. Next to the door was a uniformed guard, a member of the *militsia*.[72]

"I'm Ivan Pavlov," Ivan hoped his voice sounded controlled and nonchalant.

"Oh, yes. There you are," the railroad employee replied. Ivan couldn't read the small almost imperceptible smile playing around his mouth. "Where are you going?"

Ivan responded, hoping his speech did not sound rehearsed, although it was. "For the holiday before school resumes I'm going with a friend to visit my cousin who works in Zlatograd. We're taking the train to Kurdzhali, and a bus to Zlatograd.

"Have you lost anything?"

Ivan reached to his pocket. His wallet was gone! In it were all his important possessions, his passport, his train ticket, his money, a fishhook, and his father's picture in military uniform, the uniform that any current official knew belonged to 'the enemy'. He knew that if he wasn't careful he might expose his escape plan. He tried to act grown-up, although he felt like the not-yet-sixteen-year old that he was. His courage left him, his knees got weak. He tasted gall as nausea leapt from his stomach into his throat. Somehow, in spite of his weakness, he was able to admit not having his wallet as calmly as though he was answering a math problem in school.

Then he saw it. The ticket man was holding it toward him.

"The excitement of the game, eh?" he grinned. "Tell me what's inside so I know it's yours?"

Ivan enumerated the items being careful to not express fear when mentioning his father's picture.

"You must be careful with your passport. Next time you lose it, it may not go well for you." Handing the wallet to Ivan the man's eyes were dancing with delight. Was he happy that Ivan was uncomfortable under his rebuke or that he was restoring a lost treasure? Ivan would never know.

"Thank the gentleman at the door," he said motioning to the guard. "If he hadn't found it you might never have seen it again."

Vanko took the billfold gratefully, thanking them and apologizing for the inconvenience.

He casually walked to the empty platform where his friend was waiting alone. The train had come and gone.

A missed train was the responsibility of the ticket holder. They must buy a second set of tickets and wait for the next train. They were poorer by the time their train came, but wiser.

The boys slept several hours on the platform benches before the next train arrived. Because the city was large, no one, thought it unusual for them to sleep at the station.

Several days later Ivan realized that had they taken the missed train to Kurdzhali, a very small town, they would have been there before dark with no place to stay. Their bus did not arrive until the next day. Certainly they would have been suspected, their plot discovered, and they would have been returned home.

The all-knowing Father in heaven had allowed the change in their plans, but the boys never thought of Him, much less recognized His intervention.

11. HIKE

Arriving in Kurdzhali by mid-morning, they saw the bus depot within walking distance of the train station. It appeared that the bus would depart within the hour.

"Incredible!" Vanko said. "We are right where we need to be."

His nervous tension and excitement were building as they approached the line waiting to buy tickets for the bus. Soon the two friends would get off the bus and walk a few hours to the border. No one could track them now. He wanted to laugh out loud, to sing.

Fully aware of the somber attitude Bulgarians assumed while waiting in line, he curbed his desire. Certainly people would recognize something "fishy" were they to demonstrate their feelings. They adopted the "normal" serious attitude and prepared to wait the probable thirty minutes for their turn to pay the meager bus fare.

Feeling an elbow in his back Vanko turned to look at his friend, following his gaze with his own eyes. There above the ticket sellers' window was a sign:
HAVE YOUR PERMIT PAPERS READY

Only then did the boys realize that any travel close to the border required documents, which they did not have.

With only a few more people ahead of them Vanko stepped out of line and slowly walked to a trash bin near the back of the line. As he waited, his friend joined him. With no apparent hurry they walked out of the depot and down the graveled road back toward the train station.

Once out of sight of people and vehicles they left the road, finding a footpath through the trees leading south toward the Greek border, their intended destination.

Their strategy was to walk during the day and sleep at night. They felt certain that anyone trying to escape would be expected to move at night and to lay low while the sun shone.

They had walked for a day since leaving the train station. Their first night in the woods was uneventful except for the unanticipated cold which woke them at four o'clock in the morning, motivating Vanko to get on the move. His friend also readily rose to begin traveling for the day.

Their escape plan included walking barefoot. They tied their shoelaces together and flung the tied shoes over their shoulders in an attempt to look like country boys out for a stroll. Their callused feet from having worn shoes at home only when working added to their authenticity. The paths and dirt roads they trekked on this journey didn't cause them pain except for an occasional stubbed toe when a stone didn't yield to a kick or a tree root tripped them. Those weren't serious hurts, and Vanko barely noticed his bloody toes.

There had been a few police to whom they had shown proper respect. No one had asked for their passports. Men lounging around a village shop had greeted them with, "Good day," and a smile.

Their journey went smoothly until the next day when they came out of the woods and saw what looked like a roadblock and checkpoint.

What are we going to do? Vanko wondered when he saw the people.

Two trucks and a bus had stopped on the road. Men in military uniform were talking to the drivers.

If they ask us for our passports and travel papers we're in trouble. Of course, we have our passports. They are proof of citizenship. Without that proof many people have been jailed. Some have been jailed in their own cities because of non-compliance with the law and are still waiting for release. Sometimes they stay locked up for weeks. Our passports are in order but without permits showing a reason to be here we too will certainly go to jail. Then, after release, we will probably be sent home, never to see the 'Free World'. The surveillance on us afterward will be total. With our attempted escape everyone who knows us will be alerted to our dissatisfaction with current life in Bulgaria, our dissatisfaction with the Communist Party. We both have tried hard to act in agreement with the Party's policies so as not to arouse suspicion. We can't get caught now.

I didn't even tell Mama of our plan because she would have turned me in, Vanko thought.

That's how they do it. They build all kinds of fear into everyone so that even family members are willing to "cooperate." Some of my schoolmates have reported a family member for something. The interrogation following has usually been unnecessarily hostile. Most of those who were interrogated had done nothing wrong.

I'm glad I'm not going through this alone. He's a real friend. It's still amazing to me that without talking about our escape we both understood it.

"I wonder if the West is really free." I had said looking intently at him.

He answered, "Why don't we find out?"

That's all the communication we needed.

98

We had been listening to the "Voice of America" in the Bulgarian language in my home before Mama came from work this summer.

That home was the room made available to Mama by the government that determined the owner had too much space. That owner is a good man. I like his family. We kept onions and bread in the desk drawers. Mama slept on the desk. My bed was a cot across from the door. Our ten-inch diameter and three-foot tall cast-iron coal stove was in the corner. A curtained window, which overlooked the street, was between the stove and the door.

When my friend came we locked the door, closed the curtains, and sat on my cot. It was risky to listen to "Voice of America." Maybe the risk made it more attractive. "Voice of America" was a refreshing change from the party propaganda, part of the party's "public education" effort, which was broadcast regularly on AM radio. I hate propaganda.

I remember telling him how I enjoyed jamming the reception of that propaganda in Rogozen during summer vacation two years ago. No one knew why the radio reception was so bad and blamed the government. Propaganda is the party's mind-game used to create fear in people.

We began getting information about the border and its patrol. We talked to each other about the things we needed: binoculars and compass, milk chocolate for its calories and taste, water, bread, and sausage, which wouldn't spoil. During the planning we never spoke outright of our intent. It was encoded in case anyone was listening. We needed a plan, a destination from which we could walk out of Bulgaria. That's why we determined to take the train from Ploviv to Kurdzhali and expected to take the bus to Zlatograd, where my cousin is stationed. A few miles beyond Zlatograd is the Greek border.

We have been lucky. No one suspected either of us.

If any one had, they would have reported them for a reward. The boys would have been apprehended and perhaps arrested.

Vanko began to search for a way out of their current dilemma. How would they get past the "roadblock?" He hoped that their luck would continue.

Vanko's friend rose to this new challenge. He looked at Vanko and winked. "Let's take a look at these trucks," he said, loud enough to be heard by the *militsia* who were conducting the "roadblock."

In typical boy-curiosity fashion they hurried to the trucks looking under them. They kicked the tires and ran their hands lightly over the fenders like people who had never seen such vehicles. Being city youths they knew all about cars and trucks. They had dodged them as they crossed streets back home. Neither one had been wealthy. In villages animal carts were used for traveling and hauling. Now the young men acted mystified by the machines.

"Wow! Look at the size of this thing!" Vanko said to his friend. His voice was excited. He thought himself convincing. *Now my acting in school plays in Rogozen is paying off,* he thought. *You never know when what you learn will be useful.*

"Hey, what do you think this is for?" Vanko's friend asked. He too sounded amazed. He was kneeling in the dusty roadbed, head under the front of the truck, stretching to touch the oil pan.

"I don't know. Maybe it's where they put the fuel." Vanko responded from his contorted bent-over position.

As they continued to examine the truck and make their comments to each other one of the *militsia* came over and roughly pulled Vanko's friend to his feet.

"Move along!" he ordered. "Get out of here. Or are you hoodlums looking for trouble?"

"Oh, no, Sir!" They both replied as one voice.

"We didn't mean anything. It's, it's, it's…they're, they're so…Wow!" Vanko stammered in his "best performance" attitude.

"Go on. Get going!" The policeman growled at them while shoving Vanko's friend forward. Turning his back to the kids he chuckled and shook his head.

The two quickly followed orders but as they shuffled off they kept looking back as in genuine awe of the trucks.

Crossing the next mountain ridge along the road with the men and vehicles out of sight and well out of hearing range they sang and laughed.

"It worked! They really thought we were just some country kids who stumbled onto them. They even pushed you in the right direction." Vanko did not know God, to thank Him for the protection and narrow escape He had provided. He simply felt lucky and very happy.

Later, as the sun was about to set, they walked into the woods stopping about fifty yards off the road. They had been going steadily uphill at a thirty-degree angle on the mountain road for the last two hours. Vanko's legs felt fatigued. He was hungry.

They had filled their water bottles as necessary at bright streams that churned over the rocks in the valleys between mountains.

Their first drinks of stream water were tentative, testing it to see if they would be poisoned. They realized that without water they would die, so they chose to trust the streams. Earlier they had refilled the bottles. There was enough to last through the night and into the next day before they estimated that the next stream would be reached. The crisp coolness of the mountain water revived them, unlike the mineral water that they had carried from Sofia. They drank deeply and exhaled noisily, completely refreshed.

Their adventure so far was exceeding their wildest hopes.

"I almost feel free," Vanko risked saying after his cool drink. "But I'm still tense, because I know that until we cross the border there will be no true freedom."

"I know what you mean," Vanko's friend replied. "I don't want to think about that yet."

"I'm really getting hungry." Vanko spoke more urgently. "Let's look for berries."

"Yes, without salt this milk chocolate doesn't taste good anymore." Vanko's friend replied. "I would love to have some *lukanka* right now. Too bad it's gone. Let's hunt for food before dark."

They wouldn't eat any berry they didn't recognize. Both had been taught that some were poisonous. Usually they were able to select ripe ones on the first try. In twenty minutes they found enough to end their craving. After drinking more water they were ready for rest.

Finding some leafy branches, Vanko laid some of them under a tree to act as his mattress. A big tree trunk shielded him from the evening's breeze. Other leafy branches became his coverings when he lay down for another night under the stars. In moments his tired body was engulfed in sleep.

He dreamed of walking into Greece and being welcomed by town officials. In his dream he and his friend were treated cordially, as though they were dignitaries. It was a short, pleasant dream demonstrating hope as he looked forward to being in the free world!

Waking with the sun filtering through the trees the young men began another day of walking and searching for their food and water.

They had learned another survival skill. A long sleep was possible if they stayed warm in the early morning hours when the dew falls.

Suddenly Vanko's friend's arms and back began jerking in strange ways. Vanko was concerned. "What are you doing?" he asked.

"Trying to get at my back. It feels as if something is there."

"Take off your shirt and let me check." Vanko responded, reaching down to scratch his leg. He noticed a small, slightly raised red spot. Soon there were other areas of annoyance on his limbs and he felt a "crawling" sensation all over his body.

With his shirt off Vanko's friend scratched at his stomach and chest, which were becoming as spotted as Vanko's legs and arms. After inspection, Vanko saw a few of the culprits scurrying to get away.

"They're ants," he said. "And they have a vicious bite. They must have found us during the night and sought our warmth". Many had left imprints, itchy welts, which were not serious, but certainly not welcome. After a few minutes of helping each other rid themselves of their tormentors the boys were ready to move on. The sensation stayed with them for several hours. If it wasn't itchiness, it was skin 'crawling' that reminded them that indeed they were far from being free.

Maybe our adventure isn't totally enjoyable after all, Vanko thought.

After another day the duo found themselves in a strange situation. They had just crossed a wide meadow and were in another wooded area. There appeared to be a man-made trench among the trees. Vanko had never seen anything like it.

"Let's get in and follow it," he suggested.

The two dropped down into the four-foot ditch. Grass grew in the bottom of it, weeds from the sides. They knew that it had been made a long time ago from the growth. It was only wide enough for one person. They walked single-file toward the east in this sinuous conduit, realizing that it was getting deeper. They walked for several minutes curious as to where they were going. After one particularly sharp turn the ditch dropped another several inches to about six feet deep. It widened into a small five-to-six foot diameter room-like area. The ceiling of the room was soil with small tree roots hanging into the room. In the center was the underside of a hollow tree. Actually it was only part of a tree, two feet in diameter, not much different in size from other mature trees in the region. Disease had overtaken this tree and rotted its inside, allowing the weak bark to remain. In time the upper part of the tree had fallen from lack of support leaving an eight-foot-tall stump.

"This is strange," Vanko's friend said. "Walking under a tree. I wonder if there is a purpose for it."

As they moved into the opening under the tree Vanko saw a crude ladder leaning against its under part in the middle of the "room."

"I'm checking this!" Vanko said, using the ladder to scramble up inside the hollow tree. About two feet above ground he looked out a rectangular hole six inches long and three inches high. "Hey, I can see the big meadow we just crossed. The trench isn't going into the woods. It circles back to the forest's edge."

"Let me see," Vanko's friend said pulling Vanko down in his impatient curiosity. Climbing he was able to look out. He let out a long whistle.

Jumping back onto the packed earth covered with moss he said, "This is a look-out. If anyone was in here when we crossed the meadow they could have shot and killed us. I wonder if this place is currently functional or used only during the Second World War. If someone still uses it we have to get out of here...! Fast!"

As they rushed back through the snaking conduit they realized the reality of their naiveté. What other 'traps' or unknown difficulties lay ahead for them?

They were beginning to understand that their attempt to escape from communism to freedom was tricky at best and life-threatening at worst.

12. Escape

Hurrying from the "lookout" the two youngsters followed their compass southward. The walk was rarely level. They went up one side and down the other so often they lost count of mountain ridges.

The young men began struggling to maintain positive attitudes. Escaping was strenuous work. Their legs were tired and their stomachs were never filled, but they kept going. Invariably they would work their way to the top of a crest, climb a tall tree, check with binoculars and pinpoint the tree toward which to go on the next ridge. The compass on the binoculars worked well, keeping them headed South.

As they dipped into the lowest point of the valley between ridges they stopped to bathe in the stream, to fill their water bottles, and to talk as they rested. Somehow they pressed toward their unseen goal.

It seemed they would never come to the last ridge. On each ascent they let their hopes soar, believing it to be the last time they would be climbing. At the top when there were more peaks and trees ahead their spirits dropped...but they kept going.

They had anticipated only a few hours walk to the border from the end of the expected-but-not-taken bus ride. Now, in their fifth day of walking in the mountains, Ivan wondered if their escape plan had been wise.

"That's the tree, isn't it?" Vanko's friend asked heavily as they neared the top.

"I think so," Ivan answered without enthusiasm. "We walked with the compass and the tree looks right. I'll climb this one. You did last time."

The boys plodded to the tree on the ascending side of the mountain. They saw the familiar tops of trees beginning to descend not far from their target tree.

Climbing their latest lookout Ivan saw something different. They were still in the forest. He saw more ridges but near the top of the next one, amidst the trees, he saw a tall, narrow guard hut with two people. One of the people was sitting on a stool. The other was standing and appeared to be working on something in his hands.

Breathlessly he told his friend, "This is it. We are at the border! Take a look."

Quickly the older boy climbed one branch at a time, pulling himself up to a vantage point. Studying the scene he became quiet with an almost somber attitude. Slowly climbing down the tree he turned to Ivan standing wide eyed. He was breathing hard with his nostrils flared.

"It looks like we have made it," his friend said with reserve. "What is our next move? That guardhouse at eleven o'clock east has to be avoided. I didn't see any dogs, did you?"

"No, I didn't but I know that there must be some. Since that guardhouse is slightly to our left the next one is five hundred yards to our right, according to what the soldiers said in Rogozen. I didn't see one there, but we have to assume there is and try to cross halfway between them. I'm going back up for another look."

Ivan scurried up the tree. With the binoculars he scanned the area.

There was nothing more to see than what he had first seen.

"We must walk down this ridge and up that one to determine what our next move is," he said.

They began walking. In the valley they didn't stop at the stream but pushed on to get up the other side.

Approaching the top toward what he believed was the border; Vanko studied the terrain in the distance to determine what the best way to cross might be. He didn't notice that the ground under him was plowed until he stumbled. Regaining his balance he moved on. *Why is there a twenty-foot strip of cleared land? It seems freshly plowed and raked. The soil is obviously soft or I wouldn't have stumbled.* His mind struggled to make sense of this fresh strip of soil but he had to stay alert for what was ahead.

Then he saw it, a barbed wire fence stretching from east to west. He couldn't estimate how tall it was. There were trees scattered at random between the dense forest on their side of the fence and the similar forest on the other side. There seemed to be a guardhouse next to the fence. Apart from these few new observations he had nothing more to add to his knowledge.

The two stopped within the security of the forest to share ideas.

"Well," Ivan offered, "let's keep heading west through the trees. Then we'll cut out of the woods. When we're in the open we have to run for it."

"I keep seeing glimpses of the fence, Ivane," Vanko's friend said as he loped with renewed energy through the cover of trees. "I hope there's a way over."

"Head directly toward it. We are each on our own now."

"Go! Ahead of me! Over the fence! I'll see you on the other side. This is it! Come on!"

Vanko sprinted with his friend on his heels.

When they left the safety of the heavily treed area the boys' hearts, lungs, and bodies conditioned from the five days of mountain hiking, fresh air, and unrefined food that God had conveniently provided, surged in response to their urgent need. Adrenaline pumped through their arteries for an added boost.

Ivan headed due south toward the fence. He saw that it was much higher than he was tall, over six feet. In addition it had tent-like sides. The sides swung from the top to the ground reaching about three feet toward him from the center fencing and three feet away on the far side. It was a formidable wall of barbed wire. Tied loosely here and there were empty tin cans, which would rattle with any disturbance.

He sighted a tree not far ahead on his side of the fence. It had a branch several feet from the ground barely above the fence but reaching to the other side. Adjusting his direction he ran toward the tree hoping that his friend was still behind him.

He also hoped that the tree was not one that was regularly watched by the patrol, although it seemed like it should be since it was a perfect tree for crossing.

Ivan was a tree-climber, not a jumper, but with seemingly no effort he rose from the ground.

"Thank you," was unspoken as he held tightly to the lowest branch and walked his feet up the trunk swinging a leg over the branch. Another branch reaching over the center of the fence became his next path. Crawling quickly along it as far as he could, the branch bending to the breaking point, he let go. It was a short drop but his body had not cleared the sloping portion of fence. He landed on the barbed wire and rolled painfully to a stop at the bottom.

In his rolling descent he heard the cans clanking their alarm.

Vanko's clothes had caught and torn on the barbs. Worse, he felt trickles of blood from his head, neck, back, chest, and arms. His face was sticky from blood. He could see that his arms and hands were nicked with half-inch deep jagged gashes in several places.

Vanko got up and again began to run downhill toward the stream. His heart pounded in fear as he heard an unfamiliar sound. Risking a glance behind he saw his friend, who had caught up with him and was again at close range.

"Keep going!" he heard.

"They sent dogs after us!" Ivan called guardedly over his shoulder when he heard barking.

The two refugees, sprinting, splashed across the stream and found safety in the trees on the upside of the next mountain.

Lying on the cool ground, Ivan's lungs felt like fire. Never had he asked his body to work so hard. For several minutes he lay motionless breathing deeply to restore energy.

Finally he was able to talk.

"What was the purpose of that strip of bare soil?" he asked. "It caught me off guard. I almost fell."

"I don't know. Maybe it is there so that when the guards walk near the fence they can see if anyone crossed. If they look they for certain will see our footprints. And those rattling cans, do you think the guards heard them?"

Slowly Ivan got up. He looked back toward the guardhouse they had avoided. With binoculars he could see the man still leaning against the house as he sat on a stool appearing immersed in a book. The other fellow was now sitting on the ground looking at something in his hands. Checking the vicinity through the binoculars Ivan saw a dog. It was running away from his master, away from the boys, chasing a bird.

"It looks like we weren't seen." Ivan said. "The dog didn't spot us and the guards don't seem interested in anything we have done. They might even be asleep for all I know.

"I've got to get these cuts clean before they get infected. I'm going to the stream." Ivan headed back toward the gurgling brook.

At the stream's side they both knelt and drank deeply before rubbing their sores in the cool water.

Both boys kept their attention on the guards, now far from them. Motion from this distance would not arouse suspicion but the two still used caution. They had risked much and were not willing to be discovered and returned to Bulgaria. Would they go to jail or be sent back to their families? They hoped they wouldn't find out.

After cleaning their wounds, filling their water bottle, and taking one last long drink they stood turning their backs on that horrible fence and walked up into the new woods.

"It looks like we're free. This should be Greece," Vanko's friend said.

"When we see someone let's say 'good evening' in Bulgarian and ask for a cigarette. If the person responds in Bulgarian and offers Bulgarian cigarettes we'll know we're not out yet."

As they walked through the trees they came to a small footpath. Turning left they followed it as it meandered southeast. Soon they saw a hut-like building on the other side of the stream. Returning north across the shallow water they approached the structure and walked around it but could see no opening. What was it? Neither of them knew.

Vanko's friend moved near Ivan and whispered, "Let's stand apart from each other, so that when someone comes along the path he will be between us. If we need to kill him we can use our pocketknives."

"I don't want to kill anybody." Ivan replied. "You do that. I'll talk to him and you can stab him in the back."

Being prepared, they watched. Eventually a man came down the path toward them as though to test their plan. He was a man unlike any Ivan had seen. He was stripped to the waist, wearing a heavy pair of knee-length pants. The muscles in his arms and chest were so large that Ivan doubted that a pocketknife could draw blood, much less kill him. Swung over his burly right shoulder was an ax. A tangle of hair covered the massive arms and chest.

Quickly the boys exchanged glances from their pre-planned positions and watched as the man purposely stopped on the path to face both boys at the same time. He smiled and greeted them in Bulgarian. "What are you two doing here?" he questioned.

With such good command of Bulgarian he must be Bulgarian, reasoned Ivan.

"Oh, we were just walking from Kurdzhali to Zlatograd and came here. I guess we're lost," he answered hoping his voice did not betray his fear.

"What are you telling me?" the man laughed cynically.

Ivan couldn't read the man's mood. *Is he angry?*

"This is Greece. Kurdzhali and Zlatograd are in Bulgaria. You can't come from either of those cities without crossing the border. Not even birds come to Greece from Bulgaria!"

Ivan looked to his friend for resolution to this problem. The boys' eyes met. They were both caught off guard. Quickly they pretended to be happy.

Vanko's friend asked, "Um. How 'bout a cigarette?" According to plan.

The cigarettes offered were familiar foreign imports in Bulgaria. Vanko's friend stared at the package as he took an ovoid length of paper-wrapped tobacco from it. He smelled it like the smokers he knew always did. Ivan did the same.

What was Ivan to do? What was he to think?

This man is speaking my language; he smokes the same kind of cigarettes Bulgarians smoke, yet he tells me we're in Greece. What should I believe? Ivan's eyes pleaded into his friend's for a signal as to what they should do next. He saw a look of dread in his friend's eyes.

Cold filled Vanko's body going to his core. Muscles tightened. He felt a rush of adrenaline pushing the cold away, preparing him for flight. He knew that neither of them had any idea what to do.

Replacing the crumpled package into his pants' pocket the man withdrew his hand. In it was a small item. Ivan recognized it as a matchbox. While the flickering flame was offered to him Ivan felt the knot in his stomach begin to loosen. On the matchbox was a picture of a Greek goddess. Vanko had never seen that type of matchbox or a picture of the goddess but he knew that the needed sign had been given. He could now confidently believe that they were in Greece.

Again the two friends' eyes met. This time Vanko's friend's were dancing with relief.

They were in Greece!

They were safe.

There would be no more walking.

They were free!

Now relieved, they could talk to the giant-man and tell the truth about their frightening trip across the barbed wire.

Ivan felt better.

His mother had instructed him that telling the truth, no matter what, was the only way to live. He had felt troubled by his willingness to lie, even to plan to help kill. In this matter of life and death he had chosen the easy way.

All three men continued walking.

Nearby, inside an area enclosed by a picket fence was a small child who could have been five years old but not much more.

"Is this your boy?" Ivan asked.

"Yes, he is. I came back from the woods to get him and head home. He loves to play near the stream. I've been chopping wood for the winter. Later I'll bring a cart and pack it home."

"I hope you won't mind if we give him the rest of our chocolate. We can't finish it. After two days it doesn't taste like food."

"Thank you. We don't get much chocolate here. I'm sure he'll like it. It won't hurt him. I don't doubt you were tired of it."

"Here," Ivan said offering the remaining candy, "This *shocolad* is for you if you want it. Do you like *shocolad*?"

"*Da*," the boy affirmed in Bulgarian, reaching for the candy without looking at Ivan. His eyes were on the chocolate until it was safely in his own hand.

His father laughed at his boy.

"You look hungry," the man said to the ragged twosome. "Are you?"

Vanko's friend responded, "Yes, sir, we have been eating berries for four days. I'm wanting to eat something else, some real food."

"I'll take you to our village where you can eat all you want."

"Thank you, but now we want to walk slowly. We'll come later."

The stranger took his son, rounded up his five or six donkeys, and headed home.

Giving the man and his little group a head start of fifty to a hundred yards, the boys followed at a slower pace.

On the other side of the rise at the edge of the village their new acquaintance was waiting for them.

"You'll see our school building on the left in the clearing up ahead. Up the stairs and inside you'll find food. They'll give you milk, bread, and whatever else is available."

"Thank you," Ivan said. "That sounds good."

"Welcome to Greece. Enjoy your visit."

13. Walk

Strong singing burst from deep within, belying their five-day near-fast during their excursion. The boys walked down the path toward the village school.

They were free. Their journey had been long and tiring. Soon they would eat and rest.

Ivan had an abnormal awareness of shapes, trees, and underbrush. Everything looked beautiful, with a new reality.

"So here we are. In 'Freedom,'" he said.

"After eating at the school what do you suggest we do? Where should we go?"

"I don't know," Vanko's friend replied. "I guess we'll take one step at a time. First we will have to look for work. Then, I suppose, we can pay for a room in which to live. Little by little we'll manage. Maybe we should think about working our way toward a big city where we can continue school...Now that is a thought...It's time to move on with life!...Speaking of life, my stomach is telling me that if I don't eat soon there won't be any life left! I'm looking forward to real food!"

Increasing their pace, they soon broke into the clearing. They saw a couple of dirt roads with homes sitting back from them at a comfortable distance. The forest wrapped itself around the far side of the village, which was smaller than the ones either of the two had been raised in.

Not far from them on their left, as expected, was the stucco building described by their big benefactor as the village school. The boys turned and hurried toward it, taking the front steps two at a time. A ten-foot-long hallway went to the back of the building. It was midnight-dark when the door closed behind them. A large man opened a heavy wooden door near them.

"Come in!" he said.

Entering, Ivan saw rifles.

One rifle leaning against the wall was an arm's length from the chair on which the "door-opener" sat. Another rifle was lying on the desk with its apparent owner sitting beside it. The third rifle rested across the legs of a man sitting on the deeply recessed window ledge.

"Desk-sitter" greeted them with a quick nod, "Sit on the floor, there." He motioned to a place four feet from the wall, almost in the center of the room.

"We'll give you some food. Then you'll tell us what you're doing here." Ivan detected a hint of friendliness in his voice but, at the same time, it was cold and demanding.

The boys quickly sat where directed.

Their anticipation of food became audibly evident as their stomachs churned noisily.

The next orders were barked in rapid-fire staccato.

"Take everything out of your pockets!"

"Put the contents in front of you!"

"Sit still until told to move!"

Stunned Ivan instantly felt tired. Anybody would have been weary after the last five days of hiking but there was another, deeper reason for this fatigue. *Could we have come so far just to be captured and returned?* He thought.

The situation was out of his control. He wouldn't cry, he didn't protest, he couldn't think. He sat tiredly looking at the men...and the guns...while emptying his pockets of their meager worldly treasures.

"Desk-man" looked through Ivan's wallet, removing everything. Absently he tossed the empty leather into the corner waste can. The resulting clatter spoke to Ivan: *"You'll never be free! You'll never be free!"* None of the wallet contents were returned: Ivan's father's picture, gone forever. 'Desk-man' kept the passport, leaving Ivan without security. He was ordered with the same pistol-shot-delivery to:

"Slide back!

"Sit against the wall!"

Complying he wondered, *Now what? When do I get my things back? How can we go anywhere? How can we work or go to school without passports? Is this the 'freedom' we worked so hard to achieve?* His mind was almost frozen by fearful thoughts. *I wonder what my friend is thinking,* he continued talking within himself. *Is he as frightened as I am? They have taken all of his possessions too. All we can do is wait.*

His mind drifted to nothing in particular. Then the rumbling of his stomach brought him back to reality. *I wonder if they are really going to feed us?*

"Chair-man" and "Ledge-man" got up abruptly and left the room quickly returning. Each carried a glass of milk and a bowl. Covering the bowl was a slice of dry bread. They gave a glass and a bowl each to Vanko and his friend.

Removing the bread Ivan saw green bean stew. Though he was hungry, his stomach tightened and lurched at the sight. He began to perspire and saliva gathered in his mouth as he fought nausea. The stew appeared to have been someone else's meal before the remainder was offered to him.

The captors resumed their places and watched silently as the two travelers tried to eat.

Ivan couldn't focus on the task at hand. Thoughts were racing. *How can I eat this? It will probably make me sick and I'll vomit.* Each time that thought came he struggled to overcome his instincts. *Will that make them mad at me? Will they get mad if I don't eat it? Then what?"* he wondered. *They already seem mad but why? We haven't done anything wrong. Are we really in Greece? The men don't seem to be afraid of us but they don't avert their eyes. They don't look like mil*itsia *but I don't like their eyes. Their rifles scare me.*

He ignored the beans. After drinking the milk and eating the bread Ivan told the guards he was finished.

"Do you want more milk?" "Ledge-man" asked.

"No, thank you."

Taking the dishes "Ledge-man" disappeared into another room while "Chair-man" picked up a pen and notepad and sat down.

"Now then, who are you and how did you get here?" "Desk-man" asked. His eyes had narrowed into a hard look. Was it anger, hatred or something else? While the boys were eating he had slowly lifted his rifle from the desk and was now holding it across his lap, his finger conspicuously on the trigger.

Are these men looking for someone to shoot just for the fun of it? Ivan wondered but then successfully forced the terrible thought from his mind.

While "Chair-man" took notes Vanko's friend told the truth, "We escaped from Bulgaria because we wanted freedom. I don't want to go into the military and he wants to study electrical engineering. The communists would have made me become a soldier. They wouldn't let him into electrical engineering school."

Nothing more was said for an hour or more. All five sat and waited.

As dusk settled "Ledge-man" walked to a machine on the wall and cranked its handle. A few seconds later he was talking into it. He stopped and talked again. He continued in this fashion for several minutes.

Ivan, unfamiliar with the sounds, assumed the man was speaking Greek. Bulgarian secondary school graduates knew Bulgarian, a smattering of Russian and a little German or French but no Greek.

The man's voice became progressively more agitated. Just before the conversation ended his face became red as he grimaced, baring his teeth in anger. Slamming the receiver into its cradle "Ledge man" barked an order in Bulgarian, "Get up! We're going for a walk. Put your shoes on!"

Again the boys complied. Ivan saw no option. His shoes were tight. Having gone without any, he hoped he would be able to walk as commanded while wearing them.

When shod they followed the "Chair-man" outdoors. The other guards walked two-rifle-lengths behind them. No one spoke. Were the rifles aimed at them? Ivan was too nervous to look.

Once outside three more armed men joined them. A new formation took place. Two guards positioned themselves in front and to each side of Ivan. One of them carried a small, essentially ineffective lantern. Two guards moved behind him, squaring themselves behind the front guards, blocking Ivan into an open box with guns at the corners. Vanko's friend, who was followed by two more rifle-bearing men, walked within his own guarded box. If they had been dignitaries they would have felt protected. Under these conditions there was no security.

They walked quickly with night's darkness surrounding them. The smooth, packed village road became a narrow path through the woods. Most of the time the path was nearly vertical before leveling or descending for a short distance. The dim light from the lantern swinging from the front guard's hand helped keep them from tripping over tree roots as they trudged along the winding path. What must have been several hours later they were again on a dirt road. This one was deeply rutted and much wider than the village road. It was difficult to find secure footing with their limited light. The lantern did little to help. Ivan was glad to be wearing shoes, which no longer felt too tight.

Buildings, looking like shadows in the blackness of night, became discernible on either side of the road.

Maneuvering the ruts was increasingly difficult.

Suddenly Ivan heard a man's voice growl loudly and unexpectedly to his right. His captors returned equally ugly and angry sounds.

Lurching to keep from falling, Ivan was startled by floodlights, which suddenly glared into existence revealing his immediate surroundings. The armed formation was standing in front of a large, closed iron gate. A guard was on duty to open it when necessary but it appeared to Ivan that the guard did not believe that this group of people was important enough for him to act officially. A huge, salivating, straining dog was held close to the guard by a chain. The dog focused intently on the eight newcomers.

In the bright light Ivan saw that indeed two of his captors had rifles pointed at him. The captors themselves, however, were looking toward a soldier dressed in a khaki uniform entering their circle of light.

Striding toward them with military attitude was a tall confident man. The hat he wore seemed familiar to Ivan. Bulgarian cartoons often showed United States of America military officers wearing hats like his. The grip of a six-shooter pistol was sticking out of the officer's pocket. With knowledge of that gun's destructive power and the apparent anger of the men around him, Ivan looked for a place to dive for safety if shooting began. Only ruts greeted his searching eyes. He feared that he might not live to be sixteen. Although the confrontation was but a few moments it seemed to Ivan to take place in slow motion, lasting at least half an hour.

Eventually however, the men managed to control their voices and perhaps their anger. The boys were turned over to the new soldier. The gate opened and the long walk resumed.

Finally that "endless walk" which had begun in the Greek village of expected "freedom" seemed to be coming to an end. The three of them turned toward one of the lighted buildings. Steep steps went up to a small porch in front of a second story door. Climbing them they were led into the building.

"You need food," someone understated to the young men.

Soon the captured boys were given steaming bowls filled with rice, vegetables, and bits of meat. Cool water seemed the best beverage they had ever been offered.

This food looked acceptable and Ivan ate it with gusto. No doubt any energy he had received from the earlier meager snack had been used up in the walk hours ago.

Ivan's bowl was filled as often as he emptied it. His stomach felt too full but he was grateful as well as fearful that he might not eat again soon. He consumed as much as he possibly could.

The men in this building were friendly and talkative. They seemed curious about the newcomers. One of them knew a little Bulgarian.

"What's going on, kid?" the young soldier asked. He spoke broken Bulgarian but his friendliness made it easy to understand. "You look tired. Has it been a rough day?"

"Yeah," Ivan admitted. "My friend and I started walking from inside Bulgaria about sunrise this morning. We escaped a few hours later over a barbed wire fence. We surrendered, thinking we had entered a school in a Greek border village where we could get a meal. We were mistaken. Well, we did get a meal but it wasn't a school and the guards who escorted us here obviously haven't given us freedom. After leaving that village we've been walking again for several hours. I guess it must be about midnight now. We've had few hours today where we weren't walking, so it's good to be here. I wonder if we're going to stay. I wouldn't mind bunking with you fellows."

"I don't think you'll be so lucky," his new pseudo-friend said. "Refugees are rare here. I've never seen any before you but I've heard that they do sometimes come through. I've been told that when they come to this base they don't stay for more than a night, and never inside. Sorry."

"What do you mean, 'never inside'?"

"I don't know. Like I said, I haven't been here when there are refugees but the guys say the border guards spend the night inside and the prisoners sleep outside." He shrugged. "You kids seem to be okay though. Who knows what will happen? Maybe you will be in here with us."

The boys and the young soldiers sat around, talking. The soldiers asked many questions. Ivan sensed warmth from them and didn't mind answering when he could. Some of the questions had to do with the escape, but the men were mostly curious about his future plans.

As the dozen or so chatted lazily and pleasantly Ivan noticed a man near the door whose uniform bore the insignia of an officer. Using a pair of fingernail clippers, like women in Bulgaria, he was clipping his nails!

What is he doing? Ivan's mind jolted him. *I have never seen a man use anything but a knife to cut his nails.* His mind locked onto the sight, adding an imagined sign across the officer's chest..."SISSY." He could not take his eyes from the soldier, who was supposed to be a fearless, military man.

A couple of hours later he and his friend were ushered outdoors at gunpoint.

Moments later a third guard came with a German Shepherd and two blankets. The dog was put on guard. The armed men went indoors.

"Get under the porch," the dog's owner ordered. "That's where you'll sleep tonight. Here's a blanket for each of you. Don't try to escape. You won't get far. The dog will see to that."

The under part of the stairway was enclosed except for an uncovered door-like opening. There was barely enough room for both of them in the area protected by the porch. They went in as ordered. Rock hard ground was to be the boys' bed that night. There were no soft tree boughs, with or without ants, to cushion their tired bodies.

As the two friends tried to get comfortable on the ground Ivan asked, "What do you think about these men? I hear the Greeks believe in gods. Do you think that's true? I've never known a man who believes in God, have you?"

"That is interesting. I think they do believe in gods here. It's strange. They look normal, don't they?" Vanko's friend paused to reflect. "No, I don't know anyone who believes anymore. My parents used to. Maybe my grandparents still do but they're old. When socialism replaced the monarchy people were dissuaded from believing, I guess. Boarding up the churches like they did and forcing the 'popes' to shave and take other work to earn a living for their families, who knows now what people believe? I hadn't thought about it before, but I think you're right."

The guard dog lay with his head on his paws. Patchy grass outside their enclosure was a natural place for it. His eyes never strayed from his charges, his nose a foot from Ivan.

Ivan had never been fond of dogs. He thought, however, that this one seemed nice. He had always been afraid of them because he had heard that they could attack, hold on, and create serious problems for someone not their owners. He had heard that they were intelligent animals. Even though the dog was watching him intently Ivan felt no fear. He liked the gentleness that he saw in this particular dog's eyes.

After curling up and covering himself with the blanket Ivan's curiosity peaked about their location. He was bone tired but one look wouldn't take long. He intended only to orient himself.

Lifting his head as he attempted to see out the opening he heard a growl. Turning he saw the dog. It was partially raised on its front feet, its teeth bared and its neck hair standing straight up. The dog knew its job well.

Slowly Ivan lay down again, closed his eyes, and despite his curiosity fell into a bone-tired sleep.

14. KOMOTINI AND XANTHI

Early for his tired body but not as the sun marks time, Vanko was roused by the guards.

Opening his eyes he saw the rifle which had prodded him awake. Stiffly he rose, the dog no longer on duty. In fact, it was a safe distance away seemingly oblivious to the fact that it had been their "jailer" minutes before. It was eating ravenously from a huge bowl.

As Vanko left the protection of the hide-away under the porch he saw a string of donkeys tied not far away. They were saddled ready for riding.

Both he and his friend were allowed a few minutes to wash in a bucket of clean water and quickly eat a breakfast of tea, bread, and fruit. Ivan was not anxious to leave but it was apparent that his captors were.

Ten minutes after awakening he was firmly handled, handcuffed, placed on one of the donkeys, and led out of the heavy iron gate onto the mountain trail, heading up.

Vanko's feet hung nearly to the ground at the donkey's sides. Riding felt good. He no longer needed to push himself to climb up the mountain and forward.

As the donkey moved, however, Ivan shifted from side to side. The cuffs rubbed. His arms, shoulders, and back ached. He tried to relax but the restraints made it difficult. To overcome the discomfort he forced himself to think of more pleasant things.

He remembered the long-ago, lazy days of Rogozen before socialism, when he was a small boy. His memory focused on a time before the Germans and Russians had passed through his village. He was remembering a time early in that Second World War. Bombers and fighter planes flew in the sky over his head. The people of his village knew that when there was an air raid the windows needed to be opened to prevent them from imploding as bombs exploded. Fresh air was always welcome in homes, so open windows were nothing new. They didn't need to 'remember' or to rush inside to open them. Whenever fighter planes flew overhead everyone outside needed to find safety under trees to be hidden from the fighter pilots who might strafe those in the open.

Mama ran to me and knocked me to the ground one day when a single plane flew in from the North dropping toward the ground as I stood watching, Ivan remembered. *That day she covered me with her body and my head with her hands. I thought she would crush me. We were okay. Watching the plane I realized that it had maneuvered to avoid being hit in an aerial fight. I'm glad Mama came to my rescue. She got mad at me. I guess she should have.*

I had heard all that she had said before that day and had understood it. I knew it was for my safety, Ivan thought, *but small boys don't consider danger. How could I have denied my desire to watch dogfights overhead? I couldn't see them from under the trees.*

Another day in particular I remember watching a German fighter shoot down an American plane. The smoke trailed and the plane nose-dived, down, down...it was falling and spiraling into a field near our home! I ran. Ivan laughed to himself as he remembered the little boy with stubby legs that he had been, running as fast as he could along with the rest of the villagers. *As I ran I saw a parachute open and a man dangling from it almost motionless compared to the plane zooming to its fate. The plane crashed with a huge noise. Flames radiated from the crash site, the grass in the field burned, but the whole village was focused on the paratrooper. Each wanted to get there first. We had heard reports of women from other villages killing frightened, downed, enemy fliers with their pitchforks. They reportedly had believed it was better to kill than to be killed by the 'enemy'.*

Diado, who was acting mayor of Rogozen, had told us often that we must always protect human life, even the life of our enemy. He wanted to be the first person arriving to anyone in trouble to prevent an atrocity from occurring in our village.

We did get there first! I was so proud to be Diado's grandson. He folded the parachute and let me sit on it as it draped over his arm. He carried me in this fashion while we walked the pilot back to city hall.

The frightened soldier with us was thin and blond, maybe five feet ten inches tall. He looked like a giant to me next to my grandfather, who was at least six inches shorter than the soldier was. I had never seen a man with such fear in his eyes, a face so white. He stumbled as he walked. Maybe his legs or feet got hurt when he landed. Or maybe he stumbled from trauma. He probably knew that he would be turned over to his enemy, the Germans. We would be instrumental in seeing that he got safely to them since Bulgaria was pro-German during those years. I wonder what happened to him during the rest of the war and afterward. Did he ever return to his home?

That was an experience I shall never forget.

Once the paratrooper was in Diado's custody the other villagers became treasure hunters and their focus turned toward the wreckage of the plane. Chicho still has a rotor from a gyro or motor he found in that wreckage. Many of the villagers found other pieces of the plane, which had scattered far from where it fell. They call their treasures, 'War trophies' and are proud to show them to anyone who is interested.

How things have changed in Bulgaria! I wonder if I would have wanted to escape if it hadn't become socialist.

Vanko's musings helped pass the time. They kept his mind from focusing on his aching arms and back. He enjoyed sightseeing and talked with his friend. He did what was necessary to not focus on his discomfort.

Vanko was in no hurry since he had no place to go. Everything during this donkey ride to the top of the mountain was pleasant except the handcuffs.

Somewhere over the crest a truck was waiting for them. One of the guards helped them dismount. With hope of his hands being unshackled Ivan waited, arms slightly outstretched. No one seemed to notice his unspoken request for release as a guard helped him into the back of the truck still handcuffed.

A tarp, which blocked the view as well as the wind, covered the truck bed. Sitting in the back Ivan could tell that they were descending the mountain. The road seemed not as bad as some they had traveled but the ride was anything but smooth.

On the way the guards sat with the boys but spoke no Bulgarian. The boys knew no Greek. They all tried to communicate. After attempting to use sign language and meaningless sounds they each attempted to speak in the various school languages which they had studied. Finally when Vanko attempted German, the guards responded. They all seemed to enjoy the meager attempt at conversation. Vanko learned that the guards were not happy that the boys were handcuffed but that was the way it had to be.

Vanko took comfort from their concern for them.

After the bouncing trip the truck came to a stop.

Struggling from the back of the truck Vanko saw that their destination was the city jail. No one explained why they stopped there. Later they learned that they were in the city of Komotini[73].

As instructed, the boys waited several minutes inside on the wooden bench in the outer office of the jail.

Guards came. Grasping each boy's upper arm in a firm grip they pulled them roughly to their feet. The guards led their captives through a door opening into a long corridor. There were several cells along both sides. In the afternoon's filtered light coming in from small barred windows, it was difficult to see the cells near the far end of the corridor.

Opening an empty cell near the door to the outer office the "jailer" pushed the boys inside. Reaching into his pocket he pulled out a key and unlocked the handcuffs freeing Vanko's friend's hands. Immediately Vanko stretched out his aching wrists. His shackles were removed. His wrists felt raw but they were basically okay, a little red but neither bloody nor bruised. How wonderful to be able to move his arms freely again!

Vanko was amazed at what he had been able to endure the last few days. Never had he done what other people had decided for him without some form of rebellion. Maybe sometimes he looked compliant on the outside but inside he had always disliked being told what to do. Such independence does not lend itself to being a good prisoner. These last two days, however, he had not felt anger. He had been at peace with what was happening. He had been disappointed that events had taken such drastic turns but was hopeful for brighter days ahead. Sometimes he wondered about this change in him but he accepted it.

As they stood looking around their small quarters Vanko's friend said, "The floor looks like we're back in a village in Bulgaria but our home had better dirt floors than these."

"It was my job to maintain our dirt floors." Vanko admitted. "If I had left any holes even a tenth the size of the ones here I would have been scolded and made to patch them.

"It's strange to see the wooden subfloor," Vanko's friend said. "It's too bad they won't let us out to get more dirt. We could fix this cell in no time."

"Yes, but then they would risk our running off."

"I doubt anyone from inside ever offered to help them maintain this place. I don't intend to offer. I'll just live with three-inch deep holes in the floor. I hope we're not in here very long."

"What do you suppose these marks on the walls are?" Vanko asked.

"I thought it was more dirt. There is so much smeared everywhere. But now that you call my attention to them, they look deliberately written or scratched, don't they? Look under the window here, these are tick marks. Look. Five, ten, twenty...three. What do you think they mean?"

"It has to mean the number of days someone was here."

The boys looked deeply into each other's eyes.

Will we be here three weeks? Each read in the other's silent stare. Neither knew the answer. Neither spoke.

I've got to keep thinking positively. We'll be out of here soon, Ivan thought.

"Over here! What do you think this is?" There was another series of marks but they were dots and slashes.

"Maybe it's a code of some kind." Vanko responded. "Let's see if we can make out anything else."

For the next half-hour the boys scoured the walls with their eyes walking slowly around their small cell. They found several patches of "notes" that they could not decipher. There seemed no discernible pattern. Searching kept them busy, keeping dark thoughts away.

Finishing the work of investigating their living area, if indeed you could call that "hole" a living area, they began to focus on the people in the other cells along the corridor.

No one could be roused. Apparently no one spoke Bulgarian.

Dull filtered light was fading to dark. *I've never been in such complete absence of light before,* Ivan thought. *Not even during the walk through the woods the night before last. I can't even see my hand when I hold it up six inches in front of my face.*

A guard with a flashlight took them to the bathroom, one at a time. Carefully he locked the cell after he took each one of them out. He waited outside the bathroom door. Inside there was no window. Throughout their stay the boys learned that this toilet routine was regular. Three times a day at the same times each day they were escorted to the facility and back to their cell or interrogation room.

Being returned to the cell that first night they were locked in and, they assumed, told to sleep. They were given nothing to eat. Vanko's stomach was empty. The morning's meager breakfast before the donkey trek had long since been used. In spite of his poverty in Sofia he had always eaten something in the evening.

Two wide boards that looked like doors lying on the floor next to the side wall were apparently their sleeping pads. The two of them lay down, one on each, and tried to sleep. It was chilly with drafts keeping Vanko awake most of the night. Before the sun rose he finally fell asleep.

After the two had breakfast, a cup of tea, some juice, and three slices of a sweet orange bread, they managed to ask the guard for some paper. He brought them one piece and a pencil. Carefully the boys fashioned a chessboard from half the paper. The rest they folded into various shapes, marking some of them to become identifiable chessmen. They played chess when they were able during their five days of confinement. Both of them increased their chess skills as well as their ability to reason.

When I play, Vanko thought, *it's as if I can see what my partner is thinking. I'm really getting to know him well through chess.*

The second night after the bathroom stop one of the two guards brought leftover bread, soup, and a bottle of milk for Vanko and his friend.

Ivan, who was not quite sixteen, with the appetite of any sixteen year old, ate with gratitude though there was no way to speak his thanks.

The guard also had two warm blankets.

Sleeping under the blanket was better than the previous night.

Ivan awoke to a guard pulling his arm and insisting that he get up. The guard took the blanket away.

After a stop at the toilet Vanko was taken into a small room with two straight-backed wooden chairs and left with another guard.

"Hello," the man said in Bulgarian, extending his hand in a formal handshake.

"Hello," Vanko responded taking the hand and searching the man's eyes for signs of friendliness. He found none.

He was asked about the conditions in Bulgaria, about the schools, about the Communist Party, and the Young Communist Society. He was asked about weapons.

"Did you own any?"

"No."

"Did your parents?"

"Yes."

"When and for what purpose?"

"My father was a soldier," he answered.

"Did you ever see your father shoot a gun... or point it at another person?"

"No."

"What kind of gun did he have?"

"I don't know. A handgun. A pistol. It was heavy."

"Was it issued to him in the army or did he own it?"

"I don't know. He kept it after the service."

"Where is that gun now?"

"We wrapped it in cloth and buried it under the threshold of our home in Rogozen when guns were outlawed. I don't know what happened to it when we moved."

"Where does your mother live?"

"In Sofia."

"How does she live in Sofia when she is a peasant?"

"We moved to Sofia five years ago. She became a bricklayer."

"Who gave her shelter before she became a citizen of Sofia?"

"How long did that process take?"

"Who are their sympathizers?"

"Who besides your mother is in your family?"

"Where does your sister live?"

"Why did she marry someone in the Communist army?"

"We warned her not to but she did."

"Who helped you escape?"

"My mother knew nothing about it. No one except my friend knew. We asked our friends and neighbors questions about the border if they had served there, but no one knew or suspected our plans."

"Do you really expect us to believe that no one helped you?"

"Yes!"

"Was your brother-in-law the key to your escape...to gather information about the West and report back to him?"

"No!"

"When was your scheduled time and place of meeting?"

"I told you the truth! There was none. He did not know! No one knew!"

"During your escape did you notice the roads in Bulgaria?"

"Not especially."

"Were they built to carry heavy equipment? Equipment like convoys of army trucks, tanks, or heavy artillery?"

"We never saw convoys."

"Were the roads dirt, brick, or cement-type pavement?"

"Could Bulgarian bridges hold five tons of weight?...Seven tons?...Ten tons?"

"What provisions were there along the roads for hide-outs or road blocks?"

Although the questioning was intense and annoying it took only an hour or two. He was taken back to his cell and locked in. The day was over.

Thankfully his friend was returned to the cell after his session ended and they played chess.

Each evening the friendly guard brought them extra food and blankets.

On the fifth day, by Vanko's calculation, the guard awakened them, taking the blanket. He gave them breakfast and took them to the bathroom for the morning break.

Then unexpectedly he took them outside and helped them into the back seat of a jeep.

To freedom! At last!

Ivan felt like a specially privileged individual. *After the misery we've been through this is great treatment*, he thought. *I wonder where we're going. From the look of things, we're headed west into the mountains toward Xanthi*[76] *if I remember my geography correctly.*

He settled back for the ride and enjoyed the passing landscape. While the back of the jeep had a canvas cover there were windows on the side. The front seat had no cover. The wind blew over the windshield and whipped into the back.

As the wind drove past him it stung slightly and pinked his cheeks. He opened his mouth to the wind and noticed how quickly his lips and tongue got dry. *How fast this jeep goes! I don't think I've ever gone this fast! Poor donkeys just plod along no faster than I walk and the public tramvi*[77] *in Sofia is always crowded and in demand. It must make frequent stops and doesn't build any speed.*

Occasionally he and his friend shared a word or two about something trivial but the road and jeep noise made conversation difficult.

Once his friend said, "I'm glad we're not handcuffed. That hurt my wrists."

"Did it?" Ivan responded. "Mine were not bad." He had forgotten how sore he had been. "But I hated people seeing me in those things. It made me angry. I'm glad you were willing to talk on that trip so people would know we are not Greek. I hope that they figured us for refugees."

It was good to be free again. He had begun to think that escaping meant only imprisonment.

After a long ride over difficult terrain on the twisting road with many bumps and jostling they came to a small town. It was perhaps the size of Rogozen. The driver slowed as they drove along the village streets. More traffic required skill in keeping the vehicle to one side of the road while still missing the potholes that seemed to be everywhere. Traffic was not all motorized. There were the familiar donkey carts, sleek horse carts, bicycles, and a few cars. Mostly there were pedestrians.

During the drive to this city over the mountain there had been no "driving side." The driver had steered from one side of the road to the other trying to find the smoothest roadbed. There had been no thought given to other cars since there were none.

Maybe that building up there is the hotel to which they are taking us, Ivan thought. About two blocks away on the right he could see a sign to welcome hotel guests.

As they drove, some pedestrians stopped to stare at the passing jeep with the two young men smiling like ambassadors in the back. The boys waved to those on the sidewalks and many waved or smiled back to them.

The jeep continued down the street at its moderate speed. When they reached the hotel it did not stop or even slow down.

That's okay, reasoned Ivan. *There are other hotels in this town. I wonder where they will let us out. I hope they remember that they have our passports. We can't go anywhere without them.*

I wonder if they will give us money to stay the night. They know we don't have any of our own. Maybe they will simply ask the hotel people to let us stay. They probably have some kind of agreement with them.

They continued through the town at the same measured speed until they were traveling on the outskirts, away from civilization.

Without traffic the jeep picked up speed. They traveled for another fifteen minutes.

When they stopped Ivan's heart also stopped. Low rows of rooms built into long buildings were on their left. The uninviting buildings were wooden. In front of each door were three narrow steps. This obviously was a military barracks.

Ivan turned toward his friend, whose chin was set, the muscles of his jaw working as he clenched his teeth against his anger. His mouth was drawn so tightly that Ivan could barely recognize his close friend.

"What is this?" Ivan whispered.

There was no answer. Ivan's friend turned his face toward him and narrowed his eyes. A puff of air from his nostrils brushed against Ivan's cheek. His friend was beyond words, maybe beyond thought. Anger or fear consumed him. Ivan did not like what he saw etched on his friend's face.

The driver came to the side of the jeep yanking the door open with deliberate force. There was no conversation. Not one word for the young men. Taking Ivan's friend by the arm he pulled him out. The passenger next to the driver was busy roughly removing Ivan from the jeep in the same manner.

As Vanko stumbled trying to walk next to his new captor, his arm in the vise-like grip, he saw that his friend was being hurried to a room away from the road while his own captor was walking more slowly. Vanko was jerked to a halt in front of a door not far from where the jeep had parked. The man holding his arm opened the door and pushed him in slamming the door. Vanko heard the lock engage. As it did so he heard, coming through the door, his captor's voice for the first time since they left Komotini.

The voice snarled, "Welcome to Xanthi!"

15. PRISONS

Vanko stood dazed, numb, and betrayed. By whom? His mind was frozen. Hadn't his friend and he been released from jail? This was Greece, their new freedom and the end of their escape. Bondage to "the authorities," those who "spoke and everyone jumped," was behind them.

He looked around the room. There was nothing but a metal bed, chained and locked against the wall. Vanko sat on it. The bed seemed to give way beneath his weight. He had never sat on anything so unstable. Carefully Vanko lay down putting his head on the pillow. Slowly he placed his legs onto the bed. He was now wonderfully supported, though it was anything but comfortable while sitting.

Curious, he lifted the mattress and saw several intricate square patterns of metal strips and springs attached to the frame. The bed's design now made sense to him.

At least my mind still works, he thought lying down again.

From his prone position he surveyed the room. It was ten by twelve feet with a wooden floor. Looking through the only window he saw the darkening sky. The window had twelve small panes, arranged with three horizontally by four vertically. The lower nine panes were painted black from the outside, leaving the top row transparent. The sealed window had no bars.

Getting up, Vanko walked across the room to look through the window's clear upper portion. He immediately realized it was too high for him to see anything near the ground. As he approached however, a tall, slender, finger-like building close to the barracks came into view. A balcony circled its top. Ten feet above the balcony the structure began to narrow. It became a needle-like spire at least thirty feet tall piercing the sky. He recognized the structure from his acquaintance with a Moslem mosque and its attached

125

minaret in Sofia. From the narrow balcony of the minaret a *mohala*, an Islamic clergyman, calls people to pray to Allah, their god, as he himself chants prayers. Vanko knew little about the Moslem faith.

Seeing the minaret he began to think about what he did believe.

His Bulgarian Orthodox Christian heritage was from early childhood. For him it had no relevance to modern life. No religion other than atheism[76] was openly practiced in socialist Bulgaria but Vanko had neither embraced socialism nor atheism. He had chosen to lose touch with his parents' faith. As a child he had attended church services and had liked the village pope, but had long ago dismissed what was taught as being uninteresting and probably fantasy. Who, after all, could believe that a man-like being with a long flowing robe and white beard could sit on a throne in the clouds and rule the world? He didn't know where he had gained that vision but it was firmly implanted. His mind logically concluded that it was untrue. Therefore, for him, all that the Christians believed must also be untrue.

Socialism had brought about many "good" changes; total literacy through rearranging the language phonetically and 100 percent employment, so people willingly believed its total philosophy until they realized that their freedoms were gone. Vanko later likened the result to the proverbial frog being placed in cold water, which was heated slowly and being boiled to death because it adjusted to gradual change.

"People," he would say, "react the same way. We lose freedoms to governments little by little until there is no freedom left."

Some of Vanko's school's social training added to his lack of faith in God.

"If man does not water and feed young trees they die. Simply praying to God will not make them grow," his teachers had told him. He knew that was true. He did not know that his teachers' lack of relationship to God biased their view of Him. It was God who first gave mankind work. Misrepresentation warps the truth.

The classroom pictures further illustrated the secular worldview. Every day he would see them and in time his mind accepted the half-truths they put forth. In one group the first frame showed a student praying as the sun disappeared. In the next picture he was walking from the classroom, his head hanging, an F on his paper. Another student was portrayed studying late at night. After that he was smiling, raising his hand with his test in it, showing an A. Vanko had learned from these and similar "proofs" that God does not exist. The points made came from the socialists in his school and in his society. He had been taught well. He thought that anyone believing in God must be very strange, similar to an alien from another planet.

Vanko would not accept Jesus Christ as God but neither would he accept atheism. He had become a young man with "his own" convictions of right and wrong, albeit from his mother's Christian training.

Back in the cell, lying on the bed with nothing to do, he reasoned, *It is strange to see a minaret here. I thought that Greece was where everyone believed in many gods, like Zeus and Athena, not in Allah.*

I wonder where my friend is, he thought. *Obviously the guards don't want us together, maybe not even near each other. Will we ever be together again? This was not the plan.*

The sky turned black.

Vanko drifted into sleep.

When he awoke the sun had created a pattern of three diamond-like squares on the floor. With his mind in a morning blur he couldn't understand it. Slowly Vanko realized that the design was the light shining through the mostly painted window, evidence that he was still in the cell.

Before long a uniformed man brought a straight backed chair and Vanko's meal of cool milk, bread with jam, and tea. The man settled on the chair, which he had placed close to the bed in front of his prisoner. He watched Vanko awkwardly sitting on the bed balancing the food while he ate.

When Vanko finished eating, the man leaned forward, lacing his fingers, his forearms on his legs, his face a foot from Vanko's.

He asked many questions concerning road conditions, military vehicles, and weapons in Bulgaria. Where had Vanko lived in Bulgaria? Who were his family members and friends? What was the reason for his escape? He wanted the details of Vanko's travel. Every time Vanko spoke the man wrote on a tablet before asking the next question.

Vanko's answers were as follows:

"I didn't see any problems with the roads as we left Bulgaria. These in Greece are more rutted than those were. In Bulgaria we saw a few trucks carrying soldiers, some of whom had rifles but I don't know what kind. The trucks were like the one in which we rode yesterday from the top of the mountain to get here; you know, with a tarp over the back and troops inside. Um, my father isn't living. My mother and sister live separately in Sofia. My sister is married and has a son about two years old. I think she might have another child too but I haven't seen her in a year, so I don't know. Mother is a bricklayer in Sofia. When school was out for the summer I worked with her on the construction site. There's another friend of mine in Bulgaria but I escaped with only the one you know about. We didn't tell anyone our plans. My mother would have stopped me. Maybe she would have preferred me in jail rather than to risk my death at the border. I wanted to leave to become an electrical engineer. Um, what else do you want to know?"

"That is all for now. Thank you. Your friend will talk to me next. I hope you have told the truth."

Vanko was worn down. He felt emptied of all fight, all ambition. *Why won't they leave me alone? It's always the same. Prison, questions, prison, questions. I'm tired of it!*

One day followed another. He lay on the bed except for occasional periods of self-imposed exercise. Even that was half-hearted.

He had nothing to do, so his mind began improvising. He had listened to the *mohala* pray for thirty minutes four times each day for five days. He tried to ignore the dolorous sounds. He watched as the priest walked round and round his minaret chanting first toward the sky then toward the earth. Vanko, unfamiliar with the language, began to believe that the *mohala* was praying specifically for him. His mind said it was possible that he would soon die. Perhaps, through the priest, God was asking him to do something while he was still alive. He was truly a 'captive audience' to the *mohala* but what was the appropriate response? He could only listen, try to control his thoughts, and hope for the strange voice to stop. When quiet reigned he found himself waiting impatiently for the next 'time of the *mohala*' calling from his tower. With the attempts to shut out the chanting at least Vanko had some mental activity. Nothing about the situation was normal.

On the sixth morning after his interrogation began, according to his fingernail marks nicked in the wall, he was awakened before the sun had risen, about three or four o'clock.

Although sleep-fogged he sat up to face the now visibly angry questioner to whom he had answered earlier. With him was a man new to Vanko.

"You are a liar!" the familiar voice exploded inches from Vanko. His face a vicious red with corded veins raised in his neck as he bent toward his prisoner.

"You are not who you said you were! You tried to fool me to save your skin!

"We have spies in every house in Bulgaria. We found that you told us some truth but mostly lies.

"Your friend told! He has confessed to being a spy!" The man paused, not to assess the situation but to gather more fury. His clenched fists revealed white knuckles as he stood up, stiff-armed and jaw set.

Between his teeth he hissed, "You have a chance to confess. If you do you will be my best friend. If you do not ... you will be killed as a spy! Do you understand?"

Vanko, fresh from sleep, sat facing his accuser. He had nothing to say. He had told the truth. His life was in their hands whether they chose to believe him or not.

"You say nothing?" the man asked as though fighting for emotional control. He paused.

Then spat, "You will be treated as a spy!"

Turning to the other soldier he said, "Let's go!"

The door slammed shaking the room.

"Ca-chunk!" The lock told Vanko he could not leave.

He felt nothing; no fear, no emotion.

What next? What will they do to me now? Did my friend tell them something other than what I know? Maybe he is a spy, he thought. *But I can't worry about what he may have said.*

That morning the *mohala's* sunrise prayer seemed to have a pointed message. *It is confirming what the man said.* Vanko believed.

The day dragged. No breakfast. No lunch. *Not feeding me makes sense if they are going to kill me. Why waste food?*

Mid-day he lay on his bed willing himself to sleep, to get away from his wretched, tiring thoughts. He was convinced. *They think I'm a spy. Since they kill spies they will kill me.* There was no sleep, only hunger.

A truck rattled to a stop nearby. His door opened. Hoping to see the light of late afternoon he saw only the dark cavern of a truck-bed interior covered with an army-green canvas. His friend, looking tired and discouraged, was sitting inside near the cab. He nodded recognition and heaved a sigh when Vanko joined him.

The boys quickly exchanged information. Each had been told that he was lying, that he was being treated as a spy, that he would be killed, and that his friend had revealed the truth.

Vanko saw movement through the murky yellowed plastic window between the cab of the truck and the truck-bed. Three soldiers were approaching. One carried a white package. The other two had rifles.

Turning toward his friend Vanko said, "They mean what they say. They have guns to kill us and white sheets to cover our bodies."

"So maybe," his friend said, "we were told the truth in Bulgaria, 'The West is immoral. People are not treated with reason. They kill prisoners without a trial.'"

The two settled down for the ride with the terrible end. They were silent for several hours. It appeared they were slowly moving southwest through mountain forests. There was nothing to see but trees.

When the truck lurched to a stop the boys continued to sit still.

One of the men came to the back, taking Vanko outside.

In the distance was a large body of water glistening in the sunshine.

It must be the Mediterranean, Vanko thought. *Not a pleasant way to see it!*

Joining them were the other two men with the rifles. All four walked into the woods. A gun in his back pushed Vanko forward. They stopped. Vanko could no longer see the truck, hidden by the trees and brush.

"Dig!" Vanko was ordered as the unarmed man shoved a small field shovel into Vanko's hand.

"How big? How deep?" Vanko asked.

"Big enough for you to fit."

When the hole was five and a half by two feet, the "leader" barked, "Enough! Stop! Stand there!" pointing with the barrel of his rifle to a place next to the 'grave'.

"Look at me! ... Now ... This is your last chance to tell me the truth ... Do you hear? ... Tell me! ... Admit you are a spy!"

Vanko's heart raced. His knees were weak. He thought he might lose consciousness but he could not say a word. He looked at the two rifles pointing at him. He had no rational thought.

Was it a clock or his heart ticking? He didn't know. It seemed like hours. Then he heard, "Cover it."

There was energy to fill the hole. Vanko didn't know from where it came.

Relief washed over him when he heard, "That's enough."

As the guards led him deeper into the woods away from the truck Vanko heard a shot. It rang with lasting resonance. His stomach lurched. He knew that his friend was dead. He tried unsuccessfully not to vomit. With no food in his stomach he only retched violently, a bitter taste leaping into his mouth.

Moments later he heard the truck's engine. The vehicle approached and stopped when it came into view. Vanko was again ushered into the back.

His vision blurred by tears of loss, Vanko clambered into the truck.

A familiar voice, tense and low, broke through Vanko's revulsion, bringing confusion.

Incredulously he heard his friend; "They told me you were dead and buried in that grave. You have no idea how good it is to see you—alive!"

"I thought that shot killed you," Vanko squeezed out in spite of his bewilderment and the taste of bile. "What did you tell them?"

"Nothing. What could I say with the threat of death facing me? I have told the truth. Only the truth works, but I was afraid it wouldn't this time. I don't know how much more I can take."

"It's bad. But we have to stay focused," Vanko said. "We will get out of this. We *will* be free."

"How do I know you're right? I can't believe that anymore. I am fearful."

An hour later the truck stopped again.

Turning and smiling incongruously at the boys through the old plastic window, the driver said, "This is it. See that house? Go inside."

As they began walking toward the house Vanko noticed that the soldiers were walking ahead of them talking among themselves, totally disinterested in the two youths.

"You see," he whispered, "We're free."

Taking the outside stairs to the second floor two at a time, Vanko was exhilarated. Inside no one was waiting for them. They walked a short distance down the long hallway. A door opened.

"Welcome, brothers! Welcome to Drama[77]" a cheerful man greeted them in perfect Bulgarian. "You are now the representatives of Bulgarian youth in Greece. You have passed strenuous tests. Forgive us, but we must always make certain that we can trust those who come from Bulgaria."

He walked with them to a small room with a sink and soap-scrubbed the now infected wounds they had received from the border's barbed wire fence. Then he applied a disinfectant.

Vanko winced, withdrawing from the sting of the medicine on the festering wounds. He laughed self-consciously realizing that this discomfort was nothing compared to almost being shot a few hours ago.

As the chatty man helped them he seemed interested in the troubles from which the two had come.

A few minutes later when the burning had stopped and the boys looked relaxed again, the man said, "Accept from me a present from the people of the United States of America." He handed them each a blue vinyl bag, twelve by five inches and six inches tall. Inside was a bar of soap, a razor, shaving brush, shaving soap, and after-shave lotion, a hairbrush, toothbrush, and toothpaste. Vanko had never seen a toothbrush. A soapy finger cleaned his teeth.

"Now, go downstairs and take a warm shower. Clean up. We have more for you."

When they had finished showering, two luxuriant towels had been hung on hooks for them. Clean robes to wear were folded on a chair. The dirty and ragged clothes they had worn were gone, never to be seen again.

The two were taken into a comfortably furnished room and given a meal that was unlike any they had eaten since they left home, maybe even better than at home. First came a large salad of tomatoes, cucumbers, green peppers, feta cheese, and Greek olives with an aromatic dressing of herbs and olive oil. Then tender, juicy fish was served with a lemon wedge. There was tasty rice with bits of lamb. A large plate held fried onions, eggplant, and zucchini. Their beverage was a not-too-sweet fruit juice and for dessert they were served custard, fresh grapes, and oranges with a light cookie. They both declined the coffee and smokes which were offered.

"Okay. Come with me," the man said in a friendly manner. "We must find you some decent clothes."

The clothing room held many full racks. Each youngster was allowed to select whatever he wanted.

"I'll take this," said Vanko reaching for a navy pin-striped suit. "It looks like the one Tatko had for special occasions." Trying it on, he noted, "It's a little tight across the shoulders but it's the best one here." He found a white shirt to complement the suit. Influenced by Western movies from the United States he selected a pair of pointed toed shoes resembling cowboy boots.

Dressed in his new clothes, Vanko felt like a king.

It wasn't long before Vanko and his friend were fully relaxed and able to talk with the others, to begin making new friends.

Socializing, they learned more about the city of Drama in which they were.

"This house is full. There's no room for you," they were eventually told. "Gather all your possessions. Don't forget anything. You won't be coming back."

"There's a soldier in an open jeep waiting to drive you to your lodging. It's not far from here; still in Drama.

"It was good meeting you. Hope things turn out well for you."

By then Vanko's feet hurt from being confined into pointed toed shoes. Most of his life he had gone barefoot, letting the bones of his feet separate. Bulgarian shoes were wide. Now it was too late to seek a kinder pair.

It was easy to find their chauffeur. Eagerly they climbed into the only waiting jeep. They toured through town again, past the hotels and into the outskirts. This time it was all right. They had been tested and accepted.

Approaching an army barracks Vanko remembered the friendly encounter with the soldiers at their first stop after escaping. He had enjoyed being with the soldiers. Happily he anticipated going inside and "hanging out" with the young men. Maybe they would eat again in the open mess hall where there would be interesting conversation. The jeep proceeded without slowing, however, until it arrived at a secluded building securely surrounded by rolled barbed wire. They stopped.

Vanko's heart sank. Glancing sideways he saw a tear roll down his friend's cheek. Nothing was said. They were led inside to a waiting cell, five by ten feet.

Although his heart felt squeezed now, like his feet, he thought, *At least we are together here. I'll not let the tactics of these people break me. I've done nothing wrong.*

His friend's face was masked in disappointment and disbelief. He did not, perhaps could not, lift his eyes to look at Vanko. His shoulders sagged in resignation. He sat on the only cot in the cell looking at the floor.

Vanko's mind again went numb. He could think of nothing, much less anything to say. He remained silent, leaning against the wall for thirty minutes.

Hearing footsteps he looked toward the heavy wooden door, watching it slowly open.

A guard stepped in and motioned for Vanko's friend to get up and follow him. When the two were gone the lock clicked into place. Vanko was isolated.

Well, he thought, *I'd better accustom myself to this place.* He checked out the cot. It had a metal frame and a three-inch thick mattress. Near the head of the cot the wall was splattered with cinnamon-smelling blotches of dried bedbug blood. *I can't sleep on this bed,* he thought to himself as he scooted to the far corner of the room. *If they keep me here I'll sleep on the floor. I'm not risking those things biting me. Who knows what diseases they carry?*

Huddled on the cold concrete he felt disappointed, hungry, and hopeless.

Clutching the handles of the vinyl refugee bag tightly in his fist he held the bag away from him to read the logo. On it was written 'United States

Escapee Program'. Its picture of two hands clasped in a friendly handshake mocked him. Looking at the gift from the United States of America he made a wry face. Then an ugly laugh burst out.

Sarcastically he muttered softly under his breath for his own benefit, "Sure, I've escaped. I'm free! Doesn't it look like it?"

Then he thought he heard a whistle. *Yes, there it is again. That's my friend's whistle!*

He opened the small eye-level window of the door through which food would be passed. Across the hallway Vanko saw his friend looking through his seven-inch square directly into his own eyes. They talked in soft voices. The pleasant conversation began to build new hope in Vanko.

Suddenly a guard was standing between them his back to Vanko. His anger at the talk between the two friends was evident.

As he watched Vanko saw the guard open his friend's door and push him hard. His friend lost his footing, lurching backward and stopping his fall by slamming into the back wall of the cell.

Angrily the guard opened Vanko's door and roughly yanked him from the cell. He pulled him down the corridor and shoved him unkindly into a wood-storage room. He locked the door.

Sitting on the logs Vanko began to sing. He sang songs he had learned in school, songs of any sort, just to show strength in this new awfulness. *They won't break my spirit*, he thought.

Although obviously irritated, the guard kept his temper and did not retaliate again.

Soon the guard removed Vanko from the storage room and almost dragged him into another cell. It was on the same side as Vanko's friend's cell. The new cell felt body-warm. *Someone has been here recently*, Vanko thought. The bed was ready for use. It looked comfortable and inviting but he was determined to keep his resolve to sleep only on the cold concrete.

He remembered when he and his mother had had a room in the old hospital on the construction site in Sofia after they had been homeless and sleeping in the stairwell. The first night they each had crawled into their own bed. Sometime during the night Vanko had awakened. Perhaps the newness of his surroundings had intruded into his sleep. Whatever the cause he had raised himself into a sitting position to look around. He saw the white of the sheet where his back and head had been. The rest of the sheet was dark. A shadow quickly began to cover the white area. Without thought Vanko was out of bed watching as the shadow moved to cover the white created by his legs. The shadow was alive. It was hundreds of bedbugs drawn to the warmth from his body. He would never again sleep in a bed where bedbugs lived.

He settled into his new cell.

For two days this was home for Vanko. He tried to communicate. He could not hear his friend's voice. One neighbor responded with knocks on the wall.

At least I am not alone, Vanko reasoned. Messages were written on the walls: I was here ... tick marks ... indicating the length of stay.

Hoping against odds he tried again to speak into the unknown.

"Do you speak Bulgarian?" he asked as he tried to make eye contact with one and then another of the unfortunates behind bars. Only grunts or shrugs met his inquiry. Finally a man, who was out of sight at the far end, answered in a guarded voice.

"*Da. Az govorya Bulgarski. Casvum ce Borko*[80]."

Vanko didn't immediately recognize his own language, spoken in a heavy dialect. He had believed that there were no other Bulgarians in any of the jails. His quest had been merely another mental diversion to relieve anxiety.

"Hi, Borko. I'm Ivan. How long have you been here?"

"I don't know. I lost track of time. I started to make marks, but I got mixed up. Maybe a week. Maybe more. Some men have come and gone. I can't tell you and I'm not Bulgarian. I'm from Yugoslavia. You want me to welcome you?" He laughed a short cynical laugh.

"Maybe we can talk later," he said in dismissal.

The guards were strict, speaking in gruff, surly voices. They brought food only twice a day. It wasn't the best but it was nourishing and Vanko welcomed it.

He thought, *How strange the whole idea of food is. It must be relative. In Bulgaria I liked everything, some things more than others. Then when we crossed the border just the sight of the food they gave us made my stomach turn with disgust and I couldn't eat. Now this food is probably worse than that but it seems good to me.*

On the third day he was led to a reception/interrogation house. It was clean and tidy. There was no barbed wire to prevent escape.

"This is your new room," his guard said leaving him alone and locking the door.

Unexpectedly his friend was ushered into the room. The door locked behind the retreating guard.

With excitement Vanko said, "Things are getting better. We have gone through the worst."

His friend looked as though he had not eaten or slept since they were brought to this latest prison. His face was damp, his eyes red, and his head hanging. Vanko hugged his softly sobbing friend for a few seconds. He himself felt no need to cry even though his friend was broken.

"Look! These are clean beds. No bedbugs! And they gave us magazines to read. My friend, listen to me, we're going to be okay."

Their first meal was a feast compared to the food they had grown to expect in prison. The main dish was sauce with meat and vegetables served over rice. Feta cheese was sprinkled over the salad. There were bread chunks and milk. They were offered a pastry with a cup of coffee. They gladly accepted.

"You see," Vanko encouraged, "We are near the end of this. I can tell. You need rest. You'll be fine."

"I don't know," was the mumbled response.

Someone, obviously not a guard, came into their room. He held two copies of a stapled manuscript.

"Read this, please," he said in perfect Bulgarian. "We want your opinion."

Looking at the first page, Vanko was puzzled. The title was *Animal Farm. What other kind of farm is there?* He wondered.

"Is yours, *Animal Farm*, too?"

"Yeah," his friend responded. "A foolish title. I'm going to stretch out on the bed and read. It will be good to think of something besides my misery."

It is strange that the author personified farm animals, Vanko thought as he read. *The pig in the story is a controlling, demanding sort of animal. He expects the other animals to do what he wants. They in turn look to the pig as a leader.* It became evident to Vanko that the pig had become powerful through the compliance of the others. It was hard to tell whether he had earned his position or had simply assumed it.

Over the next two weeks the boys read their manuscripts. Between readings they did other things.

Even though their window had been painted on the outside there were a few small scratches in the paint through which the boys could watch other prisoners walking in the yard. After a few hours of reading it was good to get up, stretch and 'see the sights' through those scratches.

"Do you think the one at the far end is a Bulgarian?" one might ask.

"I think so. He looks like one of my cousins."

Or, "No, how could a Bulgarian look so sneaky?"

Or, "...so mean!"

Once a day they were taken out under guard to walk and bask in the Greek sunshine. It's warmth felt good.

Sometimes there were other prisoners outside. When they met another Bulgarian they were allowed to chat for a few minutes without the guard becoming angry.

Meals were an event. After that first dinner each meal was equally wonderful in sight, taste, and quantity. Their recent hunger motivated them to eat everything even when there was more than what was comfortable. Sometimes the guards let them consume their food slowly.

One of the other prisoners sang as he played his guitar. The guards were Greek, understanding no Bulgarian. The guitarist sang telling his "story" in song. He was "Popeto," one of two Bulgarian brothers who had escaped from Sofia. They had crossed the border with another family of three.

The guards in Drama seemed not to suspect anything unusual. Then the "song" turned to practical matters.

After the brothers had introduced themselves this way they sang a "song" about how to send notes to one another.

"When you go to the bathroom leave messages on top of the elevated flush tank. We will do the same and get to know one another."

The plan was executed for the rest of the time the four Bulgarians were in the facility. The guards either did not suspect them or did not care that they were building camaraderie.

The days seemed to go quickly.

Two weeks passed. The man who had given them *Animal Farm* returned.

"Have you read what I gave you?" he asked.

"Yes," Vanko answered.

"And ... What did you think?"

"At first I thought the title was silly. What is a farm if not for animals? And I thought it silly to use pigs as the leaders. Pigs are dumb animals that like to wallow in mud. But as I read," Vanko continued, "it seemed that the character of the pigs, their aggression and apparent irritability, was more the focus. As I got to 'know' the characters they seemed like people I know in Bulgaria. There is one person wielding power in each group and the rest do what they are told or suffer the consequences. Taking the 'pigs' as a group, they run the country. It is the same in Bulgaria. The manuscript is really about Bulgaria, isn't it?"

Without answering but shifting his attention the man asked Vanko's friend, "And what do you think?"

"It was good reading. I felt like one of those other animals, always doing what the pigs ordered," said his friend. "Yes, I think the story is about Bulgaria and the way the country is led by uneducated, unthinking power-hungry people. Many Communist Party members are good people but they can't say or do what they want for fear of harm to their loved ones or themselves. The powerful few are making the rules and enforcing them. Good ones like my father are caught in a vice from which they can't get out. Maybe in part that's why I risked leaving.

"Are we right? Is this book about Bulgaria?"

Again avoiding the direct question the man stood. He took the copies saying, "Thank you. You two have given us information."

With a smile the man opened the door, locking it behind him.

The next day began with the usual breakfast and bathroom visit.

Having no manuscript, Vanko settled down with a magazine planning to spend the next few hours lost in its pages.

After a few minutes however, a Bulgarian-speaking man took him into an interrogation room. What appeared to be a casual conversation ensued.

Soon Vanko heard the familiar confrontational tone in his questioner's voice. He found himself saying, "No, that's not true," to many statements put to him. Often he repeated himself, stating facts as he remembered them when he was questioned about his reason for escaping or what military strength Bulgaria had. The questions were rapid. They seemed endless. This was more grueling than anything that he had encountered in Komotini.

That day, lunch and dinner were brought during fifteen minute breaks from questions. He was given an additional ten minutes for bathroom breaks.

The day wore on. Ivan answered, as his mother had always taught him to, with truth. Most of the questions seemed to hinge upon strategic military information. He could give only his opinion of many of the things they asked since his knowledge was limited.

When returned to his cell he fell gratefully to sleep. He woke and then slept again.

When interrogated, day or night, his friend remained in the cell. When it was his friend they questioned, Vanko was alone. Each session lasted from one to several hours. The isolation became as intense as the questioning.

Vanko felt foolish in his new suit and the pointed-toed shoes, which hurt his feet. He had no wonderful place to wear his new things.

Vanko's friend no longer wanted to talk about what was happening.

It had appeared to Vanko that reading had restored his friend. However, it took only a day of questioning for him to withdraw into himself again, often crying softly during the night. The two hardly spoke about anything anymore. Everything worth saying had been said.

Vanko would not believe that they were to be detained much longer. Even while being interrogated he held onto his hope of release to freedom.

One disturbing repetition during the two weeks was the assertion that there were spies in every home in Bulgaria, that the interrogator knew what was true and what was a lie. Vanko chose to tell only what he knew to be truth and to hope that his adversary was grasping at straws.

After those two weeks it appeared that the questioning was over. The 'authorities' seemed content that these Bulgarians were not spies.

The boys remained in their room, eating good meals, reading magazines and listening to guitar songs for six more weeks.

Again they found themselves in a jeep. They were taken to the Drama city jail and kept there overnight.

It had barred doors, barred windows with no glass, and no privacy.

The boys put their escapee bags on the windowsill.

There were writings on the walls. Other Bulgarians had been there. The messages kept the writers' minds occupied and encouraged others. Vanko added his own.

Two blankets were on the floor by the wall.

During the night Vanko heard sounds. He looked toward the small window and thought he saw hands reaching for his bag. *Let them take it*, he reasoned. He pulled the blanket over his head to defy the fear that was trying to creep in.

That sound is awful, he thought, listening. *I know what it is! It's rats. No one is trying to take our bags. The rats are everywhere.*

He felt something brush against his blanketed leg as he huddled on the floor in the inky dark. A repulsed shiver ran through him.

I hope there is food for the rats somewhere, he thought. *So they don't consider us something to eat.*

Covered by the blanket, with his legs drawn up to his chest, no rats entered his personal tent. He tried to sleep while blocking out the sound. Heavy-heartedly he listened to his friend sobbing again.

In the morning there were no bites, no wounds. They were still alive.

Soon they were again transported by jeep. The city, which they approached, looked like a metropolis. It was Thessaloniki[81].

The three-storied brick building in front of which they stopped was massive. It was the most beautiful estate that Vanko had ever seen. It looked to be a home of a wealthy person.

Surrounding the house was a large well-manicured garden boasting green grass, flowers, well-pruned shrubs and trees. Around that was a wrought iron fence. On one side was the shore of a large body of water, the Mediterranean.

The boys walked through an arched doorway through heavy wooden doors with their guards a step away. Evidently this was not a private home.

Another young man, a refugee from Turkey, was put in a cell with them inside the house.

The cell had only two beds, which were next to each other; padlocked to a two inch metal pipe built into the wall.

"Wonderful accommodations here, don't you think?" Vanko joked wryly and loudly.

"Maybe the beds can walk. The guards probably have enough trouble keeping track of prisoners and have no time to chase beds," his friend tossed back.

Vanko enjoyed hearing his friend's humor. It had been too long since they had joked.

The other youth's name was Kalin. After a couple of hours the Bulgarians had learned a few Turkish words.

However the three were not to stay together. Kalin was taken to his own quarters and the Bulgarians had the two beds to themselves.

There was a light fixture which either would not work or gave a very dim light. The days were often dark but the bedding was clean and the boys were not handcuffed. They were comfortable.

After a few days they were led in darkness into an outdoor open area surrounded by stone walls adjoining the house. There was no roof. The inside walls were lined with small metal cubicles, cells six feet tall, four feet deep, and five feet wide.

Each cell had a metal covering welded onto it as a roof or ceiling. Nothing could stop the scorching heat of the daytime sun from turning them into mini-saunas nor prevent the cold nights from making them into refrigerators.

Vanko watched as his friend was pushed into a cubicle. He was led to another one twenty feet away and shoved inside. The door clanked with finality. It was pitch black. The familiar click of the lock was the last thing he heard before retreating footsteps. At eye level was a three-inch square opening in the steel. What light could find its way came through the opening and in time Vanko's eyes adjusted. Aside from two coat hooks welded on one wall there was nothing to see.

"Here's your food," a guard said at the first mealtime, passing a small bowl of unattractive syrupy cereal through the opening in the door.

The lights went on.

Vanko could not eat the gruel in the bowl.

If I live through this without dying of starvation, I'll never die, he thought.

The next day Vanko gingerly tasted the ugly looking food. It had no flavor but was not totally repugnant. Twice each day the same food was given to him. Within a few days it seemed good.

A guard took him to the bathroom once every day at the same time. He was allowed fifteen minutes to complete what needed to be done. Anything else he had to do in the cell.

During the day the sun beat on his steel cage making him sweat, threatening to melt him in the high heat. At night the temperature plummeted and he tried not to worry about his shivering body. Only for a short time at dawn and at dusk was the temperature tolerable.

At three or four o'clock every morning the doors rattled loudly, startling Vanko out of his fitful sleep. For the rest of each night, there was silence.

Then one morning his own cell door clanging awakened Vanko. He was taken into a clean room in the adjoining house.

A bowl of grapes and some other food was on the table.

"Help yourself," a forty-year-old man greeted him in perfect Bulgarian.

"Thank you. These look good. It has been a long time since I've eaten grapes." Vanko replied, taking a large cluster and settling into an overstuffed chair.

For what seemed to be hours the two of them had an easy conversation. One asked a question of the other, who responded openly and then asked his own. Back and forth the volley went. By the nature of the questions Vanko could not call it an interrogation. The older man was, however, gaining information about the things they always seemed intent on learning; what was the Bulgarian bridge capacity, did his brother-in-law have any guns similar to the pictures shown to Vanko?

After two weeks of long talks it appeared that Vanko was considered a 'no-source-of-information' refugee.

He continued to be called by the man in the early mornings. There were no more stressful questions. A friendship developed between them.

"Some day you will be asked where you want to go. Be sure to say America...my brother is a machinist in America. He earns four dollars an hour. He thinks he will become a millionaire. It is good in America."

Vanko's new friend wrote some English words on a piece of paper and gave it to the youngster. The words were "water," "bread," and the numbers from one to ten. Vanko read them aloud. His new friend approved his attempts. Carefully folding the paper, Vanko put it into his shirt pocket.

At meal times when the lights were on he practiced the strange words, repeating them in the dark after the lights went off.

Five weeks had passed since he had come to this prison.

Vanko wondered why his new friend had stopped calling him for their informal chats. It had encouraged him to talk about a future freedom.

He continued to practice the English alone in his cell.

A twist had been added to the continuing pre-dawn ritual around him. Names were called before the doors clattered open and shut.

Periodically he heard as many as eight names. At times there were only one or two.

Vanko became familiar with the routine although he did not know the reason for it until the beginning of the sixth week. Then his and his friend's names were called. Hearing his name, he instinctively stood up straining to see through the little opening, gathering his suit coat and bag.

They joined a dozen men being marched to the house by the guards and were ushered into an unfamiliar large living room with a stone mantle above a dark fireplace.

A soldier in front of the fireplace looked at them. He issued food rations to each man as they stood in a single line around the room.

Speaking in a foreign language, the soldier began a physical search of the waiting refugees. Coming to Vanko he ran his hands up and down Vanko's sides. Then, searching, he found the small piece of paper on which Vanko had written his new English words in his captive's shirt pocket.

The guard bellowed something, looking at the paper. The light was not bright enough to allow him to see clearly. As he squinted the electricity failed, plunging the room into darkness. Irritated the man reached onto the mantle, taking a match and striking it on the fireplace. The match broke. The man swore.

Roaring, he motioned Vanko away as he took back the food.

"Take my coat," Vanko's friend quickly whispered to him. "You will need it more than I." He tossed it to Vanko, who caught it just as a guard, grabbing Vanko's arm, began "escorting" him down the stairs to his cage once more.

Peripherally, Vanko saw his friend being moved in the opposite direction toward a door.

During the week that followed the problem created by the paper was apparently resolved. Vanko was accepted as not being a subversive and was given another chance.

When Vanko's name was called a week later he knew what to expect.

He was taken to the "fireplace" room again. This time not even lint could be found in any of his pockets. Taking his rations, Vanko left with several others.

He would never look back. He would do whatever was required to stay out of trouble for the rest of his life. If he had any choice in the matter he would never be imprisoned again. He believed he had been given a chance to be a "new" person. No one he would encounter except his friend could know who he had been. He would build his character into one of decency, integrity, and kindness.

Having lost fifty pounds he was weak and skeletal. He was five feet six inches tall. The starvation his body had undergone had taken his muscle-mass to support life. His weight had been one hundred and thirty pounds, but had dropped to eighty. He wondered if he had enough strength to go where they were taking him.

Thankful to be riding, he was transported by truck with others to the Athens train depot. A few of the refugees departed by train. The rest, including Vanko, were loaded onto another truck headed to Lavrion, a refugee camp on the eastern side of the peninsula.

Vanko reflected on all that he had been through. Was it worth it? His body screamed from lack of food. In spite of aching from not being able to sleep on anything but hard soil during his last imprisonment he decided that it was. He was going toward a refugee camp, toward freedom. Soon he would see his friend again.

16. CAMP

Freedom!

I hope my friend has recovered his strength this week, Ivan thought as he surveyed the city block surrounded by ten-foot high walls coming into view. *How will I find him?*

Jerking the truck to a stop in front of the facility the driver waited until the refugees jumped from the back of the truck to the street. With a nod of his head he drove off.

Ivan stood where he landed holding his only possessions: the blue vinyl "Escapee Program" bag picturing the "friendship handshake" with toiletries inside and Stoyan's coat over his arm. He had slowly eaten the food that had been given him.

The unpainted cement wall was uninviting. A large doorway opened into a barren courtyard. Huge double gates of heavy-gauge chain link were secured against the outer wall in the open position. When swung shut and padlocked they covered the gaping doorway leading to the street. Obviously no one entered or exited after they were closed.

Several groups of three to five people stood outside the facility. Some groups of young men were smoking. Some were simply talking or laughing. They watched Ivan stand in the street. No one offered to help. Two men sat in the wall's shade talking quietly. They didn't look at Ivan. Most of the refugees appeared thin and tattered but clean.

Approaching the building Ivan spoke loudly to get people's attention.

"I am Bulgarian. My name is Ivan Pavlov. Who speaks Bulgarian? Have you seen someone who came last week from my country?"

A response, "Yes, I speak. He inside."

"Thanks"

Ivan headed toward the wide gate of the complex. Someone came around the corner toward him.

"*Ivane! Kak see*[82]?" The "someone" was Vanko's friend.

"I'm well. It is good to catch up to you again. How are you?"

His friend's smile faded momentarily then he wrapped his arms around his buddy's shoulders hugging him.

"Welcome to Lavrion," he said. "I wondered when you would get here."

Gladly each looked into the eyes of the other for several seconds as he clasped the other's forearms.

"Let me show you around."

Tiredly but obediently Ivan followed.

From the courtyard the youths went into a building. The dark interior causing momentary blindness, wrapped Ivan with a cool that seemed to revive his weakened body.

"Here's the recreation room. Ping-pong on that stage. Cards and chess over there at those tables. These old couches and chairs for reading or music. The radio works."

As they retraced their steps Vanko's friend gave him useful refugee camp information. They walked slowly across the packed, dry, dirt yard.

"This camp is for all people who have fled their countries for whatever reason. Everyone without a home is welcome to stay," he began. "There are currently six-hundred and fifty people here from five countries. Every year the Red Cross sends people to examine the camp. Basically, they run it. They give everyone who is registered eighteen cents a day. That doesn't buy much but when combined there is enough food to stay relatively healthy. There's usually no money for anything else.

"They require us to help with the work. We have kitchen duty, general maintenance, yard work, repair, and painting when there is money for paint.

"They'll tell you that the more you help the better it will be for you. You hang around the camp and they yank you into some kind of work. I try to stay away most of the time. You know, have a smoke with the guys in town or something."

It was the first Ivan knew that his friend smoked. It had been only a week of separation. Ivan remained quiet, waiting for him to continue.

"We have a head count every night at six o'clock dinner. The doors are locked shortly afterward at eight. We must be inside the gate by then.

"Because there are not enough jobs for Greek nationals there is no legal work for us.

"Stay out of trouble, obey the rules, and you can stay as long as is necessary for you."

"How long do people stay here?" Ivan ventured.

After looking into the distance for a few seconds his friend sighed and replied, "That's a question I can't answer. Some are here for a few weeks, some for years. I know an old man who will probably die here. He's been here thirteen years. One Bulgarian has been here a couple of years. He swam from Macronis. Why the sharks didn't get him no one knows."

"What's Macronis?"

"A rock. A prison. It's offshore, eight miles north of here. When Greece was struggling against Communism Bulgarian refugees were suspected as Communist spies even more than now. When they were caught they were sent to Macronis to die. Most have or will die there. That man is happy to be here. It's better here than there or dead.

"So what's your plan, Ivane?"

"I have no plan. You know I don't speak Greek. The German we learned in school isn't much help.

"The day you left they sent me back to the hole. The guard got mad at me when he found notes in my pocket and the lights failed. The notes were the English numbers to ten and a couple of other words for me to learn. Basically, I speak nothing but Bulgarian.

"With luck maybe I'll go to America if I can learn some of the language. Without money or papers what plans can I make? I still hope to get an education somehow and become an electrical engineer. Then I'll be free the way it matters, even more free than here."

"Well," his friend said rubbing a hand across his eyes as he shook his head, "I wish you the best. I don't think I'll ever be free." Quickly, apparently impatient to change the topic, he added pointing "Maybe there's a bunk in there."

Across the yard the boys selected sheet, blanket, pillow, and pillowcase from a storeroom, signing for them on the way out.

As they entered the bunkhouse which was to be Ivan's quarters his friend said, "My place is not far from here."

Ivan saw a row of double-stacked beds arranged on the opposite wall. Heads were against the wall and feet toward the center. A four-foot wide aisle the length of the room between the feet of the two flanks of bunks separated them. On the side they had entered the bed arrangement was the same, heads toward outer wall, feet toward the center aisle. Several windows let light from outside into the murky room. Four bare light bulbs hung from cords equally spaced above the aisle. They barely provided light for reading but kept the room maneuverable.

Against both walls two sets of bunks were pushed together with a three-foot access to each on opposite sides, grouping them into fours. There were at least one hundred beds in the room. Ivan thought there must be more than were needed. Most were reasonably neat. On a few young men were resting, trying to read, or sleeping. Ivan noticed that most bunks had the blanket pulled up covering the pillow with sheets neatly folded at the foot. Occasionally there was an undressed mattress.

"You choose," Ivan's friend instructed.

Crossing the room, Ivan found a vacant top bed.

"I'll take this one."

"You can spend all your time here if you want to. The sleeping rooms are to be quiet, whispered talk is okay. You'll find out soon enough who to stay away from."

Ivan wondered about that statement but got busy. He arranged his blanket casually on the bunk, stuffed the pillow into its case, threw that at the head of the bed, tossed his bag up and laid the sheet at the foot of his bunk without unfolding it, asking his friend, "Why not use the sheets?"

"They get dirty if we use them. Washing in the bay gets them salty and stiff, so most of us just leave them. For Red Cross inspection we put them on. If the Red Cross doesn't see them in use they might take them and the other things away."

Ivan thought the logic made sense, but it was strange, nonetheless, to have something you didn't intend to use.

"I'll give you a tour of this place if you want."

"Yeah, let's see it," Ivan responded in spite of his fatigue from his day of travel and little food.

"Follow me. You saw the rec. room. That's the main place we can talk, laugh, or sing but if we're there during the day, we'll likely be delegated to K.P.[83] or some other job. It's not a prison, but it might as well be with all the rules."

He told Ivan when breakfast and lunch were served. They walked to the kitchen and saw the evening meal being prepared.

"We get our food through a line. They'll issue you a plate, spoon, and a cup at your first meal. Be sure to bring them each meal or you won't get anything. We're supposed to clean our own plates. Most of us just wipe them after use. There's only a drip of water from the faucet.

"You might be interested in fishing in the nearby bay. Some guys have fishing spears. There are even eels if you can catch the slimy things. The cooks will show you how to fix them. It supplements the diet of those willing to spend the time and energy to get and prepare their own meat. Some of the younger guys go out to find metal and sell it. Since that isn't a real job it isn't restricted."

Back in the rec. room a man of about twenty-nine years old approached them.

"I am Milco from Bulgaria. I was told to watch for someone coming here from home. I want to welcome you, Ivane. My family and I escaped together. There were also two brothers from Sofia with us. One is named Vlado, the other we call 'Popeto'[84]" Milco introduced himself.

"We were in a cell block with two Bulgarian brothers named Vlado and Popeto. They helped us by singing information to us." Ivan said. "Are they here?"

"No, we haven't heard from them. We hope they're okay. So, they sang information," he laughed. "It sounds like them. They're really good boys.

"My wife and son are walking outside somewhere now.

"Since I escaped with my family we stay on the other side of the camp from where you are. Families are given very little space. We spend much time in the rec. room playing ping-pong, listening to the radio, playing guitar, and singing. Join us tonight or any night if you can."

"How long have you been here?" Ivan asked.

"Oh, maybe two weeks. It's okay here as long as we can leave soon," Milco said. "I'm very thankful that my wife, our young son, and I escaped as a family. We hope that you, your friend here, the two brothers, and we will be able to emigrate to the same place when the time comes. There are very few Bulgarians in the camp." Sensing Ivan's tiredness he said his good-byes and left.

An inviting overstuffed chair beckoned to the fatigued and hungry Ivan who gladly dropped into it, only to find that it was broken-down. He sank deeply into it and felt that it would either swallow him whole or shoot him out when the springs found their resilience. Apparently they had no more strength than Ivan did. He kept his position in the depths of the chair whose arms flanked his shoulders.

One of the boys playing ping-pong motioned with his paddle that he'd like to play a game with the "newcomer."

Ivan felt weak from all that had happened during these past six months, especially the near-starvation of the last prison. But knowing he was free from prisons gave him strength. He thought some activity might be helpful to begin the process of rebuilding his body.

Struggling out of the "hugging chair" he took the outstretched, semi-decent paddle and the challenge was on.

They didn't try to keep score but maintained a volley for several minutes. It appeared they were equally matched. It felt good to be using muscles that had been forced to remain inactive for so long. He suspected he would ache as a result of the exercise. He was right.

The two boys were limited in their communication. His opponent did not speak Bulgarian and Ivan had never heard the language the other spoke. They took turns talking, as though conversing. They played for an hour.

Finally the other placed his paddle on the table and signaled that it was dinnertime. Despite the difference in language Ivan understood. He knew that food was what he had needed for a long time. His stomach did not feel empty, his head had long ago stopped aching from hunger but he knew that his body and mind were in desperate need of nourishment.

He looked around for his Bulgarian friend and saw him at the far end of the rec. room, playing cards with three other men. One of them was Milco, the Bulgarian he had recently met.

"Ready for food?" Ivan asked.

"Yes. This is the last hand. Wait for me."

Walking to the kitchen together Ivan's friend said, "Ivane, I'm going to Athens tomorrow."

"Can I go with you?"

"Not yet, you have to be here for a week. In that time you'll learn the camp's routine. There's paper work to fill out to go to Athens. Then they'll let you go on a day pass. On Saturdays a truck takes people to and from Athens."

They joined the lengthening kitchen line working their way slowly toward the smell of food. Ivan finally received a bowl of thin soup, being told he could return for more. He was given a chunk of bread and an orange. With his friend he followed the crowd to the courtyard where they sat on the dry packed dirt and ate quietly.

Ivan had never seen an orange. He waited to see how others ate theirs and was soon enjoying the sweet juiciness of the fruit.

Shortly after dinner he climbed into his bunk. His muscles were tired but not yet aching from the ping-pong. He was weary. Lying down felt good. He hadn't been able to stretch out comfortably for several weeks. The last cell had been no luxury.

He pulled the three by five-inch mirror with its wooden frame from his refugee bag. For diversion he began playing with it, reflecting the light from one of the bulbs. The mirror bounced the reflection off the wall, the ceiling, and the floor. In the process of play he noticed a young man near his own age of sixteen watching from five bunks away on the other side of the room. Playfully he splashed the light onto the other's face. In a split second the youth was off his bed glaring at Ivan as he lay in the bunk with a look of absolute hatred on his face.

"Why? What have I done?" Ivan pleaded in Bulgarian, which was not understood.

A sharp volley of unintelligible words and Ivan knew that whatever it was had not been, and would not be tolerated.

The other young man with the curled lip of a sneer dusted his hands and swaggered back to his own bunk, satisfied that he had delivered his message.

Ivan would remember to not shine a light into anyone else's eyes although to him it had been only play.

Not long afterward the youth next to Ivan crawled onto his bed. He was Albanian as were most in the room. Soon he began to speak. Ivan could understand a little of the different language.

The two conversed in Slavic languages similar enough to be understood. The Albanian spoke either Serbian or Macedonian from Yugoslavia, having lived in the Kosovo region all his life.

"Why do you look so upset?" the boy asked.

"It's a crazy thing. I was playing with my mirror. You know, shining light around the room. When I played with a guy down the row over there, shining the light in his face he came after me. I thought he was going to kill me. I don't understand what happened."

"Oh! That was your mistake. In Albania only perverts, you know, guys who like guys, shine lights into another guy's eyes. It's an invitation to...you know. Isn't that universal?"

"I don't think it is in Bulgaria, at least I've never heard of anything like that. I'm not that way. I've never run into anyone who is. I've never shined light into anyone's face before. I just thought it would be funny and maybe a way to make a friend."

His new bunk mate laughed. "I guess neither of you wanted that kind of friend. That makes me glad since you're my bunk mate."

"I'll never do that again," Ivan said with conviction. "I guess there's stuff to learn about people from other countries. Since I'm not going back to mine I'd better be careful."

"That sounds safe to me," his new friend agreed.

"I met a man with a wife and child here. It was before dinner. He said that families stay on the other side of the camp beyond the rec. facility," Ivan said.

"Yes, the families have it rough. Just like us there isn't much room. Each family has an eight by eight foot area separated by hanging blankets," the boy said. "I've only been into family quarters once to see it. There were about three kids under the age of five that lifted the blanket 'wall' and looked around. There's no privacy."

"Where are the single girls and women who escape?" Ivan asked.

His new friend thought for awhile. "I guess there aren't any. At least I haven't seen them. The only young girls or women seem to be with families."

They rested while talking quietly. It was a long time before Ivan fell into a much-needed deep sleep.

When he awoke the sun was overhead. He rolled over to sit up. His leg muscles screamed in agony and his arms and back ached. *What's wrong?* he thought. Then he remembered the hour-long game he had pushed himself to play the day before. *Now I'm paying for it. I hope this pain won't last long.*

Gingerly he got out of bed, cleaned up, and began his day.

Ivan couldn't find his escape friend. No one had seen him since breakfast, which Ivan had slept through.

Remembering that his friend had planned a trip to Athens he started inquiring.

"Yes, the truck went to Athens this morning. It will be back tonight about five o'clock," he was told.

He questioned other Bulgarians in the camp.

Someone told him, "The only reason your friend went to Athens was to go to the Bulgarian embassy to get back home. The embassy regularly sends people to the camp telling the refugees to return to Bulgaria in exchange for full amnesty. They are promised no repercussions but any previous obligations must be fulfilled." the man told Ivan. "I overheard him saying he was going back. He'd had enough of the 'free' world. That was two days before you got here."

Wounded by his friend's betrayal of not confiding in him, he remembered his mother leaving him and now he had left her. Ivan retreated to his bunk, hoping to get his emotions under control. He needed the rest anyway but he felt abandoned by his closest friend. Tears wouldn't come, only disappointment, anger, and bitterness.

Why didn't he tell me he was leaving? his mind questioned. *I thought he trusted me. We planned this escape together. I trusted him completely.*

He never said goodbye. I won't write to him or seek him out. It's the last time I will get close to anyone. Finally he could no longer hold back. A warm, salty trickle found its way down his cheek. He let the tears flow.

He will still have to serve his two year military term. Ivan thought. *How foolish to go through all we did to escape and then to turn his back on freedom, running back to a military commitment and to socialism. He won't get out again. And I don't care! If he doesn't care about me I don't care about him!*

I'll never admit I was wrong about the West. Maybe this camp isn't what I'd hoped for but it's not another prison. I am free! It is going to get better! I'll never go back! He fell asleep.

Waking, he was hungry again. His body seemed to dictate alternately between sleep and hunger. For two weeks he was slave to those masters. After eating he would immediately sleep. After sleeping a few hours he would wake, ravenous. Usually he had to wait for meals, so he would play chess or ping-pong before eating. He was slowly making friends. On the rare occasion when he woke just as a meal was being served he ate, slept, and lost his opportunity to socialize.

One developing friendship was with the young man in the next bunk. The other was with Milco from Bulgaria and his family. Milco was patient with him. He wanted Ivan to join in the evening sing-alongs in the rec. room, but for Ivan, staying awake that long seemed impossible. Whenever they met, at the food line or sitting in the courtyard eating, Milco joked with him and held the door of friendship open. Ivan hardly noticed.

Finally Ivan's strength returned and he was ready for anything. He generally spent the evenings after dinner singing with the group that enjoyed that activity. Milco became a friend that almost replaced his lost one. Ivan's resolve to not get hurt again was strong, so no friendship could ever be the same.

Milco introduced Ivan to a gentle, quiet Bulgarian man who was Milco's age. He repaired watches for people in the camp. Ivan enjoyed observing him, asking questions. Becoming his apprentice. Ivan became known for his attention to detail and was soon sought after to fix watches without requiring the careful eye of his mentor.

Ivan and his bunk buddy went out of camp and explored the small town of Lavrion. There was no legal work for them but 'when there's a will, there's a way.'

Outside of town was an abandoned railroad track. It ran through the entrance of an underground operation, maybe a mine. The two new friends made a mental note of its location.

Getting back to town Ivan's friend inquired in passable Greek at a building supply store about their possible need for railroad ties and rails.

"We always have a great demand for rails and other scrap metal," the store proprietor responded.

"Do you fellows have some to sell? "

"Uh, yes, we do. Rails."

"How many?"

"What do you think?" Ivan's friend asked him in 'their' language, "About twenty?"

"Yes, I think that's about right."

"I'll buy the rails from you for one drachma each," the proprietor said. "How soon can you get them here?"

"We can bring you three tomorrow and three every day until they are all here. We don't have a truck."

"Good. I'll pay you as you deliver," the proprietor said. "Don't bring any on Sundays. The store is closed. I don't have any use for the ties. Maybe you could sell those to that shop a few blocks away." With no further comments or questions the man shook the boys' hands sealing their business deal.

The next day the two worked until their hands were blistered and raw. Their backs were fatigued. Sweat soaked through their shirts within the first fifteen minutes of work but they continued until they were successfully carrying one heavy rail, ten feet long, into town on their shoulders. The metal was painful on their relatively unmuscular shoulders but Ivan loved having "his" money to buy oranges. To him they were worth the sacrifice.

Throughout the day they struggled. By the time they headed 'home' each had two drachmas in his pocket. They were amazed that they had been able to deliver four rails that first day.

"This is good money for guys who aren't allowed to work!" Ivan's new friend said. They laughed.

"There is always a way," Ivan stated.

"Finally this is freedom. I can do something again!

"After we deliver the twenty rails let's go spear-fishing. Can we do that?"

"Yes! Great!" his friend said, "I've got a spear gun. I used to get about five fish every day. That will be good. Do you swim?"

"I don't know," Ivan said. "I've never tried. How hard can it be?"

Laughing, the two friends entered camp minutes before dinner was served.

17. GREECE

Several times Ivan and his bunkmate went spear fishing. The first time in the water Ivan was amazed at how easy it was to swim. The difficulty arose when he tried to stay underwater to chase a fish or an eel. He kept floating to the surface.

Occasionally they speared two-pound fish that had light, succulent meat. When Ivan's friend was using the spear gun Ivan hand-fished for eels. It was tricky holding onto those slippery lengths of muscle. He soon learned to weave them through his fingers to prevent their escape.

Reaching into submerged holes for eels isn't the smartest thing I've ever done, Ivan thought, *but they sure do taste good when they are grilled fresh.*

People from the Red Cross visited late the next spring. All refugees were required to remain in the compound during the visit. The Red Cross guests were shown immaculate bunkhouses with clean-sheeted beds. They were given the royal tour of the facility and with smiles made it known that they approved.

In the kitchen they found 'volunteers' busy at KP duty. Ivan had earlier served as "volunteer" several times and had spent many hours at the task, when he hadn't escaped the inevitable. Today he was playing ping-pong with an Albanian youth.

Late in the afternoon the manager of the camp called Ivan into his office.

"The Red Cross has decided to send a youngster to summer camp. We have selected you. It will give you an opportunity to learn the Greek language and culture. Do you want to go?"

There might be good food there, Ivan thought. *It will be a change from this.*

"Where and when is the camp?"

"It is on the island of Salaminis. It will be in June for two weeks. We must have your answer now so we can ask someone else if you are not interested."

"I would like to go."

"Very well. When it is time the truck will transport you. Everything will be arranged."

The next few weeks passed uneventfully. There was always fishing, music, and games.

Ivan played ping-pong with the most challenging players in camp. He enjoyed equally matched games but preferred playing someone who played better than he did, so that he could learn new techniques. Chess was the same. Both games honed his skills.

Time flew quickly by until he was taken to Salaminis and the Greek boys' camp.

A dozen cabins, each shared by several boys, dotted an area amongst the trees. Ivan immediately felt at home but couldn't speak Greek. That didn't seem to matter to the others. They were able to communicate with gestures and tone of voice.

After two days the Greek sounds at the ping-pong table began to form words. Ivan found himself understanding increasingly more. It was no longer 'Greek' but an understandable language. His new friends helped and by the end of the first week he was conversant.

The waterfront time was fun. Learning to swim, splashing fights, racing, grabbing both ankles and upsetting someone standing in chest deep water and sparring from the shoulders of a friend were activities Ivan enjoyed as he became united with the boys.

Their swim cove looked over open water toward a girls' camp.

"How long would it take us to swim there?" one of the boys thought aloud on the day before the camp was to end.

"It isn't far," another said. "It will be a ten minute swim."

"Who's going with me?" Yannie called over his shoulder as he dove toward open water. He surfaced five feet away, swimming strongly.

Like dolphins in a pod the others dove in and followed.

This is taking a long time, Ivan thought trying to keep up with an obvious newly half-learned stroke. He had fallen behind but kept swimming. Looking up he saw the girls' camp seemingly as far away from him as it had been at the start. He paused and trod water. Looking back to his beach he felt defeated.

Whoa! Look how far I've come, he thought. *And I haven't gotten any closer! I'm glad I learned to swim but I can't do this! I won't make it all the way.* Reluctantly he changed course, swam back to the beach, and waited. He had been in the water thirty-five minutes. One by one the exhausted boys returned, disgusted with themselves for their lack of perseverance and strength. Fifty minutes after starting Yannie returned. They were all safe again on the beach.

153

Fatigue and the awareness of their foolishness overwhelmed them. Laughter took over. They laughed until they gasped while their sand-covered bodies rolled on the beach.

Dinner that evening seemed "inhaled" in larger than normal portions. The swimmers had gained greater respect for open water. Upon reflection they realized that even had they gotten to the girls' camp there might have been dire consequences.

Falling into bed Ivan reflected on the day and on the past two weeks, *What a wonderful break from refugee-camp boredom.*

What is ahead for me? How will my life work out? Will I become an engineer? Will I be able to meet the goals I've set?

I'll miss the guys from camp.

Sleep won and his racing thoughts were silenced.

As the sun broke through the next morning's grayness Ivan woke to smiling faces looking at him. His cabin mates were sitting on their beds, dressed and looking like they had just found their treasure or "got caught with their hands in the cookie jar." Excitement played around eyes and mouths as they sat waiting.

For what? Ivan scanned the cabin. Each of his cabin mates were there, each was silent, each had expectation written on his face.

He was the last one up. What was going on? What was the joke? He became uncomfortable and slightly suspicious. No one spoke. Rising from his bed he felt their eyes follow him. He hardly heard breathing. Silently, with questioning mind, he went outside to wash his face in the basin. The eyes followed. Now he was curious. He walked the short distance to the latrine. When he returned no one had moved. They were like statues with grins on their faces.

Maybe this is a last day initiation or something, he thought.

"What are you doing?' he finally asked. "Is something wrong?" His muscles tensed for flight to get him quickly away in case of need.

The smallest cabin mate stretched and stood while ceremoniously reaching under his bunk. Dragging a seemingly heavy bag from under his bed he walked in a controlled manner as though he were a dignitary, which in this case he had indeed been elected to be, to where Ivan was standing just inside the cabin door. Ivan braced himself; his body angled half toward the group and half ready to plunge back out the door.

"This," he said, "is from all of us. You can use them better than we can. We have families. You don't." He gave the not so heavy bag to Ivan who looked inside. At least a hundred vitamin pills were settled at the bottom. His puzzled look prompted one of the older boys to explain as though giving a speech.

"We decided to take several vitamins each day. We did not consume ours but saved what we took for you. You can use them wherever you go. Just a small friendship thing we wanted to do for you."

"Thanks." Ivan said. The gift was unexpected and appreciated.

As though that gift, making a huge impression on the refugee, was not enough, a friend from camp, Georgo,[85] sought him out at lunch.

"Come home with me," he said. "You can live at my house without needing to go back to Lavrion."

"Can I?" Ivan asked.

"Talk to the camp director. My dad said I could bring you. He has money and wants you to come, really! We have a big house."

The camp director quickly phoned the refugee camp.

"It is arranged," he said. "They like the idea of your having somewhere else to live. It takes some burden off them. They will however, keep you in mind for emigration. Check with them every month or two. Have fun with Georgo."

Life with a rich Greek was different. Different from the boys' camp, from the refugee camp, from prisons, and even from his home in Bulgaria. Ivan had never asked for wealth. He had only hoped for an education. Now he found himself in the center of opulence. The home, a fifteen room Mediterranean mansion, had more than enough food. Not only was there ample meat and oil to give food flavor; there were bright fresh vegetables and fruit. Each tasted better than the next. Oranges were still Ivan's favorite. He ate as many as four daily. The family never seemed to run short of anything. There was fresh milk, yogurt, cheese, and always ice cream. Anytime he was hungry he could eat but he preferred to wait until meals were served except for an occasional orange. Meals were more than sufficient and the table conversations were interesting.

After dinner Georgo went to parties almost every night for the next two months. He took Ivan, who at first went eagerly. He liked the rock and roll music of the West. A few nights of sameness wore on Ivan and he began to dislike going. Then Georgo practically dragged him. The kids drank too much wine or beer and smoked cigarettes. Ivan did neither. The girls were silly and the boys acted stupidly. Some of the kids kissed and cuddled. He began to see the emptiness in Georgo's chosen activity.

One evening he said, "Georgo, go to your party. I want to stay here."

"Why would you want that?" Georgo sounded disgusted, as if he didn't believe him.

"I'm tired of those parties. You go. Say, 'Hi,' to everyone. I'll be okay. Your dad has some good technical books in his library. I'll read something."

"Technical books?" Georgo almost snarled. "Whatever you want. I guess I don't have to understand."

Many evenings Ivan sat in the library or in his room trying to learn technology from books. Written Greek was not easy. Ivan thought he would never understand.

Georgo's father was a kind man with decent values. He always spoke respectfully to Georgo and Ivan.

While Ivan studied in the library one evening near the end of summer Georgo's father came in.

"May I talk with you, Ivan?"

"Yes, sir."

They sat comfortably across from each other with a small Oriental rug separating their chairs.

The host carefully placed his fingertips together one at a time watching his hands as he did so. He cleared his throat and looked into Ivan's eyes. He sighed. There was a deep, dark look that Ivan's youthfulness could not read.

Discomforted, Ivan asked, "Sir, may I ask if I've offended you in some way?"

"Oh, no! Quite the opposite. I like you, Ivan. You have a way about you that is uncommon will the current Greek youth. No, my heart is heavy for my own son. I want to ask you a personal favor. I hope that I don't offend you by asking."

"Please, feel free. I have been through some difficult things, sir, so I suppose I am not typical, as you say, of youth today. I have dreams and goals like everyone. I don't know how I can reach them. I intend to do everything I can, however, to fulfill them. I don't like wasted time. Much has already been lost with my escape and imprisonment. I am anxious to move on."

"That's what I mean. You have dreams and goals. You don't like the party life of most youth. My son, my precious son, my only son, burdens my heart. He is not maturing well. He wants only to play, not to plan for the future. He thinks I will always be here to provide for his foolishness. I love him. I want what is good for him. He seems to be wasting his youth, and therefore wasting his life. When I talk to him he appears not to listen. He acts as if he doesn't care. Will you help me?"

"How can I help? If he doesn't listen to you he will certainly not listen to me."

"No. Do not talk to him about these things. I have hopes that by your 'doing' something together an interest will be sparked in him. Then his inner motivation will take over. I want to send him to an engineering school here in Athens. Apparatuses seem to interest him. I believe he would enjoy operating machines and would do well in that field. He says he does not want to go. If I send you perhaps he would be willing. He likes you. Would you let me send you to this school with my son?"

Stunned to silence, jumbled thoughts in his mind, Ivan stared at his benefactor. No one had ever offered him such an incredible gift.

"Do you need time to think about this?"

"Oh, no, Sir. I'm sorry for not answering. Yes, I will accept. But, Sir, I cannot repay you for the tuition."

"No, it is not a loan. Thank you for accepting this gift. I hope it will be a turning point for my son. I will register you both tomorrow. Classes begin in one week. Oh, it is a live-in school with meals provided." Georgo's father got up, leaving Ivan to his thoughts and racing heart.

Maybe this is the beginning of my electrical engineering studies, he thought. *Georgo and I will have a great time studying together. Now that summer is over he will be ready to study. Older people seem to be too serious. They often misunderstand their children.*

Moving to the school in Athens Ivan found his studies interesting but not demanding, leaving him much time after school Monday through Friday for exploration and a personal life.

Georgo chose to run with his own crowd, basically ignoring Ivan who soon learned the short cuts in and around the ancient city. In one of his explorations he surprisingly reacquainted himself with the two bothers from Drama, now in Athens, Vlado and "Popeto" originally from Sofia, Bulgaria. They had escaped with Milco Moushmof and his family.

In Athens the two brothers had formed a close-knit group with three Yugoslavians and a Romanian youth. Ivan joined them and the seven spent most of their free time together. All wanted to emigrate. The youths Ivan joined had already put in their requests with various embassies.

They went with Ivan for his registration. He was willing to live in Germany, Australia, Africa, or the United States of America. He was willing to serve in the armed forces of any country in exchange for a permanent home. He knew that there was also a chance for him to find a home through the Refugee Camp connections with the Red Cross.

He sensed that freedom was finally within his grasp. Even now, he had more freedom than he had had in almost two years in Greece and for the last eight years in Bulgaria.

He and his new friends roamed the city until it felt like home.

The Acropolis became their playground after tourist hours. Large blocks of marble made slippery stairs to the ruins. They seemed out of place next to the grassy fields that surrounded the Acropolis. The ancient Parthenon and the Temple of Venus were structures of awe and beauty attesting to man's God-given gift of creativity. The majestic view of the city from atop the hill was breathtaking. Sunsets were highlights of most summer days when seen from that vantage point.

All of the Acropolis' attractions became passé when the boys used it as their site for "hide-and-seek." It afforded many unusual places to hide. Although it was a kid's game, no one was around to make fun of them for being childish. The young men didn't care about appearances. They simply had fun.

Ivan also liked the harbor, where he could sit and think as boats busied themselves on business trips.

As much as he liked Athens, he was more grateful for the school, the learning, the opportunity that had gotten him there.

During school Ivan focused on learning. He liked having a direction in life and working toward a goal.

When the tests were announced Ivan studied but Georgo didn't.

Since the boys were roommates, Ivan was aware of Georgo's behavior. He felt somewhat responsible to Georgo's father for his son's schooling.

"Let's study together." Ivan urged. "It'd be more fun than doing it alone and it would help me."

"I don't need to study. I know this stuff," Georgo would say. Then he would often fail. It didn't seem to bother him.

When Ivan saw Georgo outside class and asked him questions pertaining to school Georgo seemed disinterested or blankly answered, "I don't know" or "I don't care."

Georgo's lack of interest in the opportunity for training was evident. Ivan began to reflect, *Was his father right about this young man?*

At least twice a week Ivan noticed that Georgo was not in class.

"Where have you been?"

"A couple of us went for wine (or beer)," he answered.

Sometimes Georgo would say, "I went to the beach. Petros wanted to fish," or, "The day was too nice. We had to go swimming."

"Georgo, your father expects you to finish this course. What will you tell him when you don't pass?"

"I don't know. He wanted me to come, I didn't ask. School is boring. I've spent my whole life in school. I plan to be a businessman when I grow up. Who needs this? My dad's okay but he's old-fashioned. If you want to waste your youth on learning this stuff go ahead. Besides, who says I won't pass?"

It wasn't long before Ivan knew that he could no longer cover for his kindly benefactor's son and to allow the father to wrongly believe that his son was making good use of school.

The following weekend Ivan went to Georgo's home and sought out his father.

Sadly he reported, "I can't continue school at your expense. Your generosity is not doing what we had hoped. I'm afraid that Georgo is not making the most of his opportunity. He wants only to continue to play."

Georgo's father sighed deeply. After several seconds he said in a soft voice, almost a whisper, "I guess I knew that Georgo wouldn't put much into this, any more than he has into anything else worthwhile. I have tried to help my son. Maybe my affluence is the problem. Maybe he couldn't sense my love for him because of my wealth. Well, thank you for helping get him to the school."

He paused, "Ivan, I want you to finish the term. Stay in the dormitory as long as you like even after the term finishes. I will pay for your stay. The people that run Lavrion's refugee camp will know where to find you."

"You are a very kind man, sir," Ivan said. "I like to think that my father would have been like you. Thank you for the help you have given me. I'll never forget you."

They embraced before Ivan went back to school.

When he received his certificate for completing the term he had time on his hands. No school, just leisure.

He and his friends spent much time playing ping-pong, chess, and singing. Fall was moving toward winter.

One Saturday in November when the truck from Lavrion came to Athens the driver sought out Ivan.

"Because you are among the youngest registered at the camp in Lavrion, the Red Cross has chosen you to be one of the next immigrants to the USA. Do you still want to go there?"

"Yes, I'll go anywhere!"

"A sponsor has been found for you. He lives in Cincinnati, Ohio. He expects you to wash dishes in his restaurant. He in turn will give you room and board in America. Does that sound agreeable to you?"

"Yes," Ivan said with emotion.

"There are no entrance visas to the USA available from Bulgaria or Greece. Your group of refugees must first travel to Germany by plane and go to the USA from there, on the German quota," he was told. "Go to the US embassy in a week. Your papers will be in order. Take this document of identification with you. Bon Voyage!"

With the good news came a sense of loss. He would miss his friends.

They, in turn, decided to give him a 'going to the New World' party. None of them had many possessions or money but with generosity they gave what they could.

One gave ten American dollars. The others pooled money for clothes. He decided on two pairs of underwear, two pairs of socks, and a sport jacket for travel to his new home.

Wearing the jacket and one pair of each of his new possessions, the other new items fit easily into his Escapee Program bag with toiletries and the remaining vitamins.

"We're not saying good-bye here," his friends said. "We will go to the American consulate with you."

The consul gave Ivan papers and airline tickets.

"I have ten American dollars," Ivan said. "Is that enough to take with me to America?"

"Ten dollars American is a lot in the States," the consul told him. "But I must tell you that you cannot legally take anything but drachmas out of Greece. When the officials find it, it will, at their discretion, be taken away or exchanged.

"Tomorrow morning at eight o'clock," Ivan heard in an abrupt change of subject, "You are to be at Athens airport to depart for Germany."

Ivan never let "No, you can't" stop him. In fact it enticed him to find a way.

After leaving the consulate he and his friends went to the harbor. Leaning against the rock retaining wall, his friends around him, he took the tubular shaving soap from his Escapee Program bag. Carefully he removed the foil that was wrapped around its base forming a handle. Using a friend's pocketknife he routed the bottom of the center out of the soap, making a hole about two inches deep and a half-inch in diameter. Folding, then rolling the bill he placed it into the newly formed compartment. Then he again covered the end of the soap with the foil. It looked normal. One would not suspect that it contained contraband.

"How's that for a hiding place?" he asked putting the soap back into his bag.

They all approved and laughed.

The next day they escorted him to the airport.

The year 1956 was ending. In ten days a new year would be ushered in. A new life was about to begin for Ivan.

Surely I will be free in the "free world," he thought.

18. Transplant

Dirt and grime flew in the stiff breeze. Papers rose effortlessly from the tarmac and whirled around the rundown airport in Athens. Others caught in tufts of grass scattered around the field. Winds whipped the overgrown grass back and forth like a dog shaking a toy, as though the grass was trying to free itself from the foreign material caught in its long blades.

Shielding his eyes from the dust and dirt, Ivan hurried outside to the portable steps rolled up to the airplane door.

He turned to look through the fence at his friends waving their good-byes. Blurry vision made him aware he thought he would never see them again. He waved back and again turned toward the plane.

The group of passengers boarding was poor, wearing threadbare coats or, like Ivan, only a sport coat. Their shoes were beyond scuffed. The leather had visible holes. Some of the frayed laces were long enough to lace only through two or three eyelets out of seven. Other shoes lacked laces entirely. The heels were thin at best, if indeed there were heels.

On board Ivan found a seat, stashed his belongings in an overhead bin, and began this new leg of his journey.

Takeoff was an experience for which he was not prepared. His stomach was oddly moved but not uncomfortable. A baby cried fitfully and he realized that his own ears were feeling unusual pressure from the change. Perhaps that was the baby's torment. A woman's soothing voice tried in vain to comfort the child. In time the wailing ceased.

Through the window Ivan saw the land quickly slip away. Huge mountains appeared small. He was intrigued by the strange appearance of the familiar.

Time stood still. It was an eternity...yet the travel took no time at all.

With the plane's descent buildings took shape, vehicles became crawling ants. Ivan gathered his things to leave the plane. He was ready when the doors opened and a guide led them to a waiting car. Ivan, along with several others, was whisked to a building. He had anticipated different arrangements but each person had his own room off a long corridor.

Later, meeting in the cafeteria, they decided to see the local sights.

Three of them, young men under twenty years of age, went outside into the street together exchanging names. The others were Yugoslavians. They saw a social dance club not far from the dorm and agreed that they had found their evening's destination. Entering the dimly lit hall Ivan felt his insides throb in unison with the heavy downbeat music.

Upon invitation they joined other young men in a booth. They ordered sausages and hard rolls to complement beer. Ivan saw and heard the chattering of girls in another booth.

"Are you going to ask someone to dance?" one of Ivan's companions asked another.

"I don't know. What if she can't dance?" he responded. "Or worse, says, 'No'?"

"No one will say, 'No.'"

"And what if you can't dance?" teased another.

"I can dance! Come on, let's ask someone."

The two slid out and without wasted time were vigorously dancing to the loud music with laughing partners.

"Do they all speak German?" Ivan asked of the others still at the table.

"Ya," they laughed. "What does it matter?"

"I want to dance. If I can't speak their language how do I ask?" Ivan puzzled.

"Ask! Who need words? They're here to dance just like we are."

The rest of the group left the booth and approached a few giggling young women who were not yet dancing.

They easily found dance partners. No one seemed to notice any flaws or embarrassment in anyone else. The kids were there to dance, to laugh, to exercise, and to relax.

Ivan danced with many girls that night and felt a freedom that he had never known before. Here he, a Bulgarian who had spent almost two years in Greece, was now in Germany dancing with girls he didn't know, in a club he had seen for the first time a few hours before! He was on his way to America! He didn't think things could get better.

In four weeks the necessary additional paperwork to obtain visas was completed and Ivan was on his way by bus to Bremerhaven, a northwestern seaport of Germany on the Weser River.

Boarding the long, narrow ship his ears distinguished a welcome language from all the sounds of machines and voices.

"So this is the ship that will take us to America," someone said in Bulgarian within Ivan's hearing. He couldn't see the speaker. People were packed between them on the deck as horn blasts announced that the ship was prepared to leave.

"Mamo, I want to explore the ship right now!" Ivan heard.

"Wait, *momchentse*[86], until Tatko can go with you."

Pressing through the crowd, Ivan found the vocal Bulgarian family. He was surprised to see Milco, whom he had met in Lavrion, with his wife Elena and their child.

"Hi," he said in greeting, "You are going to America too! I didn't see you on the plane."

"We arrived in Germany about ten days ago. Our family flew from Athens to Hamburg on December 31," Milco explained.

"My group flew to Hamburg after you. We've only been in Germany for four days. I was with some Yugoslavians. It is good to see you. It is very good to hear Bulgarian. Where are you going in America?"

"To Toledo, Ohio? What about you?"

"I've got a sponsorship in Cincinnati, Ohio. Maybe we will be close together. I hope so."

"That would be good," Milco agreed.

"Let me show Boby[87] around the ship while you two find quarters and settle in," Ivan offered. "It won't take me long to find a bunk. There's only one of me but three of you."

"That sounds very good to me," Milco's wife sighed. "But let's all go together to find our places, then you can take Boby around. Maybe we'll find four together that way. In any event you will know where to bring Boby back later."

Together they made their way through the thinning crowd toward the ladders to go below decks. Boby raced ahead as children do. He reached the stairs before the adults and turned to watch them as they approached. At that moment the ship rose as it plowed into a large wave and was lifted. With the sudden unexpected motion Boby dropped out of sight. There was no sound. He simply disappeared.

Running, Ivan got to the top of the stairs and looked down. Boby was sitting on the deck below. He appeared to be fine. He had no idea how he had gotten there. As is often the case with children there was no damage. When the adults got to him, Boby was up and smiling and ready for his 'adventure' not realizing he had already had one.

The *General W. C. Langfitt*, a converted battleship from the Second World War, became their floating home for ten days.

During their time on board Ivan and Boby explored every inch of the ship. Whenever he felt well enough he would play and instruct Boby, so his parents could be alone or rest.

Ivan explained to his young friend, "These platforms make nice places to sit in the sun now but they cover the mountings for big guns."

They played in the enclosed rooms and on the open decks when the ocean was quiet. Most of their time was spent exploring the many nooks and crannies.

"Do you see how narrow this ship is? It was made like this for wartime, so it could go fast through the water. Let's see how many big steps it takes to get across the deck. Because each big step is about one meter we can figure out how wide it is. Being narrow and long, it isn't stable. I think we will have trouble walking like we used to when we get back onto land."

On board the German ship the meals were often "brats" and "kraut."

After a few days Ivan started having nausea. He began to leave Boby in his parent's care and spent much time hanging over the rail of the lowest deck or over the toilet as his insides roiled like, and because of, the sea. Day after day of sea-sickness reminded him that they were afloat, isolated from all other humanity.

He played ping-pong when it was possible or when he wasn't enjoying Boby.

Talking to the captain several days into the trip, Ivan asked. "Why are we not in America yet? I thought we would be there by now. Hasn't it been eight days yet?"

"Yes," the captain answered. "You're right. We expected to be in New York by now. There's a storm up North we are avoiding. Going through it on this ship would be difficult at best."

"When will we get there?" the now regularly greenish Ivan asked.

"We anticipate making harbor tomorrow. Do you think you can survive?" he added with a knowing chuckle.

Ivan inwardly groaned as his stomach churned.

"I hope so," he answered as he dashed again to drape himself over the railing.

Long after the voyage the smell of boiled bratwurst, hot dogs, or sauerkraut plagued Ivan with the memories of horrendous seasickness. He no longer enjoyed eating them.

Finally on January 19, 1957, Ivan saw her as he looked toward the horizon. The most beautiful lady he had ever seen. She had a flaming lamp in her right hand and a crown on her head. She was magnificent and she stood on the soil of New York. Without a word she said, "Welcome, you who are weary. Welcome, Ivan."

She became blurred through his tears.

They were in America! Freedom! Ivan stared. Did he breathe? He didn't know nor care. His ship was docking in America. He had arrived at his new home.

Along with the other immigrants Ivan half-walked and was half-pushed by disembarking passengers along the dock and into a cavernous hall.

Milco and his family were soon lost, milling in the now crowded building. The massive room stood next to the narrow walkway beside which the

W. C. General Langfitt sat gently rocking at dock. The armory-like structure had windows that were high near the ceiling, allowing the light to stream in. The only view, however, was of the deep blue-gray winter sky. Ivan saw a line of immigrants leading to a small wooden table where a person sat taking papers, stamping them, smiling, handing them back, then taking papers from the next in line. He queued behind a bent man and woman, easily in their late seventies. The man leaned on a gnarled wooden cane. Their bodies said, "We're finished!" but their eyes shone with the excitement of new beginnings.

The line crept forward and people shuffled to maintain their place. Ivan noted three other similar lines in the building.

A man who was apparently speaking came quickly from one of the tables toward the end of the lines. He seemed to be repeating something as he searched the faces in the four lines craning his neck and standing on tiptoe from time to time. He seemed to be looking for someone as he spoke. Ivan could not make out what was said. As the man got closer Ivan heard, "Ivan Pavlov Ivanov?"

Raising his hand, Ivan called, "I am Ivan Pavlov Ivanov."

Hurrying through the lines toward Ivan the stranger said in perfect Bulgarian, "Come with me."

Ivan was grateful to hear his native language. He had not yet thought how he would manage in this strange place so far from his homeland. He knew he would have to learn English but after learning Greek he assumed that that wouldn't be a major challenge.

Together the two walked briskly at least fifty yards from the crush of immigrants in their lines and across the hall to an empty bench, one of many against the walls.

The man spoke.

"You have no sponsor," he said bluntly.

"Yes, I do," Ivan defended. "He owns a restaurant in Cincinnati, Ohio. I was told in Greece."

"But since then his restaurant has closed. It is no more. There is no sponsor for you."

"But there must be! What do I do now?" Ivan felt an unusual tightness in his chest. He was glad to be seated. He became faint and confused.

"You can sleep on board the ship tonight and then go back to Germany. It departs tomorrow morning, or...."

"Or, what?" Ivan quickly asked feeling weak. *How can I endure another ten days at sea? Without being able to eat again I might die. I can't go through that again. Everything that has happened has been easy compared to that.*

"Or," the stranger was saying, "you can sit here while we look for another sponsor for you. I can't promise anything but I can look if you want me to."

"Please look. I do not want to go back. Please... please," he begged. He felt pressure from within threatening to explode his head and body.

"All right. Stay here. Don't leave. I don't know how long it will take. I'll be back. Just stay here!"

One hour passed. Two. Ivan was hungry. He got up, stretched his legs. He moved around but would not leave his bench.

Milco and his family saw him. They walked to where he was pacing.

"How are you, young friend?" Milco called out. Boby ran toward Ivan and leapt into his arms to be thrown into the air.

"My legs work good now!" Boby said in mid-toss. "But they sure were wobbly after getting off the ship."

"Ah ha! Was I right?" Ivan laughed putting the child down.

Struggling with his feelings and his hunger Ivan quickly explained what had happened.

"I have to stay here," he said. "The man promised to be back. I hope he will be here before dark. I don't know how long the hall stays open."

"We'll stay with you for an hour," Milco said. "That will allow us enough time to get to the station for our train's departure.

"Certainly by then you will have a sponsor. We are still headed to Toledo, Ohio. It would be good if you went there too. Who knows, maybe your new sponsor will be in Toledo.

"This is to be our address," he handed Ivan a slip of paper.

"Write to us as soon as you get settled. We might not be able to stay at this address for long. Each sponsorship works differently. We want to stay in touch with you. You are like our brother and Boby is attached to you too."

The next hour passed swiftly as the little group discussed many things. Milco's family left.

Alone, fighting desperation he realized his hunger was consuming him. He was hungrier than he had ever been. He hadn't felt this hungry in the cell in Thessoloniki where there was never enough food and what there was was barely edible.

A half-hour passed, then another.

Do I have the stamina to stay here? Where else would I go? I can't speak English. Few are left in the hall. No one seems to know I'm here. I wish I knew what to do, he thought.

Then he believed he heard his mother's voice, "Stay where you are, my son." He obeyed.

The next half-hour of waiting was the worst. He felt like a prisoner in this huge tomb. If he left, even to find food, he might lose this opportunity to gain refuge in America. Besides, where could he go? Thinking of staying brought confusion. He wasn't certain that the stranger would return. The minutes dragged slowly like mud-encased boots struggling to get across a muddy creek bed, being sucked down at every step.

Finally, after four hours, the stranger approached Ivan with quick steps. He was breathless but was wearing a toothy smile.

"If you would like you can go to Monticello, Illinois. Is that okay with you?"

"Cincinnati, Ohio; Monticello, Illinois," he said with a shrug, "If they are both in America they're the same to me. As long as I don't have to go back on that ship I'm fine."

The stranger laughed.

"Okay," he said. "There is a youth group with a Presbyterian Church in Monticello, Illinois, that is paying for a young person to travel from New York to their town. Their assigned refugee was from Yugoslavia but he didn't pass all the medical and dental requirements for entry. They say it is fine if you want to take his place."

"What do I have to do for them to sponsor me to stay there?"

"It appears that they only want you to live with the pastor and his family and to be part of the church youth group. There is no work requirement."

"Wow, that seems unbelievable!" Ivan said. "When do I go and how do I get there?"

"These are your train tickets to Chicago and from Chicago to Monticello. You will travel with a small group of Yugoslavian refugees. A former refugee has come from Chicago to help the new ones. He will help you too, since the language is similar."

At the train station the man bought Ivan a hamburger, French fries, and a soda. He introduced him to the young men from Yugoslavia.

"I have a group of friends in Chicago," the spokesperson and leader of the group said, "and hotel reservations for the night within walking distance of the train station. You may stay with us until tomorrow when you take another train to Monticello. The rest of us will live around Chicago with our sponsors. Do you feel okay with these arrangements?"

"Yes. Thanks. I'd be happy to stay with you. I don't know my way around. You are the first to offer a plan."

In Chicago Ivan entered the massive and beautifully designed train station. It was old but not as well maintained as the buildings he had seen in Germany.

Walking from the station on dirty, litter-strewn sidewalks, the group passed run-down buildings and derelict men sleeping in doorways, reeking of cheap alcohol. The "El"[88] ran noisily overhead, with no effect on the drunken men in their stupor.

A large brick structure proved to be their hotel. Inside the massive outer door the group waited as the "leader" went to the front desk to get the keys. He distributed them to the Yugoslavians, two men to a room, and to Ivan who was given a private room.

His key and the ten dollars, which he had retrieved from his shaving soap, were securely in his pocket. Ivan felt able to handle anything.

They stepped into the late afternoon bone-chilling wind and walked about half a block, crossing the not-too-busy street.

The group turned into a noisy honky-tonk bar and ordered a round of beers. Smoke hung heavily in the place and the murky lighting with some burned out bulbs made the atmosphere smothering. It smelled of stale beer.

When their beers sloshed to a stop in front of their owners the bartender, walking behind the bar, collected money from the "leader". Ivan pulled out his ten dollars with the intent to pay for his own.

Quickly covering the bill with his hand the "leader" whispered, "Put that money in your sock or somewhere it can't be seen. Don't wave it around like that!

"Do you see that dark man over there. If he sees your money, he'll hit you over the head when you aren't looking and take it from you. You've got to learn the ways of the big city. I'm paying for tonight's drinks. We're celebrating 'Life in America' for you new refugees."

Ivan had no knowledge of a big city in America. The big cities he had experienced were small compared to Chicago. He had never seen a black-skinned man in person. He could only accept what was told him as truth. Quickly he stuffed the bill into the inner ankle of his right sock.

After finishing the beer Ivan said, "I need some sleep. Is anyone coming to the hotel with me?"

"Nah, the night is young. We're celebrating our entry into the U.S. tonight. It will be late," someone said.

"Go to the hotel," the "leader" told him, "Take the stairs to the second floor. Go straight ahead down the hall and your room is the last on your left. It is already paid for. Have a good sleep. Leave in the morning. Have a good life in America. Good to meet you!" And they were back to their drinking and laughing. No handshake, no embrace, just a quick impersonal good-bye. Still, Ivan was thankful for their company and help from New York to Chicago.

Will I ever see any of them again? he wondered.

On his way out of the saloon there were two black men ready to enter, talking and laughing. They opened the door for him to leave. He was smaller than either of them. He hoped that they couldn't hear his heart alternately skipping beats and racing, it seemed. He hoped his smile didn't look fake. He hoped they didn't know he had ten dollars in his sock.

Trying to walk normally, trying to disguise his mounting fear he entered the hotel. Directly in front of him was the very long stairway. It appeared to rise to the third, rather than the second floor. It was wider than any he had seen. Walking to the last room on the left, as instructed, he felt the raw cold January wind as it rushed down the corridor. He shivered involuntarily and pulled his sport coat across his chest. Taking a few steps further down the corridor he saw the dark of night as clear as day. The hotel appeared to end after his room. There was no wall at the end of the hallway. It was either unfinished or partly destroyed. If he kept walking he would fall from the higher-than-normal second floor to the ground below.

This is the strangest place I've ever seen, he thought turning into the room he had been told was his. Switching on the light he saw an inviting bed beckoning his tired body. A private sink was to the right of the door. The dresser held a metal basin and a glass. A straight-backed chair sat near the window. The best sight was seeing four complete walls enclosing his room.

Remembering the warning his Yugoslavian "friends" had given him he closed the door and attempted to lock it. There was no keyhole on the inner knob.

I wonder why they gave me a key if the door doesn't lock, he thought. *How am I going to secure this room against thieves?*

He tried wedging the chair under the doorknob. *That isn't secure enough. If someone wants my money they can still get in.*

He decided to take the door handle apart and prop it in place so that from the outside it looked normal. However, the inside knob was resting precariously on the rod going through the door between the two handles. He tested it. Each time the outer handle turned, even slightly, the inner knob fell.

Perfect! he thought, placing the metal bowl on the floor under the inner doorknob. *Now I can go to sleep and if anyone wants to get in, as soon as they turn the handle the knob will fall into the pan and make a racket. I'll wake up and it might even scare the thief away.*

With his alarm in place he slept well until daylight woke him. No one had attempted to get in during the night.

Retracing his path from the night before, Ivan arrived at the train station with time to spare. Boarding the train he realized the end of his travel was in sight. Soon the train's wheels clacked rhythmically, "Freedom, home, freedom, home, freedom, home."

Looking through the window after leaving the big city of Chicago he saw a few small cities. Mostly it was farmland. There were cattle grazing or fields of grain. This trip resembled the one from New York to Chicago with miles of corn. It was strange for Ivan to see crops growing in the winter.

How am I to know when to get off? he thought as he watched the scenery. *People just get up and get off when the train stops. They must know the stops.*

Then he noticed the conductor walking back and forth through the cars continuously scanning the window area. As he walked he would seemingly at random reach over and pull a ticket from its place next to a rider. At the next stop that rider would leave. So Ivan waited. At one point the conductor pulled Ivan's ticket from its place. *This is it*, he mused silently. Gathering his jacket and Refugee bag he got up and headed for the door.

Soon the train stopped. He got off and walked a few steps. He realized he was alone.

Stopping, he looked around and saw a few cows lying in the field nearby chewing cud and watching him. The train was still next to the wooden platform on which he stood. There were no buildings, only farmland.
I have to get back on the train! he thought, panic beginning to rise. But when he turned to step aboard, the train lurched forward too fast for him. He stood watching as it quickly vanished from view down the track.

Nothing to do but wait, he thought.

So he did.

19. MONTICELLO

Mid-afternoon on January 20, 1957, seventeen-year-old Ivan was waiting alone on the platform.

A car. Is it for me? Ivan wondered.

A tall man and five young teen-aged girls got out and walked toward him.

It looks like they came to meet me. But why all the girls? The last word, "girls," echoed...*Girls, girls, girls.* His face became warm and his palms damp. A lump in his throat seemed to threaten his breathing. He had little experience around girls, feeling uneasy.

The smiling man asked, "Ivan Ivanov?"[89]

They were strange sounds but Ivan, in spite of his embarrassment, boldly patted his chest with his palm and said, "Ivan Pavlov."[90] He returned the man's smile but could not allow himself to look at the pretty smiling girls. His few English words were gone under this stress.

"Oh, Ivan Pavlov." repeated the man. Touching his own chest he said, "Bob Williams," and extended a hand in friendship. Ivan shook the hand, aware of feminine stares. He kept his attention focused on Bob's dancing blue eyes.

Then carefully with as much poise as he could muster, trying to be polite, he offered a handshake to each girl in the circle pressing around him.

Bob, recognizing Ivan's discomfort and assuming correctly that the girls were the cause, put Ivan in the front seat of the car with him while the girls piled into the back. It was a tight fit with some sitting on laps. Resounding with youthful laughter, the full car headed away from the tracks lower in the back than the front.

A five-minute drive brought them out of the country into the small town's residential area of homes with nicely groomed yards. Although it was January the weather was mild, there was no snow. They drove to a well-maintained two-story home and stopped.

171

Bob and the girls were talking. Ivan could make nothing of the garbled sounds.

Ivan expected the girls to precede him but they held back. He entered the house. He walked directly into a living room filled with boys and girls, some sitting on the furniture, most on the floor. All were looking at him and smiling. Next to him was a piece of wooden furniture acting as a divider between the door and the room, creating an entry hall of sorts. It was standing on the floor. Although the youth saw Ivan their attention was on that furniture, the television.

Ivan felt awkward, conspicuous. He thought they were focusing on him.

A woman walked to him and embraced him in front of everyone. They moved into the room a bit. He saw the flickering from the television out of the corner of his eye.

The woman said, "Welcome home," but he didn't understand. He assumed correctly, however, that she was Bob's wife.

Bob said, "unintelligible things," "Nan," several times, and more "unintelligible things."

So her name is Nan, Ivan surmised. *She seems very nice.*

Nan asked Ivan, "Do you want water?"

He couldn't understand her. He knew the word "water" but he had heard "wahr." He didn't respond.

Not far behind Nan was a four-year-old child.

Nan said, "David, take Ivan to his room, please."

Ivan felt David take his hand and sensed him smiling up at him. But Ivan's attention was now on the piece of furniture next to him at which the others were looking. In a lighted square on its front from which he had noticed the flickering was what looked like a tiny, smiling, bald man waving from inside a tiny topless vehicle which was being driven down a tiny street. Many similarly tiny people were along the side of the road. Some waved to the man in the car. Ivan could not imagine how people could be only inches tall and still look normal. Ivan also heard unintelligible speech coming from the box.

Looking around the room he thought there must be a projector of some sort for the "movie" but found nothing.

He had never seen a television.

He was viewing the historic coverage of President-elect Dwight D. Eisenhower's (Ike's) inaugural parade.

After gawking at the TV he felt David's little hand tugging him. He looked down at the boy who pulled him again toward the stairway beyond the living room. Ivan grinned at David, nodded toward those whom he didn't know, and went gratefully upstairs with the non-stop talking David. Ivan kept hearing the same word in David's chatter, "Yeroom."

On the second floor David led Ivan into a small bedroom. Inside was a bed covered with a bright quilt, big enough for Ivan's whole family in Bulgaria. There was a rustic wooden table with a lamp. He even had a chair.

David was saying, "Yeroom," again.

What does that mean? he thought. He looked around the room realizing that David had slipped his hand free and had climbed up onto the bed.

More chattering from David as his steady small-boy gaze drew Ivan to sit next to him.

I'm going to like this little boy, Ivan thought. *He's probably going to be my first friend in America.*

Ivan pointed to the table, "*Kakvo e tova?*"[91] he asked.

Not knowing the speech but knowing the gesture, David responded, "Table."

"Tahbuhl?" repeated Ivan.

"Okay," said little David.

"*Ee kakvo e tova?*" Ivan asked again, pointing to the chair.

"Chair," little David answered.

"Cheer?" Ivan asked rolling the "r."

"Yes," David laughed. He got off the bed.

"*A tova?*" Ivan pointed to the lamp.

"Lamp."

"Lahmpa?"

"No, lamp," said David.

"Lahmp!"

" No! Lamp!" said David correcting him as he turned and walked from the room.

Ivan sat alone on his bed.

"Tahbuhl, cheer, lahmp," he said softly to himself. *That's three new words. David says them some other way. I'll have to learn to pronounce them correctly.*

On the table was a pad of paper and a pencil. In the Cyrillic alphabet he wrote: *stol* = cheer; *masa* = tahbuhl; *lampa* = lahmp. He wrote the numbers from one to ten, then twenty, thirty and each additional ten to one hundred, as he had learned in Greece. He added bread, water, yes, and no and headed the page: Dictionary of English.

This is a room fit for a prince, he thought. *I have never had my own lamp, table, and chair. Studying will be easy with all this.*

He lay on his new bed.

Within an hour David returned and once again slipped his little hand into Ivan's pulling him toward the door. Down the stairs they went, Ivan reluctant to face the crowd he had earlier fled. The living room was now empty.

The wonderful aroma of cooked food tantalized his nose. By the smell he knew that it must be ready to serve. He was ready for anything and everything set before him.

I have hardly eaten in two weeks, he thought. *We were on board ship for ten days and I either couldn't eat or it wouldn't stay down. In New York I had the hamburger and fries. In Chicago only a beer. No wonder my stomach is screaming.*

In the dining room nine places were set. The table covered with a beautiful white damask cloth. Five people unfamiliar to Ivan were sitting, smiling and nodding to him as he entered. There were two married couples and a single man. As was the Bulgarian custom he went from one to the next shaking hands. Bob introduced them, the men rising while taking Ivan's hand in firm handshakes.

One of the men referred to Ivan often while speaking and spoke directly to him although Ivan could not understand the words.

"John Paul Johnson," the man repeated several times, "John Paul Johnson." Ivan had no idea why. About the fifth time the man pointed at Ivan and smiled, "You will be John Paul Johnson. That is the correct translation of Ivan Pavlov Ivanov. We'll call you 'Johnny'."

Slowly understanding settled into Ivan's mind. His name was being changed to John Paul Johnson. *Maybe that will be easier for Americans,* he thought. He said the name in his mind, *John Paul Johnson. It's okay, I guess. I didn't anticipate a name change but so many things are different. I will get used to it.*

Although he was polite he didn't try to listen to most of the table conversation. His mind was tired. Occasionally he noticed someone looking at him and he smiled into the individual's eyes.

When David and Bob were seated Nan finally brought dinner. Five minutes had seemed like half an hour.

Ivan lost himself in eating. Fried chicken, cornbread, tossed green salad, green beans with bacon and onions, and mashed potatoes and gravy were the main course. Ivan felt so full he thought he couldn't eat another bite. Then dessert was served. It was a fruit pie topped with vanilla ice cream. Ivan had never seen a pie. It resembled *bonitsa* in being round but smaller than *bonitsa*, about as deep. When he tasted it the crust melted in his mouth and the tart cherry filling was juicy with just a hint of sweetness. Ivan was not fond of sweets like the Americans, but he loved the pie.

This is living! he thought. *My favorite fruit next to oranges is tart cherries. How did they know?* Alone the ice cream was too cold but it was perfect when eaten with the warm pie. *This ice cream is smooth, not gritty like Bulgarian ice-cream. I like it. My first American meal is a great experience!*

There was enough chilled milk to swim in and he knew that his new life was going to be wonderful. His goal now was to learn the language.

Going downstairs the next morning he cautiously entered the kitchen, not knowing who would be there. Only Nan and David were.

David greeted him playfully, "Sit there, Johnny," he said, pointing to an empty chair at the dining room table.

"Cheer," Ivan said smiling.

"Sit there," David repeated.

Ivan sat at the table not knowing what David had said except for his new name.

As soon as he sat David was next to him poking him in the ribs with his finger and giggling. As "Johnny" tried to tickle back David quickly avoided contact. That was to be their regular game. Nan, in the kitchen, laughed with them.

Ivan was quickly becoming a member of the family, thanks to little David.

Soon Nan was placing a glass of freshly squeezed orange juice in front of him. From a box she poured some tiny spheres that clinked into the bowl followed by milk. Giving him a spoon she said, "Eat your breakfast," as she motioned "eating" to him.

He smiled and ate. The food was crunchy and different to any he had ever eaten but he liked it. It had a sweet fruity flavor. He hoped that whatever it was would be his regular breakfast.

"*Blagodaria*,"[92] he said.

She smiled at him. "You're welcome," she responded.

"Ooelcum," he parroted.

"No," she laughed. "You," she pointed to him, "Say, 'thank you.' I," and she touched her chest with a finger, "Say, 'You're welcome.' You say," she pointed, "...thank you...thank you...thank you." She was quiet, continuing to smile at him, waiting.

Thinking he understood Ivan said, "Sank oo."

"Yes! You say, 'Thank you.' I say, 'You're welcome.'"

He was to discover many similar exchanges with people wherever he went. Sometimes he would learn a new word or two. Other times he would be confused.

With David's simple communication skills and by using many grunts, pointing, and acting out what he needed to say Ivan was able to ask for a dictionary.

Soon after breakfast he was in his room with the big book.

Before opening it he took his notepad and carefully added: *blagodaria* = sank oo.

Tearing a clean sheet from the pad, Ivan wrote briefly to Milco in Toledo sending his address. He copied Milco's address onto the envelope David had brought him. He trusted that the family with whom he was living would put it into the mail.

After studying the dictionary for several hours the Latin alphabet seemed less formidable.

I must develop a plan, he thought. *I will learn what I can from David and his parents. I'll add each word to my list as I learn it. But I must study at least six hours a day on my own. I will learn three words beginning with each letter every day, three from A, three from B, etc. Let's see, first is "aardvark," second, "aardwolf," third, "aba."* For B, first, *"Baal,"* second, *"baba,"* third, *"babitt."* C has, first, *"cab,"* second, *"cabal,"* third, *"cabala."*

He wrote and studied carefully for his first six hours, taking twenty minutes off to go into the kitchen at noon with David for a sandwich, a glass of milk, and an apple.

By dinnertime his mind was numb. He had, however, made progress and could hardly wait to hear the words that he had carefully learned. Maybe he would be able to use a few himself. That evening he heard very few familiar words; "yes," "no," "bread," the family member's names, and his own new name.

Day after grueling day he continued to work at learning English from the dictionary until ten days later he realized that no one used the words he had learned.

There has to be a way. I don't know why I can't learn as quickly as I did in Greece.

Upon reflection he realized that Greek had come easier to him because he had been surrounded by Greek youths who constantly spoke their language in his presence. They repeated phrases while playing ping-pong and other games. At first he had heard only gibberish, like this English, but in time his brain had transformed sounds into words, thoughts, and sentences.

Ivan decided to give up the dictionary approach. David would be his primary teacher. He would learn the basic language and add more sophisticated speech later.

David enjoyed the added attention, spending time with his new friend.

Finding a magazine with pictures, Ivan began to study the captions under the pictures. These, he discovered, were more helpful than the dictionary had been, and he heard some of those words being used.

Little by little his list of known, helpful words was growing.

In mid-February Bob took Ivan, who was now known as "Johnny," to High School to register him for the second semester.

The principal with whom they met asked Johnny, "How many years have you studied?"

"Nine years in Bulgaria," Johnny answered when he understood the question.

"Then you must start as a freshman. At seventeen you are old enough to be a junior or senior but we must not let you 'fall through the cracks' of education," the principal said.

Johnny did not understand most of what the principal said but was excited about being accepted into the school.

In the dictionary that night Johnny found "freshman: a student in the first year of the course at a university, college, or school."[93]

Writing a short note to his mother he was pleased to tell her that he was to start high school, "an institution of higher education." He believed that he had been admitted to a university. After all, that was the definition, wasn't it?

Mama will be proud of me, he thought.

The following day Johnny went with Bob to school. They met a man in his thirties.

"This is George," Bob told Johnny. "From Greece."

"George, this is Johnny from Bulgaria who is part of our family now. He lived in Greece for two years and speaks Greek. He's learning English. I hope you can help him with school."

"I own a restaurant in town," George said in Greek. "*Kale mera.*"[94]

"Ah," Johnny responded excitedly hearing a familiar language, "*Kale mera! Te kan is?*[95]"

The two conversed for several minutes.

Bob stood beside them smiling, patiently waiting.

George and Bob talked. George translated for Johnny.

"I will go to school with you every day this week," his interpreter said. "Then maybe two days a week for two or three weeks. Then you will call me when you think it is necessary. Okay?"

"Yes, and thank you very much. I need the help," Johnny responded in Greek.

Johnny's first classes were a blur. He barely understood. He and George sat in the back of the room away from the other students, so that George could translate without causing disruption. Johnny grasped only the major points.

The kids in his classes seemed to accept him, or at least ignore him, after the first few awkward minutes. Not being the center of attention helped him lose his embarrassment at being an outsider.

At lunch he followed the others into the cafeteria while George went to help in his restaurant during the busy mealtime.

When Johnny sat at the long table other students joined him. He looked at his tray. His plate was heaped with a thick, round piece of white bread covered with a reddish meaty mixture. A small bowl next to his plate held a salad. Canned peaches were in another bowl and a waxy square container that he assumed held milk was also on his tray. Wrapped in a paper napkin were knife, fork, spoon, and a straw.

Looking at his tray he glanced sideways to see how the others would open their milk containers. They, in turn, were staring at him, smiling, waiting for him to start. They were being polite but he had no idea how to drink his milk. He decided to begin his lunch the way he knew. Bravely he unwrapped his utensils, fully opened his napkin and tucked one corner into his belt. A few girls giggled. His face got red but he courageously continued. Using his knife and fork he began to eat.

This is good, he thought with the first bite. He'd never eaten "Sloppy Joes." *They can serve this every day as far as I'm concerned*, he thought.

The other students began eating. None opened his milk carton.

Finally, Johnny picked up his milk. He turned it around and upside down, over-emphasizing his puzzlement. The boy sitting next to him realized his dilemma. Touching Johnny's arm he got his attention. Then, pointing to the arrow on his own carton he pulled and pushed until the carton opened, slowly showing Johnny the steps. The boy inserted his straw and began drinking.

Gratefully Johnny copied his actions, enjoying his milk.

How strange everything is, he thought.

Those first weeks were difficult. No one could converse with Johnny except George, who was busy at the restaurant most of the time but he offered respite when the need arose.

David was always happy to chat with Johnny and he was good company, but he wasn't allowed to go to school with him.

One day in study hall an attractive girl gave Johnny a note folded into a triangle. Opening it he saw a coded message. In words it would have said, "My heart pants for you." In her silly American girlish way she was saying she liked him—that she thought him "cute." In cryptic form he saw the word "My" followed by an outline of a heart. Next to that she had sketched a pair of shorts. Below that the number "4" and the letter "U." Try as he might he was not able to not figure out what it meant. He was horrified to think it might have something to do with "under pants." If it did, she was not the kind of girl he wanted to know! He didn't want to get into trouble. It would take years before he understood what the girl had been trying to say. Because American girls usually smiled at him and flirted his impression was that they were all immoral. The note reinforced his opinion. The cultures were different. Johnny had not begun to understand how different.

One day he said to a boy at lunch, "Today go dentees. Wat do dentees? Someting for teet."

"You're in for it," the boy grimaced. "They find holes in teeth and fill them," the boy acted out what the dentist would do. "It doesn't feel good. They give you a shot in your mouth, so at least you can't feel them work on your teeth. After a while the shot wears off."

"Shot mout?" Johnny asked, horrified, his eyes wide with disbelief. "Dat hurt!"

"It does," his friend said.

Their conversation ended. Johnny's apprehension grew.

At the dentist Johnny was stiff with worry.

"Try to relax," the dentist said several times, gently touching his arm. "Keep your mouth open for me during the examination."

With much effort Johnny was able to force himself to comply.

"Well, Johnny," the dentist said, "you have perfect teeth. No need for me to do a thing. Brush them twice a day. I'll see you in a year."

Because the dentist talked slowly and used hand signals Johnny finally understood and relaxed.

What a relief!

"Sank oo!" Johnny said emotionally. The afternoon had been spent with fear building. Now there was no way to release the tension except in thanks as his nerves melted into gratitude.

Every experience was new to Johnny. As he went through each he learned. Then something else would happen and he would learn again. Each day the new things were too numerous to remember.

After a month one of his teachers escorted Johnny into an empty classroom. She gave him instructions; "This is a timed test. Do your best. Work on one page until I tell you to turn to the next. Immediately turn the page even if you aren't finished. Don't turn before I tell you. We will proceed through the test like this for two hours. Do you have any questions?"

"Wen don't know?" he asked. "Ask oo?"

"No, I cannot help you," she answered, "Skip the question you don't understand and go to the next. Keep working as fast as you can."

She set the timer. He began reading. The English was difficult but he made out the first question and answered it. He tried to read the second. His mind was tired. The teacher broke into his thoughts.

"Turn the page now."

Again he tried to answer the ten or so questions on the next page but was able to answer only two.

When the test was over Johnny had a headache and a backache. He was thankful to be finished.

"We will give the test results to the Williams's at the end of the school year," the teacher told him. "It is an I.Q. test."

Johnny's brain was too tired to ask what that meant. He went back to class. The end of the day came. It was good to go home.

That evening another man Bob knew, also named Bob, came to the house to meet Johnny. He was an English teacher married to a non-American woman.

"Come to my house as often as you would like after dinner," he said. "We'll quickly get you to talk as if you lived here."

Each Tuesday and Thursday thereafter Johnny showed up for English. The two talked about many things. In three months Johnny was conversing with a "better than beginner" understanding.

During that first Spring Johnny met Nan's brother, who had come from college for a weekend visit. He was a few years older than Johnny. The two of them found much in common, particularly history. They spent hours talking about European history.

Johnny's English improved with his new friend's help. These two were never far from laughter. In time they became best friends.

When the older boy was in town on Sunday the two of them sat in the back of Bob's church and made fun of the sermon, stifling their laughter. No one seemed to notice the two cut-ups. If they did they probably figured, "Boys will be boys."

In April, still a freshman in high school, Johnny realized that he had already done the algebra. He had also been assigned to a beginning general science class.

Going to the principal's office after school Johnny said, "I want take physics, chemistry, advanced mathematics. Things I study now, I know. I study *pro-gymnasium*[96], then mechanical engineering."

The principal waited looking at Johnny a few moments. Nodding, he said, "You have no records, Johnny. You must stay where you are. Physics and Chemistry come in the third and fourth year of school. Advanced math is in the last year. There is no shortcut. You must be patient and finish this year."

"I stop school!" Johnny said emphatically.

"I'm sorry to say it, but your English is not good enough for you to take the classes you wish. Your I.Q is very low, forty-three. If you quit high school there will be no opportunity for you to learn in America and achieve what you want."

Once again Johnny would not be told, "No."

He quit school.

Bob and Nan were concerned but patiently and prayerfully watched as he took his next steps.

"I like electronics," Johnny told anyone who asked.

Bob understood. One day he took Johnny downstairs in the house, "Here's a space in the basement for your hobby. Use some of that old wood to make a bench and whatever else you need,"

"Sanks," Johnny replied. "David help make lab."

The two, Johnny and David, spent time building the workbench and shelves. David wasn't much help but his questions made the work enjoyable. When he questioned Johnny learned by answering.

After the "lab" was built neighbors began calling Johnny to their homes or stopping by.

"Here's a toaster," one would say (or a radio, a blender, a TV, or a lamp). "It stopped working yesterday. Do you think you can fix it?"

"I work," Johnny responded. "I will tell you can or can't fix." The next day, more often than not, the appliance was in good working order.

"Here's a few dollars, Johnny. You saved me a trip to the store and the expense of a new toaster (or other appliance). I appreciate your work."

Johnny always seemed surprised. "Sank oo!" he would say. "Not work money. Happy help. Like electric work."

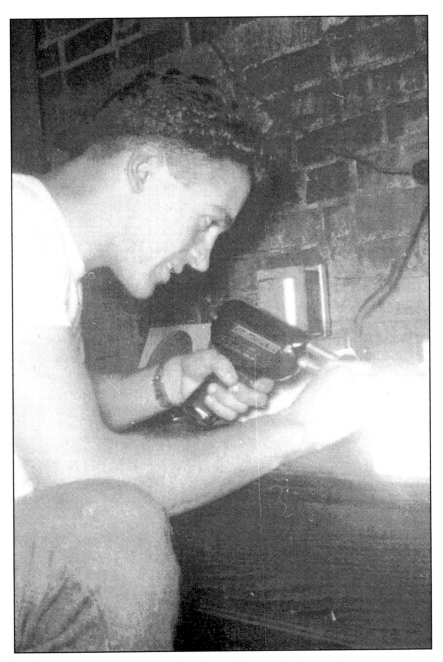

Ivan, age 18, happily working at electric repair.

Other times people would see him and say, "Here are some electronic components for radios and TVs I found in my basement (or attic)," as they handed him a box filled with parts.

"How many money you want?" Johnny asked.

"Nothing. I'm glad to get rid of them. I know you will put them to good use. Thanks for taking them off my hands," would be the usual answer.

Some gave him "How-To with Electronics" books or schematics of electrical systems.

He studied everything he could about electricity and electronics.

When Bob worked on the car or in the yard Johnny was there learning and helping.

Gradually Johnny took over the maintenance of the yard for the kind people who had opened their home to him.

In late spring Johnny and David spent hours shooting a B.B. gun at a paper target while it was still light. Little David learned to hit the target more often than not and Johnny almost always hit the bullseye.

Aggressively learning English, Ivan continued to expand his understanding.

Every Sunday Johnny went to church because Bob was the preacher. He wasn't interested in the sermons, but respected Bob. The folks were friendly and treated Johnny with kindness. Most of them were his electronics 'customers' and he liked the weekly social contact.

"Do you know that there is a cable company in town?" someone asked.

Johnny applied there for a job and was hired as a laborer. He lifted the fifty pound cables on and off from shelves. His body became muscular.

The men at work enjoyed teaching him new American words. If he repeated them and they slapped their thighs, laughing heartily, he knew that those were words of which the minister would not approve. When his factory work ended he had learned the 'other' English language and chose to ignore it.

Communication with Milco and his family was regular.

Ivan found there was work suitable for Milco in Monticello. He told Milco about it. Milco took the job when it was offered and his family moved into a nice quiet neighborhood near Ivan's home with Bob and Nan.

"Now I have a family with cultural ties nearby. You are like my own family," Ivan told them.

"We feel the same," Elena replied. "This town is better for us than Toledo as well."

Johnny registered for the military, being willing to serve America if called. In time he earned his driver's license.

"I have enough money to buy car," he stated.

"That's not wise," everyone who knew him said. "You'll find it's expensive to support a car, and you won't be able to do anything worthwhile."

As always, telling him, "No" made his resolve greater.

He bought a green 1953 Mercury.

It's great to be able to wash this baby every Saturday and see it come back to life, he thought. Each night he kissed it before going into the house.

A year and half after arriving in Illinois, July 1958, at dinner with Bob, Nan, and David, Johnny said, "I hear is university thirty miles away. I go Monday, ask I attend school."

"That's the main campus of the University of Illinois in Champaign-Urbana." Bob told him. "That's a good idea."

After dinner, poring over a local map, Bob and Nan showed Johnny the way to the University. They told him how to find the Administration Building and which people would help him there.

After Johnny's visit to the university Nan and Bob peppered him with questions.

"Where did you have lunch?" Nan asked. "What did you eat?"

"I ate Deluxe Cafe near university. Chili and beer."

"Beer?" Nan questioned in a shocked voice. "Johnny, don't joke like that!"

"Oh? Chili was good." *I wonder what is wrong with beer,* Johnny thought. He had not been served beer while at Bob and Nan's but in Bulgaria everyone drank alcoholic beverages on special occasions, controlled by parents. Once again Johnny had things to learn. He was not yet of drinking age, being only eighteen with the legal age being twenty-one.

"What did the administration tell you about school?" Bob asked. "Will they accept you?"

"They take me when pass entrance exams at three months. I no documents of education. I take English test for...place. Foreign speaking students take English second language in university. I pass high school chemistry, physics, high algebra, and foreign language. They no use Bulgarian, Russian, or Greek language. I pass German and other tests I be student electrical engineering." He smiled at Bob and Nan.

"I pass," he said with confidence.

"How much will it cost?" Bob wanted to know.

"What save from factory and more," he answered. "They tell me work 'room and board' at boarding house. Money from university scholarship and boarding house near campus may be enough to go university study electrical engineering. That my dream. Free country. I study and work hard. Thank you help make dream. You not give money for university."

He studied German every chance he could. After learning English he found it even easier than Greek had been.

Freedom was beginning to look wonderful.

Electrical engineering school was around the corner. He had only to pass a few tests.

20. UNIVERSITY

With anticipation, Johnny drove to the campus in October. He had three sharpened pencils and high hopes.

Arriving an hour early, he parked and made his way to the testing room in Altgeld Hall. The wait seemed unbearable but eventually the proctor came.

"Are you John Paul Johnson?" he asked.

"Yes, sir. Ready for exams. What first?"

"Math is first," the proctor said. "Then you will take chemistry. While you take one test I will grade the previous one. You have one and a half hours for each test. After the second there is a thirty-minute break for lunch. After lunch you will do physics and German. Again there will be a thirty-minute break while I grade the German. If you do not qualify to take the English test you will be finished by three. If you pass all four with a grade of eighty percent or better you will take the English placement test which will finish at four thirty. It takes thirty minutes to grade. You are welcome to stay until five to see what English you must take or you may leave and find out later. Do you have questions?"

"No," Johnny said. "I begin."

"You may start. I am timing you."

Johnny finished the math test with ease. Chemistry was more difficult but with careful work, he knew that he had passed.

Lunch seemed to drag. He gulped the sandwich and the apple Nan had bagged for him, getting a drink at a water fountain. He was back in the testing room ten minutes early.

"You passed both tests with over 90 percent," the proctor said. "Do as well with the rest and you will be admitted to the university."

Pleased, but concerned because his mind was tired, Johnny bore down on the physics and then the German. Some of the cases and word order in the German were tricky and Johnny wasn't certain about that test's outcome.

The thirty minutes following the last series was more difficult for him than the lunch break.

How can I help time go faster? he wondered.

Going outside he stood on the narrow porch at the top of several cement steps looking the length of the main campus. It was beautiful. A three or four block long rectangular central grassy area had wide walkways on all four sides defining it. Other walks ran diagonally across the green lawn. Mature elm trees were paired across from each other forming high overhead arches for their entire length. Dotting the lawn were smaller trees lending their shade. Between the walkways and the streets were large stately university buildings, some in red brick; others with white stone blocks. Looking to his left he saw the student union building. A large low porch was facing the grassy campus. Students were playing ping-pong on four tables.

That's something to keep in mind, Johnny thought as he began walking to the union building. *I wonder if these people play as well as those in Greece.*

He sat on the wide cement porch rail watching a game between two young Asian men. They were evenly matched and spent at least five minutes in a tie game: twenty, twenty. Finally the spin of a serve took the opponent off guard when he was down a point and the game ended. The two competitors laughed and walked into the union to return their equipment.

Johnny hurried back to the testing room just as the proctor was replacing the telephone receiver. The proctor stretched his back and arms then said, "You get to take the final test. Your German was weak. You earned 78 percent but the admitting office said that because your physics test was like the first two, above 90 percent, you're in. Well done. Do you know that these are the high school level tests you took? You will need to take college level chemistry, physics, and mathematics while here."

"Yes, I know. Sank oo. What must earn on English?"

"We don't grade this last test with a percentage grade. It is to find what class you will take when you come to school next January. You are **now** officially a student at the University of Illinois, Congratulations."

I can hardly believe I'm a student! he thought.

Being mind-weary, excited, and insecure in English, Johnny struggled with the test. Finding errors, correcting them, and writing responses to the questions was not easy. Johnny's vocabulary was limited to technical words and a smattering for social use.

After an hour and fifteen minutes he had finished the test. He tried to review it in the remaining time but the day had taken its toll. He made no changes.

"I'm done," he said. "How I know class?"

"The level of your English will be recorded so that when you register for school in January you will be placed in the right class for your ability. The administration takes care of that."

After his testing day Johnny went to the university several more times before school started. He located a boarding house at 605 East John Street that would allow him to work in the kitchen for his room and board.

On another visit he was directed to the scholarship office and applied for every scholarship available to him.

Often while on campus he borrowed ping-pong equipment and challenged anyone willing to play a game. His opponents were often better than he was, teaching him new serves and returns. They also helped to increase his spoken language.

In late December two separate letters came from the university for Johnny. Opening the first, he read that he was accepted as a freshman in the Electrical Engineering School with a level three class in English as a Foreign Language. The second letter told him that he had been given a full tuition scholarship based on his entrance exam scores, renewable every year if he performed well in his classes.

I've done it! I'm finally going to be an electrical engineer...after the escape, prison, travel, quitting school,... This is freedom!

How I wish my friend had stayed with me. He would be here too. He was stupid to go back to Bulgaria. He betrayed me by not telling me his plans. I'll never write to him!

Having secured a place to live and eat near campus in exchange for a few hours of kitchen work every day and not having to pay tuition the only money needed would be for books, fees, and personal things; clothing, entertainment, and car expenses. He had to maintain his car, buy gas, and pay for car insurance. His savings would take care of at least a year's worth of those uncovered items. It looked as if everything was in place for another "new beginning."

One warm afternoon in April, after Johnny's classes were over for the day, the union porch was teeming with students who all appeared to be from different countries.

All the ping-pong tables were being used. Johnny was playing a rousing game with a student from the Middle East.

A woman appearing to be in her mid to late thirties came from inside. She stopped to watch the games.

Johnny noticed that she smiled and talked to three students sitting at a table drinking coffee. She wrote something in a small book as she talked with them. Before long she had made her way all around the porch talking to the students and writing. When he finished his game she walked toward him smiling.

"Hi," she said lightly, "I'm a graduate student here and I really enjoy talking with people from other countries. Are you also a foreign student like these others?"

"No, ma'am," he replied. "I have Green Card. I was born Bulgaria and came America last year. I started school this semester. I stay in America to fulfill dream of being electrical engineer."

"Did you come with your family?"

"No, ma'am, I escaped Bulgaria with friend. He went back. I stayed Greece. Then come here."

"It sounds like you have an interesting life story to tell," she said. "Would you give me your address, so I can invite you to a gathering I am thinking about having?"

"Okay," he said. He told her his address. She entered it in her book.

That evening he was working in the kitchen at the boarding house. The cook was in her usual cheerful humor.

"Johnny," she asked, "what is this?" She held up the teakettle she was filling with water.

"It's funny 'pot'," he said.

"Silly," she responded, slapping his buttock with an open pudgy hand. He winced in mock pain. She quickly sidestepped to get out of his reach. "You don't know, do you?" she teased. "Go ahead, Mister-Know-Everything. Admit it. You don't know!"

He feigned a sore backside, rubbing it, while grinning at his playful tormentor, who was old enough to be his mother.

"Okay, Helen, I don't know funny looking pot. Will you tell me or no?"

"It is a 'teakettle.' Say it, Johnny. I want to teach you this new word. Teakettle."

"Teake'll," he responded.

"No, not quite. It is teakettle, don't forget the 't' sound."

"Teaket-tell."

"Closer. Say 'tea.'"

He sighed; *Will I ever learn this language?*

"Tea," he said.

"Ke."

"Ke."

"Tl."

"Helen, I can't say."

Yes, you can, Johnny. 'Tl'."

"Tull."

"Tl!... Say teakettle."

"Teaket-tul."

"Well, anyway, do you know what it is now?"

"I know, but can't say. Tongue won't say," he laughed.

It was her turn to sigh. Shaking her head at him in mock disgust, she laughed.

"Okay, you tried. I think you know the name for your 'funny pot' now. I guess we can try to get you to pronounce it later."

Reflecting on his speech he thought, *If only I could master some of these sounds, like "th", or "w" in woman. I always say. "ooman." Or "y" at the start of a word. I say "oo" for you, "east" for "yeast" and "ear" for "year." And then there is that "I" sound. I say "leeve" instead of "live" and "een" instead of "in." And now this "teakettle" thing. Maybe I'll never learn.* He felt bad. *How can I lose this accent?* he wondered.

The semester flew by quickly. Johnny met a student from Iran during that time. They played ping-pong frequently, but more regularly they played chess.

Darius asked Johnny, "How would you like to share an apartment with me next year? I saw a Quonset hut on the east side of campus. There are two bedrooms, a study/living room, bath and kitchen. It doesn't cost much. We can split the rent, take turns cooking. We both have cars to get to work and classes separately. Living together we could play chess anytime."

Thinking about the offer, Johnny thought that they shared the same life values. It would be a step toward greater freedom. He would need to work a little more at his job than he had been but he had plenty of time to do that.

During the summer Johnny worked and saved for his new living arrangements. By September he and Darius were housemates.

He was freer than ever. He had finished a semester and was proud of the grades he had earned.

Shopping for food, cooking, maintaining their home, driving to and from campus, going to classes, and studying took most of his time. The two friends rarely had time to play chess.

One day in October, similar letters came for both Johnny and Darius. They were in small envelopes. Their addresses had been crossed out and their current one written in with different handwriting.

Curiously Johnny opened his.

"It's a party. Some girl is inviting! Is yours same?"

Darius opened his. "Yes. Who is the girl? Do you know?"

"Linnea? No. But let's go. What is Open House? It's from two to five o'clock Sunday week away."

"I don't know what an Open House is either. I want to go. Maybe we'll meet someone special."

"Umm, Johnny? This is a good time to discuss something I've been thinking about. I'm a couple of years older than you are and I'm beginning to think. So, if either of us meets a girl we like, what do you think we should do?"

"What do you mean? We like girl, so what?"

"Well what do we do if one of us wants to get married? We have this apartment. It wouldn't work for a single man and a married couple."

"I'm not thinking marriage," Johnny said. "I started school and finish four or five years. Later will be time to think marriage."

"Things can change," Darius insisted. "If either of us does want to marry the other one ought to leave and let the married ones live here. Do you agree?"

"If you want to marry, yes, you stay here. I'll find place to live. Okay with me."

"Okay then. That's settled." The two friends shook hands to seal the agreement.

In less than two weeks the young friends dressed in white shirts, ties, and slacks were the first ones to arrive at the "party."

Opening the door their hostess, a woman nearly as old as their mothers, greeted them warmly, "Please come in. I expect many other people this afternoon. Help yourselves to tea or coffee and some cookies."

The two disappointed young men recognized the woman who had written their names along with those of other foreign students in her address book the previous year.

"You Linnea?" Johnny asked.

"Yes, and what are your names and the countries you came from?" she asked shaking their hands.

"I am Darius from Persia, Iran. This is my roommate Johnny. He is from Bulgaria."

"I hope you enjoy my Open House," she replied.

A graduate student, Linnea worked as a housemother in a senior girl's experimental dorm near campus. The dorm held forty co-eds in ten apartments. Each apartment had a living room/study combo, a large bedroom with two sets of bunk beds, a bath, and a Pullman kitchen. As housemother she enforced the house rules and nightly hours established by the university for co-eds: ten o'clock on school nights, one o'clock on Friday and Saturday, and eleven o'clock on Sunday.

When the other guests began arriving Johnny's disappointment continued. They were all other non-American men and their families. The children were well behaved and cute but there would be no opportunity for "socializing." No dates would come out of this party.

At four-thirty a few women from the dorm entered and visited for half an hour. Everyone was polite as they ate their cookies and drank their tea or coffee.

Two of the women talked to Ivan and Darius.

On the way home Darius said, "Nancy was nice."

"Yes, she was only girl that didn't mention boy when she talked," Johnny responded. "Nancy's too tall and maybe too old. Will you call her?"

"I might, she didn't seem too old for me," Darius said.

They drove silently home.

School and responsibilities continued.

Darius did not tell Johnny if he had called Nancy.

In late March Johnny was studying physics. A group of six friends surrounded him at a round table in the student union. He successfully tuned out his friends' chatter.

This is interesting stuff. I wonder why most Americans don't like physics. It is so easy to understand, he thought.

"Hello, Johnny," broke through his concentration.

Looking up reluctantly he saw a girl. She was sturdily built, not skinny like many Americans. She had shoulder length, almost black hair and smiling black eyes. She looked vaguely familiar.

Who is she? he thought. *I wonder where I've seen her. Maybe on the way to class or something.*

"I met you at Linnea's party months ago. Do you remember?" she said.

"No," he said. "I remember one girl that didn't talk about boyfriend. Her name was Nancy."

"Nancy! I was there with Nancy. You and I talked about many things that day," she said dragging a chair to the table and sitting next to him. "Don't you remember?"

"I don't remember anyone but Nancy," he restated.

"Okay," she laughed unself consciously, "And I don't have a boyfriend anymore. He lives in California and I haven't heard from him in at least six months, even before I met you at that party.

"I remember you," she continued.

"What's your name?" he questioned uncomfortable in the situation but trying to be polite.

"I'm Kathy Goldberg," she said. "And I have trouble believing that your name is Johnny. I know they call you Johnny. You told me your name is John Paul Johnson but you sure don't look Scandinavian to me. How did you get that name?"

He was impressed. *I hardly remember this girl,* he thought as he studied her smiling face. *She's kind of pretty,* he concluded. *She's telling me my name five months after meeting me once. This is an interesting puzzle. I wonder how I can get to know her?*

"My real name is Ivan Pavlov Ivanov. I'm from Bulgaria. I came to Monticello two years ago. They told me John Paul Johnson was new name. It was okay with me. It means the same if you translate."

"But can you translate names?" she asked.

"I never thought about it," he answered. " I didn't know English. They told me what to do. It's okay now. I'm Johnny to everyone. My driver's license, draft card, and university registration say John Paul Johnson."

"I don't think it's okay!" she countered. "I'm calling you Ivan if you don't mind. That *is* your name!"

"That's fine," he said grinning. *Maybe we will see each other again, who knows*, he thought.

They chatted for ten minutes. *I don't like her having a boyfriend and being so friendly but now she says she doesn't have one. She doesn't sound faithful*, he thought. *She looks pretty but she probably would marry someone and divorce him when she got tired of him.*

He told her that in Bulgaria things were different socially.

"There's not word for divorce in my language," he said, working one of his major standards of life, and current concern, into the conversation. "You see someone divorced you cross street so you don't look at him."

"You shun them?" she asked shocked.

"I don't know that word. We stay away from them if that's what you mean."

"Doesn't it make you feel bad to do that?" she asked.

"No. There are not many people who have divorced. I see in America girls get boys interested in them by smiling and flirting. They don't care about them. Maybe that's why divorces here," he said, baiting her, but she apparently didn't realize what he was doing. He hoped to find out where she stood on the subject, just in case.

Her response gave him food for thought.

"I hate divorce," she answered with conviction. "I will never get divorced. It is wrong. My parents and my mom's sisters were never divorced. I'm going to be like them when I get married!"

"I knew boy last year," he continued trying to present his rock solid standard, "he went into army. He was engaged to pretty girl. He was nervous about leaving her on campus. He asked me take care of her. You know, take her to movie once in awhile or for hamburger so she have male company without looking for it. He trusted me. I thought, 'Okay.' Two weeks later I asked her for dinner. She agreed. We got to White Castle she wasn't wearing engagement ring. I asked why. She said in flirty way, 'Johnny, he's gone and you're here. Why should we be unhappy wearing ring *he* gave me?' I never saw her again. Haven't written him. I'm not getting in trouble with that kind of girl."

Kathy just sat there looking at him, her eyes wide.

Johnny didn't know what more to say. He had said everything that he wanted her to know. He liked what she had said.

"I'm getting cup o' coffee," he told her. "Do you want?" he asked as he casually took his small address book from his hip pocket and inconspicuously left it on the table next to his physics book.

"Yes, thanks, but I can get mine," she said as she started to stand.

"No, I'll buy. Do you want cream, sugar?"

"No, thanks," she said sitting down. "Black is fine."

When his back was turned she quickly took his address book and opened it. Only one girl's name and number was there. The rest were numbers for boys and businesses.

Turning to "G" she quickly wrote her name and phone number. Then without calling attention to what she did she returned the book to its original position.

Coffees in hand he returned. They sipped their coffee. This time their casual conversation was focused on their studies and positions in school.

"I'm finishing my junior year," she said. "I took time off college last year, worked in a bank and came back with my new major of secondary school biology teaching. I should graduate a year after this May."

"Then what?" he asked.

"I don't know yet. Maybe I'll get a master's degree. Maybe I'll teach."

"I'm freshman in el..."

"Electrical engineering," she interrupted. "I remember. You escaped to study electrical engineering. You told me, don't you remember?"

"No, but you remember about me."

He looked at his watch, stood up, and gathered his books.

"Oh," he said, appearing to have an afterthought. Handing her his little book he asked, "Write your name, phone number in book before I leave? I'll call you."

He was startled to hear her reply, "No!" as she gave it back to him.

He couldn't understand her smile, but looking hurt he asked, "Why not?"

Breaking into a flirtatious grin she said, "Because I already did...when you got the coffee." She giggled.

He looked down at the little book in his hand, set the other books on the table and leafed through the pages. There in bold eye-catching detail he read her name and number. His heart skipped a beat as he tried hard to be nonchalant.

"Yes. I see. Thanks, I'll call." His face was beginning to get warm. He outlined her name and the number with heavy black lines.

"I've got to drive home."

"Drive? You have a car? Why didn't you ask to take me home?" she blurted.

"I didn't think...I mean... If you want...I'll drive you. Do you live far?"

"Pretty far. It takes about fifteen minutes to walk but maybe only a few minutes to drive."

They walked for almost fifteen minutes. When they got to the car, she said, " Well, I live two blocks from here. I guess I can walk the rest of the way."

"No, come. I'll take you home. I keep my word." He laughed, opening the door for her.

Stopping in front of the dorm he noted where he was. Although it looked familiar he had long forgotten how he had gone to Linnea's party.

Now I know Katia's phone number and where she lives.

Late in the afternoon after classes the next day Johnny was in the union again.

Kathy brazenly walked up to him. 'Hi," she said. "I believe you are Ivan Pavlov Ivanov."

They laughed. He stood up.

"Please, sit down."

She sat.

Without chitchat he began talking. "My friends told me there is dance Saturday after three weeks. Will you go with me?"

Kathy answered, "Sure, there are many dances on Saturday nights. I like to dance. It would be fun to go with you."

The following day they met again.

They were in a hallway of the union in a small conversation area with a sofa and plants.

Sitting down, the girl said, "I want to talk with you about the dance." She had a serious look on her face and a tone in her voice.

"What is to talk about?" Ivan said sitting next to her. "We're going. You said you would." He wondered about this girl. *What is there to discuss? Maybe it's just girls,* he thought. *I hope she didn't change her mind. I haven't met anyone quite as interesting as she is. That dance will be a good way to spend time with her.*

"The dance is the Military Ball," she said. "That's the most special yearly dance on campus. It's formal. Usually the boy takes his date to dinner. It will be expensive. I can't let you take me to something like that until we know each other better. I just can't. I don't mean to say that I don't want to go but I can't let you spend that kind of money on me. I didn't know it was the Mil. Ball when you asked," she rattled on. "If I had known I would have said, 'No.' I guess I'm trying to say, 'No,' now, but after we know each other better I'd be happy to go with you to a big dance."

He looked at her red face that had a look of confusion on it and laughed.

"I know enough about you to take you to dance," he said more cheerfully than he felt.

"How can you say that?" she asked. "We only met once months ago and you forgot about me. Then two days ago we met again and then yesterday. You don't know anything about me...really." She ended in a fluster of words.

Calmly he waited for her to look squarely into his eyes. Her dark eyes reminded him of the song, "*Ochi Chornia.*"[97] The mystery in them captivated him, intrigued him. *Who is she?* he thought.

There they stood. Her eyes were open to him. She was waiting for something. *What is it she wants?* he wondered. *Oh, yes, she wants to know how I know her. I don't know her but I know enough.*

"I know name," he finally told her firmly. "I know you are single." And for emphasis he added, "I know phone number."

He was rewarded with her happy laughter.

"Oh, you silly. Are you sure? Even after you know it will cost a lot of money? I mean, I think we should know each other better."

"I want to take you to dance!" he said. By now he knew he had to go with her if she was still willing. This girl was a fascinating puzzle and he intended to gather the pieces and put them together for his own peace of mind.

The night of the dance, after seeing Kathy every day since they met at the end of March, Ivan waited happily after ringing the bell of the dorm. He was in the tuxedo Bob has given him. In his hand was a corsage. His new haircut added to the clean-cut look appropriate for the dance.

When Kathy opened the door in her green taffeta gown he stopped breathing as he thought, *Look how much skin is showing. Boy, she is beautiful. I think this will be a great night.*

Across the dinner table, with the most expensive menu item, roast duck, on their plates, the two sat looking at each other. Neither ate much.

Ivan paid the waiter and stood, reaching for Kathy's hand.

They saw only each other that night. The dance was a blur of music and motion. Then it was over.

The next day Ivan confessed to being "broke" as a result of the night of fun.

"Darius and I share Lifesavers," he said.

"What does that mean?"

"One day I buy roll. Next day he buys. I'll get paid next week. Now I have no money for food."

The next time he picked her up she gave him a bag of groceries.

"Because of me and that silly dance you are starving yourself. I hope these will help until you get paid," she told him.

"It was worth it. I don't feel bad. Thanks for food. It will help," he responded.

Shortly after the dance Ivan stopped in at 605 E John to see Helen, his former supervisor.

"Johnny! How are you? Are your new living arrangements working out or do you want your old job and room back?" She asked the latter more to tease than thinking it might be true.

"Darius and I get along," Johnny assured her. "I stopped to tell you something new. I thought you want to know."

"And what is that, Johnny?" she asked drying her hands on her apron. Sensing his need to be heard she stood squarely in front of him to listen

"I went to Military Ball." he began, watching Helen's face for a reaction.

"The girl's name, Kathy. I think she is one for me. I've known her one month. I've begun caring more for being outside her classes and walking her

Ivan at age 19 in Monticello, Illinois

to next one, than going to mine. I don't think grades are going to be good this term. She's got me thinking, I can tell you."

With warmth and understanding Helen said, "Johnny, I'd like to meet this girlfriend of yours. She seems to have captivated your heart. Let's make a date for you to come to my farm. I'll fix you two a mid-day dinner. You can enjoy the day and meet my family some Saturday."

He was elated. She did not question him.

"It's date," he said.

But they made no specific plans.

On July 24, 1959, three and a half months after nineteen-year-old Ivan Pavlov Ivanov and Katherine Ann Goldberg met they were married in a small church in Urbana, Illinois.

It was a Friday. The previous Monday Ivan had begun working as a stock boy at the local Kroger Food Store. A co-worker from that store was his best man.

The minister who married them spoke with them for thirty-five minutes prior to the ceremony. No one else was at the wedding.

Instead of asking Darius to leave his place Ivan had rented a small apartment in a remodeled house. The two newlyweds set up housekeeping within walking distance of the engineering campus.

Remembering Helen's long ago kind invitation to her farm for a day out and a dinner, Ivan arranged to spend a relaxed day in the country instead of working. It was mid-August. Ivan and Kathy had just been married.

While they were there, Ivan asked Kathy, "Which apple do you want?"

Kathy looked into the huge apple tree with many blushing ripe apples on it. Playfully she pointed to one on the tip of a branch twenty feet overheard, "That one."

Ivan pointed to the apple.

"There?"

"Yep!"

He raised the rifle that Kathy had inherited five years earlier. He had brought it to the farm in the hopes of doing some target practice. Carefully aiming, and hoping that the sights were accurate, he squeezed the trigger. The bullet sliced through the stem. The apple fell. Ivan put his hand out. As if by an unseen force the apple landed firmly in his palm.

"For you, my lady," he said grinning.

"That was just luck."

"Do you think so?" he asked faking hurt.

"Do you see that fly?" he pointed to a cabbage moth.

"Watch."

From fifteen feet away he took aim, shot, and the insect fell lifeless.

"No! This is too much," Kathy said laughing.

"I'm going in to help Helen. Do what you want with that gun. Thanks for the apple!" Laughing and shaking her head she went into the house.

Ten minutes later Ivan went inside.

"Helen, can you fix these birds for dinner?" he asked.

"We'll have squab," she said. "Tell me, how did you get them? Kathy told me about her apple and the butterfly. Is there a story about these pigeons?"

"Yes! It was funny," he answered. "Bird was on beam in barn. I aimed and shot. It fell. Then another fell almost at same time. When I went to get them I saw that bullet must have gone through one and hit other one next to it. I didn't even see second one up there."

Helen laughed, "How wonderful to be young and in love. Everything is right!"

Ivan looked at Kathy and winked. He saw her face turn red as she looked away.

I don't understand what causes her reactions, he thought, *but she is a sweet girl.*

As head of his house he had bills to pay. He was almost twenty years old and had become the produce manager of the grocery store. Kathy worked in research on campus.

"Look," Ivan said one morning emerging from the bathroom. "What do you think?"

"About what?" Kathy asked turning to look at him. "You didn't shave?" she asked.

"I thought it would be fun to finish summer by growing goatee and mustache. If you want I'll shave."

"No. You just surprised me. How long will it get?"

"I keep it trimmed close but it should fill in and look better in three, four days. It's new look, now that I have wife. I'll leave it until we get tired of it."

That August, as in the previous year, Ivan went to see his benefactor at the University for the status of his tuition scholarship. Another few courses and he would be a sophomore.

"Yes, Ivan Ivanov, Let me check your situation," his friend said in a not-so-friendly way." There is no scholarship for you this term," he said when he returned from the records.

There was no explanation for the denial. Was it grades? Was it that he had married? Or perhaps his facial hair? Ivan was never to know.

During the fall quarter when Ivan came home from class he said, "The university offered me a part time job at the large observatory on campus. I will process signal recordings from Sputnik and Explorer. They are satellites to study the ionosphere. My boss will even teach me to use the reflecting telescope."

"Why would you want to learn to use the telescope?"

"We can take friends to see sky. We might see rings on Saturn, close views of moon, many things," he told her.

"That does sounds like fun."

"There's another benefit to job. You can come to work with me and read or sleep in research room. That way we can be together while I'm working. And I can study when I'm not taking printed data from machine."

In October their apartment was cold for Kathy.

"Let's visit my parents for the weekend," Kathy said.

On the way, they stopped impulsively to see a house trailer for sale. It was perfect, although only eight by thirty-three feet. Returning from the weekend visit, they bought it.

School and work became a full-time way of life for Ivan.

He went to eight o'clock classes every weekday. After dinner he went to work until nine o'clock. Studying kept him up until midnight or sometimes until four in the morning.

In September 1960, Pavel was born to the young couple.

Kathy left her paying work to take care of the baby. Pavel often joined his mother visiting Ivan at work.

"With new baby coming," Ivan said. "I think we should move into apartment your sister and brother-in-law are leaving. He asked if we wanted it. He will arrange things with landlady for us and will leave much furniture."

Selling the trailer took longer than they had anticipated but eventually, after paying double housing payments each month, Ivan was able to sell it as a rental unit on the airforce base nearby.

Brother Anton joined the first thriving baby in September 1961.

With the added responsibility Ivan found a ten-hour job on Saturdays repairing televisions.

At that time Ivan and Kathy received a notice in the mail: "Pay for personal property tax or you will be charged interest."

Entering the tax office Ivan smiled at the office worker.

"Hi," the man behind the counter said looking up as Ivan walked in. "What's your name?"

"Ivan P. Ivanov."

"You owe one-hundred-thirty dollars for last year's taxes."

"I'm not here to pay. I don't have money."

"Then why did you come?"

"To tell you I will pay when I can."

"When will that be?"

"I don't know. Everything I earn goes for food and rent. Maybe I'll win 'Cashword Pete.'"

"Get serious!" the man almost bullied.

Ivan laughed leaving the office.

"Are you working on 'Cashword Pete?'" members of the community asked each other as openers. 'Cashword Pete' was a crossword puzzle the local newspaper printed, offering a hundred-dollar prize each week. After eight or nine weeks of being unsolved it had become the region's popular topic of conversation.

For three weeks Ivan and Kathy sent in two or four "solutions" to the puzzle.

A few weeks later at a dinner party Ivan said, "Let's work on puzzle tonight."

"It's too late," Kathy responded. But after putting the boys to bed the two began making three by five cards into entries. Ivan cut a stamp from an eraser to fit the squares. He dipped the cut eraser into ink and marked the cards to copy the puzzle's pattern. Kathy typed all the known words then methodically filled in the uncertain ones. There were over a hundred entries when she finished at six in the morning. Ivan had gone to bed at two. The next day they deposited their entries at the newspaper's office before the deadline.

Hearing a knock on Saturday afternoon, Kathy reluctantly left the basement laundry climbing the stairs to answer the door. She was upset thinking that the knock might have awakened the babies. They were still soundly asleep.

"May we come in? We are from 'Cashword Pete'."

Nonchalantly, the young mother said, "Did we win?"

"We don't know yet," a woman with sparkling eyes said. "We have some questions."

"Please come in," Kathy finally invited.

In the living room fifteen minutes later after several questions the man looked at his co-worker and smiled. When he nodded the woman said, "Well, it looks like you did win."

With no emotion Kathy asked, "How many winners are there?"

"You are the only ones who answered everything correctly."

Realizing the truth Kathy jumped from her chair, squealing, "May I call my husband?"

"Of course."

Ivan was on a house call. Upon his returning to work his boss said, "Ivan, I want you to go home now. There is no need for you to stay at work."

"Why? What did I do wrong?" Ivan asked frightened that a customer had complained. *Was it the woman whose son I yelled at when he dumped my tool box? Was it the man I told I couldn't fix his television set?* Ivan worried. "Do you want me to come next week at the same time?"

"No. Nothing is wrong. Just go home."

"Please tell me. How can I improve if I don't know why you are firing me?"

"I'm not firing you. You and your wife won Cashword Pete's eighteen hundred dollars. You don't need this job now."

"Don't tease me!"

"I'm not. Just go home."

Until he arrived Ivan wasn't certain that the story was true. Since it was, he was able to pay his taxes.

On November 14, 1962, Ivan's Green Card was replaced by "Citizenship of the United States of America." He had passed the INS test and was sworn in as United States Citizen number 8128130. Holding his small American flag he looked into the audience. He smiled at his pregnant wife and two young sons standing near the back of the large room.

Ivan's baby girl, Theresa, was born at the end of June 1963.

He graduated in August 1963, with a bachelor's degree in electrical engineering. He had fulfilled his dream!

School had taken five years.

His children were six weeks, twenty-three months, and thirty-five months old.

Freedom had begun.

21. California

"Go West, young man. Go West," came from the 1849 gold rush, which had no bearing on Ivan in 1963. From seventeen years old he had headed west, going from Greece to Germany, then to New York, and the last stop Illinois.

Finally he was an electronic design engineer. Graduation from the Electrical Engineering School offered him some options. He chose to continue going west, accepting a job in Azusa, California, with Aerojet General—about as far west as he could be without ending up in the Far East.

"My 1953 Mercury won't make the trip," Ivan told Kathy. "Besides, with five of us we'll be cramped. We need a new car."

Loading two boys, almost twins at not quite a year apart, and their baby sister into the Mercury, they went car hunting and found a nearly new station wagon that would accommodate the family for the long trip.

"We don't have any money to buy a car," Kathy stated. "How do we do it?"

"I'll go to the Monticello bank and ask for a car loan." Ivan said, "You stay with the kids."

Driving the thirty miles, Ivan realized that he had no idea how to ask for the loan. *I had better just be bold and honest about it*, he thought. *They can only say, "No."*

"Johnny," the bank president said, refusing to call him Ivan. He and the other townsfolk would always call him Johnny. "You are one of us, like my own son. The many things you did for the people of this town were selfless. You have worked hard to achieve your goal. I am proud of you for what you have done. I will be pleased to help you any way that I can. How much do you need for the car?"

"We looked at a used station wagon in great condition. It's three hundred and fifty dollars. I think we'll have it for many years."

The bank president wrote a check and handed it to Ivan.

"This is for four hundred. Wait here. I want to give you a letter. The ways in California are not Midwestern ways. You might need financial help for awhile after you get there until you establish yourself. You can pay back the car loan as you are able."

Coming back in a few minutes he said, "This letter is for any bank. I have made it to 'Whom it May Concern'. It pledges payment of any check you write up to one hundred dollars. There is no date after which the pledge is void."

"Thank you," was all Ivan could say out of his deep gratitude.

Before leaving Illinois the family of five drove to Calumet City where Kathy's parents lived. Her mother's two sisters and their husbands were visiting to say good-bye.

"Three days is not enough," they complained. "Going to the West Coast to live! Who knows when we will see you next!"

Leaving amidst tears of separation, the new graduate's family began the westward journey toward Ames, Iowa, to stop at Kathy's sister's family, the Drexlers.

Ruth, Burt, and Marc were happy to see the large family.

"Come in," Ruth said. "Let's see that new little girl!"

"We hope you can stay at least a week with us," Burt invited.

"No, I think we have to be on the road before that," Ivan responded. "We have a lot to do when we get to California. I'm nervous about how to get established in a strange place with so many of us."

Marc was three and a half, just eight and a half months older than Pavel. He gently patted and kissed the new baby girl and played continually with his boy cousins. The children argued against eating and sleeping.

"It is time for us to leave," Ivan said the third morning adding humorously, "Thanks for the two days of 'rest'."

The other adults joined his laughter. They had been overwhelmed by the constant activity of the boys.

"Are you sure you are rested?" Burt asked. "Didn't the kids wear you out?"

"Maybe, but it was wearing out without getting tired, if that makes sense."

There followed another tearful parting.

Pavel and Tony reluctantly climbed onto the station wagon's blanket-padded platform. Their favorite toys were there. Sitting, they had plenty of headroom. When tired they could lie down and sleep. Seat belts were non-existent in 1963.

Theresa was asleep in her baby basket on the middle seat.

"We're on our way to California!" Ivan said as he headed the car toward Route 66 for the long drive.

"We've got a water bag to cool the car through the desert," Ivan said.

"How does it work?" his wife asked.

"The water slowly seeps through the tightly woven bag and the wind carries it through the grill into the engine area. It should help keep things cool under the hood."

Their plans were to drive through the night as well as the day, getting to Azusa as quickly as possible.

"I'll drive at night," Kathy said. "Car lights don't bother me and I can sleep while it's daylight out. When you get tired let me know and I'll take over."

"Thanks," Ivan said. "I'll be fine until pretty late."

He drove until ten o'clock that first night.

Kathy began driving. At three she woke, panicked, realizing that she had dozed off while driving.

"Honey, wake up. Please, wake up," she said barely above a whisper not wanting to wake the children.

Ivan woke.

"What should I do? I've never had a problem with drowsiness before," she was close to tears thinking about the possibility of her crashing the car into the rocks or falling off a cliff and killing her precious family.

"Pull over *now*, off the road," he told her. "We'll sleep here for three or four hours then I'll drive again."

Kathy did not ask to drive after that and Ivan did not expect her to.

When they were hungry Kathy brought out the sandwiches, vegetable sticks, and fruit her sister, Ruth, had packed. The little boys ate quartered sandwiches. Drinks were cups of ice water from a gallon jug and cans of vegetable and fruit juice kept in an iced cooler.

When the baby was hungry she whimpered. Kathy lifted her from her basket and cared for her. After burping her Theresa was put back in her basket where she would again peacefully sleep. She was the best traveler of all, at only eight weeks old.

Flagstaff, Arizona, was their location the second night. Ivan pulled into a motel and checked the rates.

They had a king sized bed, big enough for four. Theresa had her own little basket.

"This will be worth the money," Ivan said. "We'll get a good night's sleep and be rested tomorrow for the last long haul to California."

Having graduated after the summer session Ivan was driving to Azusa in August the shortest way through the Mojave Desert and Bakersfield. None of them had been in the desert. Ignorance is bliss. God, whom they did not yet acknowlege, was definitely smiling on Ivan's family.

Tony and Pavel's cheeks flushed from the intense dry heat in the back of the station wagon.

Ivan tried to keep Kathy from worrying about them.

"Give them more water," he suggested when she spoke of her concern. The boys drank large amounts of water and juice, continuing to look red and wilted.

"They are so lethargic," Kathy complained. "They have no interest in playing, they don't sleep. What are we supposed to do?"

There seemed to be no answer.

Little Theresa, slept peacefully, dressed only in her diaper. She looked comfortable with no flushing from the heat.

Stopped for gas, each of them jumped as the sky burst with a crash and rain gushed out of a black cloud as though a bucket had been dumped.

"This never happens!" the gas station attendant laughed, running trying to stay dry as he worked. "I don't ever remember a rain storm here in the summer. Did you folks bring it with you?"

"This is the first we've seen since we left Illinois," Ivan told him. "It feels great. Sure did cool things down."

When Kathy looked at the boys again they were asleep and their cheeks had lost the hot flush.

After a few more hours they were still in the desert but the next minute in civilization.

As they continued west the haze and smog worsened.

Eventually a city sign next to the road read "Azusa."

An unpleasant smell surrounded them.

Hot air invaded the car through the open windows.

Everyone was weary, sweaty, and quiet.

"Honey," Kathy said almost inaudibly, "Can we turn around and go back? I don't like it here. We can't even see the sky in broad daylight. It smells, it's hot, I can't live here. There were supposed to be forests. How can we raise a family in this...." She was almost crying.

"We can't go back," Ivan said decisively. "We don't have anyplace else to go. My work is here."

He pulled into a small single-story motel and checked in. A shimmering blue-water swimming pool between the building and the road beckoned to them.

"We'll relax here before we begin looking for a place to live," Ivan said.

The two little boys jumped from the car. The long drive was over.

Inside their room Kathy unpacked swim clothes and they, including the eight-week-old baby, cooled themselves in the water.

They played in the pool for an hour.

When they got out to dry and rest, Ivan said, " I'm going to start look-ing for a place to live. Do you want to come with me?"

"No!" Kathy said emphatically. "I will stay here with the children. I don't care what you find for us. Anything will be okay. Please, try to be back by six o'clock so we can eat together."

Ivan left. At six o'clock he returned.

"I found a house we can rent. It has a swing set in the yard and a fireplace in the living room. It's a junior executive home," he said with some wonder.

The day they moved into the house, the movers delivered the crib, their double bed, four packing boxes of clothing and household items, and the boys' mattresses. The other furniture they had used in Illinois was not coming with them to California.

"I am beginning a new life," Ivan had stated proudly. "I don't need old wooden furniture or worn out rugs."

"But the rug is from my aunt's house," Kathy had argued, "and I refinished the table and cabinet. They are nice antique pieces. The chairs are old but comfortable."

Her pleadings had fallen on deaf ears.

"I will have new things!" her husband had stated. And so it was.

The day after they moved into the house was Friday. There were still two boxes left unpacked. Kathy woke with a fever.

"Can you stay home and take care of the kids while I sleep?" she asked. "Maybe you could even finish unpacking."

"I really want to go to work today," Ivan said. "I can be there for six hours if I leave now. I was supposed to wait 'till Monday but I don't think you really need me here and I'm excited to know what work I'll be doing."

He left.

A new neighbor took Kathy to a doctor who said she had milk fever.

"You can continue nursing," the doctor said. "The pain will leave in a day or two and your temperature will subside."

"Guess what happened today?" Ivan asked when he returned from work at six o'clock.

"I don't know," his sick wife answered, struggling against weariness to stay alert.

"The company gave its employees a fifteen percent raise effective today. If I had waited until my start date of Monday I would have missed it but today I got a big raise."

Once again it was evident that God was smiling on them.

Kathy almost whispered through her haze of fever, "Then I'm glad you decided to go today. I'm even gladder it's Friday. I want to sleep most of the day tomorrow and get well. Will you take care of Pavel, Tony, and Theresa?"

"Agreed," Ivan said.

Their meager belongings left the home looking empty. There was no living room furniture, no wall hangings.

When she regained her strength Kathy said, "It will be fun filling this house and decorating it."

"If there is money *after* paying the bills and loans," Ivan responded.

Before leaving work his first payday, he looked excitedly at the check, anxious to see the two-week's pay written there.

Something is wrong, he figured. *If my salary is $3.50 an hour it should be much more than this.*

The accounting office of the company was still open. He spoke with a payroll employee.

"There's been a mistake," Ivan began.

"Let me see," the employee said in response. "No, this is the correct amount. You see, here is the Federal Tax deduction. This is the Social Security tax and this is taken out for workmen's compensation. Adding those three and subtracting their total from your earnings gives you the amount."

"Are you saying that this is my two-weeks pay?"

"Yes, your 'take-home' or 'net' pay."

"Thank you for your help," Ivan said weakly wondering, *How can we manage our household on this "take-home." What can I tell Kathy? I'll just do the best I can. She has been helpful, making bread every week and not overspending. I'll see how far this money goes before I say anything. I know she wants to decorate but we can't buy anything for awhile.*

Barely having any money for the next several pay periods, Ivan had to face the truth about their situation.

"This house costs more than we can afford," he said finally after living there three months.

"Making the payments, paying the utilities, and buying food takes all our money. I can't repay my college loans or make the car payments. We have to find something cheaper," he apologized, feeling he'd failed.

They moved to a two-bedroom apartment with a swimming pool, a child's splash pool, and a sand yard with swings. The monthly rent was half that of the house.

In less than a year the car loan was paid, some of the college loan was behind them, and money was accumulating in their savings.

"Now we can look for a home," Ivan said.

Finding a beautiful, large affordable home that had been repainted inside and out was a highlight for Ivan. He went through the process and bought it.

"Why should we rent and lose the monthly payments?" he told his wife. "We can deduct it on our income tax and have our equity growing by owning."

She didn't understand but sensed that he knew more about money than she did. She was pleased with the big house for her family.

The house had three bedrooms, two baths, and a large extra room where the garage had been.

Ivan was now vested in America. He had bought his own home and secured his first mortgage.

The home was wonderful for the children. The neighbors provided at least ten youngsters for playmates. Most every day someone was at the door wanting a playmate.

"Can Theresa come outside to play?" always surprised Ivan and Kathy. Theresa was still a baby under two years old.

After the first week in June Kathy said, "Ivan, you have an air-conditioned office and might not realize it but it's hot! Most of our days are spent sleeping. From eleven in the morning until four no one can move. Is there some way we can cool off? Like a pool maybe."

"Either a pool or an air-conditioner," he answered. "Not both."

"A pool would be better," she said.

After shopping for several months, and talking with five pool representatives, they decided on a company. The pool they selected was to be made of gunite with a twenty-two feet wide shallow area for the children. The other end was eight feet deep but only eleven feet wide with a springboard for diving. There would be two sets of ledges acting as seats. One would be an extension of the shallow end steps. The other seat would also serve as a deep end step across from a built-in ladder.

Work began and was finished quickly. The pool was beautiful. Maintaining it became Ivan's exercise since he wasn't fond of swimming.

The children learned to swim. Theresa was two years old, Tony four, Pavel five. They loved swimming. Whenever the weather was warm they were in the water.

Ivan's job at Aerojet was challenging and interesting.

After four years Kathy begged, "Ivan, look at this help wanted ad in our local paper. Wouldn't a move from here be healthy for the whole family?"

"I think you're right. Sounds like a good job and back in the Midwest. A college community would be fun again."

He called the number in the ad before work.

Answering the phone, a man said, "We're headed to San Francisco for another round of interviews this afternoon."

"Would you talk to me today?" Ivan queried.

"We are finished here," was the response. "What credentials or experience do you have for us to even be interested?" the interviewer asked.

"I graduated from the University of Illinois at Champaign-Urbana four years ago. These last four years I have...," and he enumerated the things he had learned and produced at Aerojet.

"Come see us tomorrow," Ivan heard. "If you can get here at nine in the morning we'll wait for you. You sound as if you know what you're talking about and have the skills we're looking for in medical electronics at the University of Missouri, Columbia Medical Center. We'll postpone leaving for a day."

"Wow!" Ivan said, replacing the phone after getting instructions to the downtown Los Angeles interview location. "They'll stay to talk with me. I'll take the day off tomorrow." He went to work that day with more enthusiasm than usual.

The next day, Ivan reported, "The interviewer was pleased with my background. We talked for a long time about the electronics with which I'm familiar. It was good talking to someone other than my co-workers."

"What did he say?" Kathy wanted to know.

"About what?" Ivan responded.

"About you working for them?"

"Well, nothing really. He said that they are going to San Francisco and Sacramento. Then to Moscow, Idaho, to interview more candidates. There's only one position they're trying to fill, in cardiology." Ivan recalled. "He told me that after they get back to Columbia, Missouri and confer with other department people they'll make their decision. I'll be called after that. It should be about six weeks."

"Six weeks!" Kathy replied, surprised. "I don't think I can wait that long to find out."

Laughing, Ivan said, "Of course you can, silly."

Two weeks later Ivan came whistling through the door after work.

"Hi, everyone!" he said. "I'm home."

When his wife came to meet him he put his arms around her and smiled.

"Guess what?" he said. "I got a call from the medical center at the University of Missouri today."

"You did? Why?"

"They want us both to go to Columbia as soon as possible for my second interview."

"Why do they want me to go?" Kathy asked.

"They said they want you to look around town to see if you like it."

"Have they offered you the job?"

"I think so. I mean it's up to me if I want the job. So, yes, I guess they did."

"I thought you said they would call in six weeks. Why did they call so soon?"

"Well, apparently when the interviewer called from Idaho before going back they asked for a rundown of the men that had been interviewed." Ivan explained. "When the doctor who's looking for an electronic design engineer heard about me, he said, 'I want to call him right away. Someone is going to grab that young man and he has all the qualifications I need for this program.' So he called.

"Can you get someone to watch the children next weekend from Friday through Sunday night? That's when I'd like to go."

Flying to Missouri on a commercial plane, Ivan was in the window seat, his wife of eight years snuggled next to him.

Ivan began thinking as he looked out the window.

"Remember this number for me," he said, giving her the number. A few minutes later he requested the remembered number, then gave her another one to remember.

"What are you doing?' she asked curiously.

He answered, "I saw all that empty space down there. I know the ratio between land and water. I know the world population so I was calculating how many people live on a square mile of land."

"I thought this was our belated honeymoon!" she whined in mock disappointment. "We never took one and this is the first time we've been without the children in seven years. Except, of course, that horrible ride to Mexico in December, 1966, when my Mom died. I just want this trip to be romantic."

"So do I," he responded. "I think it is. You are here with me," he winked and smiled at her. "Doesn't that qualify as romantic? Our being together?"

Kathy wasn't sure what he meant. Was he teasing? Was he serious? She decided it didn't matter what he meant. It was simply nice to be with him without anyone else needing him.

While Ivan interviewed, Kathy went to the administration building of the undergraduate campus.

"Is it possible for me to complete my bachelor's degree in biology for teaching?" she asked. "I have all the requirements except for American History and practice teaching."

"Yes, you can graduate with a lifetime teaching certificate after one full school year. It will take that long because there are Missouri requirements for educators."

When Ivan's interview was over, he said, "I accepted the job. It sounds interesting and will be helpful to rural doctors who don't know much about cardiology. My boss is excited about my getting started."

"Shall I stay in California with the children until the house sells?" Kathy asked.

"No, that won't work. You will all come when I do. We aren't going to worry about our house. It will sell when it sells. In the meantime we have to get a house here."

A realtor gave them his multi-list book.

"Giving this book to people to read is not our usual practice. Don't tell anyone. It could mean my license but you folks are pressed for time."

Looking through the borrowed book in their hotel room Friday night after the interview, they found a house on a third of an acre that they wished to see.

The realtor took them to the house.

"Look!" Kathy said in every room, "It's perfect! It feels like home to me. The patio with its big brick BBQ will make outdoor entertaining so much fun. Look at the tree house down by the creek. The kids will love this place."

"That section near the tree house would be a great vegetable garden, too," Ivan added.

On Sunday they returned to their family in California with tales of the new home the children would love.

"The tree house is at least fifteen feet up. There is a huge yard in which to play. It's partly in the country."

The children seemed to be excited about going to a new home where they would have a larger yard to play in.

"We'd like to rent your house after you leave," friends in California said. "We'll pay you what we pay now in rent."

"Even with the mortgage payments, the pool loan payments, and the projected maintenance costs, what you offer is excessive," Ivan said. "We have to accept less. We, in turn, will have the satisfaction of having our home cared for and we won't waste money and time looking for a renter."

"That's unbelievable," the friends said. "How can we rent a house with a pool and more space than the one we've been in for less money?"

"Sometimes what money buys fools you," Ivan responded.

The next weekend was a flurry of work.

Ivan told Kathy," Take the children to the neighbors with you for the day. I don't want them in the way while we're moving."

He and a friend did the work. One load was packed into a U-Haul truck. Then the two went to the friend's house four blocks away.

They loaded his pick-up and returned to the house to unload. The process was repeated until both households were almost moved.

Because of the fatigue brought on by the long heavy work the friend carried a chair to the patio and closed the sliding door after re-entering the house. When he tried to go back outside, forgetting that the door was closed, he crashed through the door, cutting his face and arms severely.

Work stopped as Ivan and his friend raced to the local hospital for stitches and observation.

"That was such a dumb thing to do," his friend said.

"It wasn't dumb. You are exhausted. It could happen to anyone. You just get yourself fixed up and get well."

When the doctor decided that his patient had recovered enough to leave they went back to the house.

Fortunately, everything had been moved from the one house to the other.

"You stay here and rest," Ivan said. "Your bed is in place and I don't need help to finish what's left."

Ivan continued moving boxes into the U-Haul.

Their new black Rambler sedan was attached behind the U-Haul.

It was eight o'clock that night when work was done.

"Good night," Ivan said to his friend.

The friend and his family slept in their new home that night.

Instead of leaving at five o'clock in the evening as planned Ivan, Kathy, and the three children camped on the living room floor until three in the morning. Quietly, so as not to awaken the others, they left.

"This is some adventure," Kathy said, hours into the drive outside the populated area. "I feel like a pioneer with Pavel lying at our neck on top of the back of the seat, Theresa sitting between us, and Tony curled on the floor at my feet."

"I'm glad you're seeing a bright side to this because it will take at least four days to get to Missouri," Ivan said. "This U-Haul truck won't even go the speed limit. There is a regulator on it so that we won't go too fast."

"I hope Pinkie is okay in our Rambler back there," one of the children said.

"I'm sure she is," Kathy answered. "She has her kitty litter pan, water, and food."

"When we stop for the night we will let her come in the room with us. She'll be fine," Ivan said.

When Ivan saw a park at lunchtime they stopped to let the children play. Once they went into a small zoo and enjoyed the animals for an hour or two before moving on.

They drove on, stopping as needed, toward their new home.

22. Missouri

Weary and aching from the slow drive controlled by the regulated speed of the U-Haul, Ivan stretched as he stepped into the cul-de-sac from the car.

"I'll get the key and we'll move in," he informed his family.

Answering the door, the previous homeowner asked, "What are *you* doing here? Our new home isn't ready for us. You can't stay here."

"This is the day of occupancy according to our contract," Ivan stated. His wife and three young children with all their possessions were in the street waiting.

"You can't stay here," the man repeated. "Get a motel for a week or so. We'll move as soon as we can."

Not only tired from the grueling drive but now also disappointed with his fellow man, Ivan turned away with a resolve to make the best of this latest situation.

It seems like I am really never free, he mused on the way into town where the motels were. *One thing or another dictates what happens. I'm always adjusting what needs to be done from someone else's perspective.*

"There's only one room in town for tonight," the desk clerk told him after checking his motel and all the others.

"It's Friday of Homecoming weekend. This is a college town. The game is tomorrow. All motel rooms everywhere in the city are booked for Saturday too. You can stay tonight but not tomorrow," he said sympathetically.

"What do you recommend we do?" Ivan asked later on the phone with the real estate agent that had sold him the house.

"Today is the day your contract states that you have the legal right to stay in your home."

"But they won't let us," Ivan explained.

"Tomorrow you go and don't leave!" the agent said. "Legally he has to let you move in."

The next day Ivan acted on the realtor's advice.

"The contract states that as of yesterday this was legally our home."

"What are we, my wife and I, supposed to do?" the previous owner countered.

"That is not my concern. I have a family and this is my house. What action do I have to take to live here?" Ivan said.

His family was allowed to move their mattresses into the walkout basement and sleep there until "further notice."

"Why isn't the downstairs bathroom finished?" Ivan asked the builder on the third day.

"I haven't had time. I'm building my house five blocks away. It is taking longer than I thought it would. In two to three weeks we can move to our new house. Then I'll finish the bathroom," he promised.

The bathroom was rough-framed. Ivan felt uncomfortable with a verbal agreement but decided that he would not make an issue of it.

The builder was back two weeks after he moved out. Within days the bathroom was finished, and even painted.

The Ivanov family now lived in Missouri.

Ivan became immersed in studying heart disease and how he, as an electrical engineer, could be helpful in solving a major problem facing many Americans, the problem of getting good cardiac care to rural family doctors via telephone lines hooked up to computers for diagnoses, treatments, and prognoses.

His work was rewarding.

On the homefront, the children were thriving in the clean air of rural America. Pinkie the cat was the family pet but Ivan wanted to get another more interesting animal for the family.

To surprise the children he and Kathy went to a pony farm in a nearby community. Making a decision on which baby pony to take was difficult. There were at least thirty to choose from. Ivan squatted, getting to the ponies' eye level.

"We've got to take this brown, fuzzy fellow," Ivan laughed as the pony tried to climb into his lap placing front hoofs on his leg. Had Ivan not stood, perhaps the hind feet would have followed.

"What about that one?" Kathy asked.

"Oh," Ivan responded. "She's so curious, but look how shy she is. She wants to come to us, you can tell, but she seems afraid."

He lowered himself again, and called softly to the little white one with the huge eyes. She took a few steps toward him, stopped, waited, and walked close enough for him to touch her. Her focus on him was intense but she came no closer.

"We'll take two, the brown and the white," he told the farmer.

The ponies jumped into the car and were easily transported in the back seat.

When the young ponies bounced out of the car at home the children were delighted.

"It's going to be fun to take care of 'Snow White' and 'Cocoa,'" they said.

"It will take consistency and work," Ivan reminded them.

"That's Okay. We will get up early before school to carry water and grain to them. After school we'll take hay and more water," Tony and Pavel promised.

"I will help," Theresa said. "I'm not too little."

As she had confidently stated she was not too little. She was the first up and dressed to tend to 'her' ponies.

Each day they carried four buckets of water, a cup of grain, and a flake of hay down the sloping back yard and up to the paddock that had been loaned to them as the ponies' 'home'.

Kathy watched her industrious children from the kitchen window, marveling at their strength and dedication. She laughed when the water sloshed over the lip of a too full bucket. In a few days the boot-shod children had the knack. They knew just how full they could fill the five-gallon buckets to get all the water to the ponies.

Poison ivy grew profusely around the paddock.

Nothing seemed to stop it. After trying to dig it out and finding that method ineffective Ivan poured gallons of weed killer on it only to find that it proliferated in other areas.

"We can't continue going to the ponies," Kathy told Ivan after several weeks of unsuccessfully trying to eradicate the noxious weed. "Pavel and I are sensitive to poison ivy. Without our helping with the feed and water Tony and Theresa have more than they can handle. It's hard work for children so young. I feel terrible."

With the poison ivy and other activities requiring Tony and Theresa's time, the ponies had to be sold.

Snow White and Cocoa went together to a home with children to love them.

Theresa especially was sad when her ponies were sold. The whole family felt the loss.

Columbia offered excellent education for Ivan's children. All three loved school and learning.

At work, Ivan heard about an AAU swimming program within the community.

"Would you like to see the swim team practice?" Ivan asked.

"Yes," all three said in unison.

"I really miss swimming," Tony replied. "Our pool in California was there whenever we wanted. Now we hardly ever get to swim."

Pavel said, "Swimming is fun. I like it. I don't know if I want to race, though."

Standing at the rail of Hickman High School Pool, Tony was mesmerized.

"I want to join them," said the seven-years-old.

214

The workouts were hard, sometimes two hours long and often at six o'clock in the morning. Nothing daunted his enthusiasm to swim as much as he was allowed to.

After a few weeks Pavel decided that he wanted to join and began to practice with his brother.

Watching the first meet, Theresa, then six said, "Mommy, let me join them."

"There aren't any children your age, Honey. They are all at least eight."

"I don't care. Pleeease."

The next meet little Theresa stood on the outdoor pool deck in her white swimsuit poised for her first race.

"What's *she* doing there?" Ivan asked surprised.

"She's racing," Kathy said.

She flew off the edge like an angel, feet first rather than a dive.

After one race that year a news photographer took her picture as she toweled her hair dry. It was a twenty-five yard freestyle race for ten-year-old-and-under swimmers.

"Did I win?" was the caption under the picture printed in the local sports section. She hadn't, but because there weren't any other swimmers in the pool when she finished and because she didn't fully understand the process, she had hopes.

"You are a winner!" the reporter had responded.

A few years later Theresa broke a pool record.

Swim meets became the Ivanov's weekends. In summer they were held either in their "home" pool at Hickman High School or in communities as far as two hundred miles away requiring motel stays. The nearest meets were thirty miles away in Jefferson City, Missouri. In winter there were fewer meets but they continued practicing and competing perhaps once a month, becoming top AAU competitors in their age groups.

There were Cub, Webelo, Brownie, and Junior Girl Scouts, bowling and softball leagues, summer track programs, and piano lessons for Ivan's children. Theresa had baton and dance lessons.

Little had Ivan realized that his life would revolve around his children's interests and activities. Where was the elusive freedom he had expected so long ago?

Through all the busyness of extra activities the children found time to excel in their schoolwork.

The family was like a well-tuned machine.

Kathy finished her biology degree. She began teaching in a local junior high school and was home when their children arrived on the school bus.

Teaching, she developed flu symptoms. Nothing she ate stayed down.

The doctor looked surprised when he examined her.

"How could you *not know* you were pregnant?" he asked. "With three other children weren't you suspicious?"

"Well, no, I wasn't," she said. "I was busy teaching and taking care of my home and family. I guess I didn't have time to think about it. We want a baby anyway before we get too old to have another."

The pregnancy caused the termination of her teaching contract at Spring Break. It was school policy.

Waiting until August for the second daughter's birth was easy. There were swim practices and meets.

Pavel had chosen to play the drums in the fifth grade band. Practice started in early July.

"I feel bad but I have no strength to take Pavel to practice mid-morning and then pick him up. With everything else, this is impossible," Kathy told Ivan.

"Your health is important. We won't let him continue with the band. With swimming, bowling, scouts, and the piano he has plenty to do," Ivan said.

"I know, but he likes it."

They talked to their eldest who agreed to drop his band activity.

Two busy weeks passed.

"Ivan, meet me at the doctor's office after work. My check-up is at five-thirty. Since I'm in labor he'll tell me to go to the hospital. I'll have my bag with me. You can take me to the hospital and get my car home later." Kathy excitedly reported mid-August.

Coming from the doctor's office Kathy shook her head. "He says I'm not in labor. Let's go home."

After eating a bowl of canned chili Kathy excused herself.

" I'll lie down and wait awhile," Kathy said. "If this isn't labor the feeling will go away. Finish your meal."

In ten minutes Kathy returned to the kitchen, bag in hand.

"We're going to the hospital. Don't call the doctor. They can get him after we check in."

"Kids, clean the table!" Ivan ordered.

"There's no time." Kathy said.

"It won't take long." Ivan responded.

The children cleared the dishes.

In their Fiat sports car the family of five raced across town. The three children were crammed into the space for the convertible top behind the two front bucket seats.

They felt every bump in the road as they sat two feet above it...and then they crossed the railroad tracks.

"Honey, hurry," Kathy begged, as she began the second stage of labor.

They ran across the parking lot of the hospital, Kathy in the lead. At the desk Ivan promised the clerks he'd return to check her in. He joined the rest of his family in the elevator.

At the floor below Obstetrics Ivan and the children got off the elevator.

Kathy stepped out on the next floor and was rushed to a labor room. Ivan came in, breathless.

"Sweetie, I'll take the kids home and be right back," Ivan said hurriedly kissing his wife. "The nurse says we have plenty of time. I left the kids watching TV in the waiting room downstairs."

He left.

There wasn't time.

A nurse found him, telling him to wait with his children.

Twenty minutes later the nurse called him from the waiting room.

Ivan reported to his children that they had a baby sister, Aleesa.

The family of six was complete.

The next day the older children, seven, soon-to-be nine, and ten years old, waved to Aleesa through the hospital window as Kathy held her.

The baby became her siblings' mascot, accompanying them to their activities.

"I am proud of my children. They are strong, healthy, polite, and intelligent," Ivan said. "They work hard and aren't afraid of life."

Then, unexpectedly, the government grant for developing medical electronics expired without renewal.

"With no funding we no longer have work in cardiology electronics," the doctor told Ivan. "Check for work at the university."

Coming home one evening, Ivan said, "I've been hired to teach an electrical engineering lab class."

"That sounds impressive," Kathy said.

"I think I'll like working with students again. The evening classes I taught at Citrus College in California were enjoyable. I've been given a lot of freedom with the lab. I get to set it up and teach any way I think the students will benefit."

The shift in focus was like a vacation for him. Ivan enjoyed his new position.

"While you're here," the department head said to him, "Take more courses. They are free for employees."

He studied the math and engineering classes that appealed to him, always enjoying the mental challenge.

Life became a marathon, like that of many active American families in the sixties. Activities filled almost every evening and weekend.

"Why don't you get your master's degree?" his boss asked one day.

Talking with Kathy he said, "Two more classes in math and a thesis project could earn the degree. I wasn't interested in it earlier but now that it's close I think I'll do it."

Two years after Aleesa's birth, the university life and the department politics became oppressive to Ivan.

"I don't want to play their games," Ivan told his wife.

"Everyone else in the department has a Ph.D. so my bachelor's degree is meaningless to them. Even with the master's degree close they look down on my ability. They act as if I can't contribute anything.

"They expect me to buy electrical components for the lab that we don't need, to use up our federal funds. If the money isn't spent it won't be given to the university the next year.

"There's a student who knows he doesn't understand the basics but wants to. Even with my volunteer tutoring he hasn't passed my class. He is willing to take it again but the dean wants me to pass him. If the dean thinks he needs to pass, then *he* can change the grade. I won't be responsible for a student doing poorly after his education.

"If I don't spend all Saturday working at my master-degree-board chairman's home doing household repairs for him, he says he won't approve my thesis.

"I thought that living in America and working as an electrical engineer I'd be free but now it doesn't look that way."

"Why don't we move? You can find another job," Kathy responded. "The kids will adjust. You need to find work that is rewarding again."

"I have too many responsibilities. That's part of the problem. With you and the four children it isn't easy to pick up and leave. Last time only Pavel was in school and he was just beginning. Now only Aleesa can move easily."

Several months later, after almost eight years in Missouri, a student told Ivan about opportunities with Tektronix, an oscilloscope company in Beaverton, Oregon.

"I'll arrange an interview with them," Ivan told his wife and family. "I'm not saying I'll take another job but it might be interesting to look." His voice held excitement; something that had been lacking for the last two and a half years.

Within a month Ivan was on his way to Oregon for the interview.

Returning home he was exuberant. "You'll love it there!" he told his family. "There are trees. Many trees! It is a forest. My motel window faced woods. There are hills. It is beautiful. There is a lot of water."

Looking out her window the day after Christmas, the two-year-old, Aleesa, saw a 'For Sale' sign in the yard. She believed Santa Claus had left it. Years would pass before she mentioned her childish error to anyone in the family.

Soon the movers came, packing up their household belongings.

The children, old enough to be sad at leaving friends, said their good-byes.

Ivan and Kathy also had regrets at leaving close friends. Most of their friends were concerned for them.

"It isn't safe in Oregon," they said. "There are wild animals roaming the hills. Life is difficult there."

"It's modern and settled," Ivan laughed. "We'll be fine."

"Oregon floods are all over the news," the friends reminded them.

"I guess we'll, uh-hum, cross **that** bridge when we come to it," Ivan retorted, a twinkle in his eye. "We promise to be careful where we settle."

It was January when the family of six, with Theresa's new black cat, named "Midnight," climbed into their Chevy station wagon and once again headed West.

23. OREGON

The January wind on the high plateaus along the northern route whirled the snow across the highway like cotton candy blowing inside its kettle. It flew off the ground up to ten or twelve feet high, dancing and playing like clothes drying on a line in a spring wind.

From a cozy bed the next morning one of the children moaned, "It's too cold!"

Looking out the window at the three-foot drifts another asked, "With all this snow won't we slide all over the road?"

"If we leave quickly, we should be okay," Ivan told his family.

He was right. It was a cold snow, no ice.

Watching the snow flurries around them they were thankful for the luxurious warmth of their car.

Even Midnight had her luxuries: a litter pan, water, and food.

The road became clear but the air was sharp and as crisp as a good apple.

Their spirits were good. The children sang and laughed as they traveled when they weren't sleeping or playing games.

"You've got to see what this motel has," Ivan told his family after registering for the night.

"What's so special about a motel?" someone asked.

"Let's get ready for a swim. Then I'll tell you."

"Is that it? It has a swimming pool?"

"Wait. You'll see."

"This is a fantastic pool," Pavel said. "I've heard of these. And that huge window!"

"What a view! Look at the snow on those mountains. Are they the Rockies?" Kathy asked.

"It's hard to see clearly with all the steam coming off the water in the outside pool. Let's go out there," Ivan said, diving under the wall separating the indoor pool from its outdoor counterpart. He resurfaced outside, laughing amidst the steam. "Come on over."

Tony and Theresa dove, with Pavel on their heels. Kathy asked Aleesa, "Can you hold your breath to get to the other side?"

"Sure! Let's go, Mom!" said the three and a half-year-old swimmer.

Holding hands mother and daughter dove under the wall to the outer pool.

Cold, exhilarating air filled their lungs. What an adventure!

The next day their travel resumed.

Passing through Portland, coming out of a tunnel on their way toward Beaverton the family was astonished at the lush vegetation.

"We were in snow and ice yesterday. Now look at this," Ivan said.

"Is this a jungle?" Kathy asked. "Look at the giant ferns and the other underbrush. The trees are huge."

"What's that green stuff hanging on the trees?"

"It might be moss."

The family had never seen things like these.

Beaverton seemed flat compared to what they had traveled through but all around were high hills covered with houses and trees.

"Here's the temporary lodging Tektronix arranged for us," Ivan said, pulling into the Satellite Motel. "We have two rooms."

"Pavel and Tony, you share one bed," Kathy told her sons. "The other is for you, Theresa and Aleesa. In the mornings come to our room next door. We have a well stocked kitchen and will eat there."

After settling their luggage, Tony asked, "Can we go to the ocean now?"

"That sounds Okay," Ivan responded. "Do the rest of you want to go? We've driven only five hours today. I'm ready if you are."

"Yes!" the others chorused.

Back into the car, they were off. A little over an hour and the afternoon sun glinted off the restless water. The salty spray from the waves raced inland on the wind, kissing their faces.

"Let's go wading," Tony said, taking off his shoes and socks. He rolled his jeans up as far as he could and took off, running to the water.

"It's cold," Pavel called, laughing.

"But it's the ocean!" Theresa responded.

"Yeah! It's January, too!"

Ivan watched his playful youngsters as they enjoyed their first contact with Oregon seawater.

They came to love the Pacific coast.

There were harvests of clams and crabs to catch on weekends. Idle hours of sunbathing and sand tunneling were part of most beach trips. The picnics on Cannon Beach would prove mostly gritty, as sandwiches became 'sand witches'

Summer 1998, Ivan demonstrates his love of soccer at Cannon Beach, Oregon

in the unstoppable wind. Hunting beautiful agates, shells, and driftwood at various beaches would become an interest. There were to be fishing trips to the south jetty and one special deep sea-fishing trip for the older children.

Back at the motel Ivan said, "I want to live within a two mile radius of Tektronix, so that I can ride my bike to work as I did at the university. We have these motel rooms at Tek's expense for a week but I'd like to find a place we can stay until we decide where to be permanently. It might take time to find the right house."

"While the children are in school and you are at work, I can look for a house with Aleesa. If we find one we like you can look at it in the evening," Kathy responded.

The family drove around Beaverton the next day looking for apartments.

"Stop there," Kathy said. "The sign says they accept children."

Ivan stopped.

Kathy ran to the manager's door. When the manager opened, Kathy said, "We see that children can live here. Can we have our four children in a two-bedroom place? We expect to rent for no more than three months."

"If you can manage with four kids in two bedrooms you're welcome here," the manager stated. "Let me get the key to the unit we have available."

The two women went into the apartment.

"We'll take it," Kathy said.

"That was quick. Are you sure?" the manager asked, laughing at the sudden decision.

"It's all the room we need."

Ivan contacted the moving company who put the mattresses on the bedroom floors and the TV on the kitchen counter.

They had been in Oregon for less than a week.

"You kids have this larger bedroom. The four mattresses leave no room. You'll have to walk on each other's mattresses to get to your own. Be sure to take off your shoes."

"Will you deliver my kitchen things?" Kathy asked as the movers were leaving.

"If you are home this afternoon."

"Yes, I didn't realize you would be here so soon."

The 'kitchen things' were eight boxes and the dinette table and chairs.

"Where do you want these boxes?" the movers asked after setting the table and chairs in the eating nook.

"I guess they have to go into the living room. Put the TV on one of the boxes."

Finishing the task, the men left.

When Ivan got home from work that night he looked at the box-filled living room and laughed, "What's this?"

"I told them to bring the kitchen things," she responded. "They brought all of them. I didn't have the heart to tell them to take back the extra boxes. I found enough dishes, utensils, and cookware. I thought we'd leave the others packed until we settle in our home. We can watch TV from the floor or the eating area. There's room to get to the bathroom and bedrooms around the boxes. What more do we need?"

On Sunday after they had moved to the apartment Ivan said, "Tomorrow we'll get you registered for school before I go to work."

"Dad! Why do we have to start tomorrow? We just got here. We need to rest after this move."

"You're not missing any more school. You already missed a week. No more arguing."

The children resigned themselves to school the next day.

The busiest room in the apartment became the bathroom. Not only were there three school kids and one employee to be groomed but it was needed for privacy when dressing.

Early on Monday everyone was up and ready

Walking across the parking lot next to the apartment complex, the family went to the junior high school that was to be Pavel and Tony's.

In the office the receptionist told them, "This is our winter vacation. School won't start until next Monday."

"What about the elementary school?" Ivan wanted to know.

"They are out this week also. You may register the children today if you'd like."

"Thanks. Where is the closest elementary school for Theresa? She'll be in fifth grade."

"It is three and a half blocks from here," the receptionist said. "You'll need to go there to register your daughter. Registration doesn't take long."

On the way out of the junior high school the children happily taunted their father, "See! We don't have to go to school. We get a vacation!"

In March they moved to their new home, not quite two miles from work but in a different school area.

"We want to stay in *our* schools," all three said.

The district replied, "Fine, as long as you have private transportation you don't need to change. All the schools, the ones you are attending and the ones near your new home, are in our district but we cannot transport you to the old schools."

"Transportation will be your bikes," Ivan told his children. "I won't have your mom taking you to and from the old school just because you don't want to try a new one."

Every morning Ivan and the three school children left on their bikes, heading out for the day, rain or shine.

.   Their home was large with a yard big enough for the three active young teens and a younger girl.

During the first summer the children made friends close to their new home. Over the three months all three older children agreed it would be Okay with them to attend their local schools.

Theresa's elementary school was two blocks away. Getting there was safer for the sixth grader than going to her previous school.

Junior high school for Tony in eighth and Pavel in ninth grade was three blocks from home.

"I like to bike if no one is going to pick me up," Pavel stated.

"I agree," said Tony.

Many days there were friends stopping in the morning and they all walked together.

The boys participated in a season of football.

Theresa continued her piano lessons.

"I need to teach swimming," Kathy said. "My Red Cross WSI certification from Missouri is valid here. The extra income can pay for our dental work until we sell our old home. Aleesa can come and help with my daytime classes during the week."

Often Aleesa would help instruct tots older than she was.

Parents and children were in the class together, the parents holding their little ones. Aleesa loved demonstrating underwater swimming or the crawl stroke.

"You really help motivate the shy kids, Aleesa. When they see you swimming they figure that if you can do it they don't need to be fearful."

On weekends Aleesa stayed home with Ivan and the older children when Kathy worked.

Within a year someone asked Ivan, "Would you be willing to be a volunteer soccer coach for a group of young boys?"

"It's been years since I helped coach a team," he said. "I'd be happy to do what I can."

On Saturday mornings he worked with his group of soccer players. They began to understand the game from his Bulgarian perspective.

"It's not a game of kick and chase," he'd tell them. "Dribble the ball close to you, shield it with your body. Always know where your teammates are. Always be ready to pass and receive. Don't wait until you have possession of the ball. Move! Anticipate. Don't be afraid of the ball. Be aggressive. Move in and take it when your opponent doesn't keep it close to himself. You are always a part of the game when you are on the field, not just when you have control of the ball."

During other times he'd say, "There will not be any bad mouthing your teammates or anyone. Anybody who does that; he's out for the remainder of the game. The referee is always right, even when he's wrong. Never talk back to the referee. I won't tolerate any foul language. If I hear any you'll run a lap around the field."

"Do what I do," he would say leading them in fifteen minutes of personal skills. "I don't expect you to do anything I don't do." They ran the length of the field and up the small rise and down again, forward, backward, and sideways. They ran dribbling the ball straight ahead. They dribbled the ball through a pattern of cones. They jumped from one foot to the other tapping the ball in between jumps. He juggled; they juggled; on their feet, their knees, from their chests to their feet, from their feet to their heads.

Team skills took up the next fifteen minutes, with three players working together offensively, running, passing, receiving, and defending, two trying to steal the ball with one guarding and running.

At last Ivan would call out, "It's time for a thirty minute scrimmage."

The boys yelled in enthusiasm, "Yes, let's play!"

Each Saturday Ivan's team showed greater strength and more skill. He enjoyed coaching more than playing. When his team had lost three games with scores like 8-1 or 6-0 he said, "You are learning. Play the game. Don't worry about whether you win or lose. You will win when you play well."

They began winning. At first the wins were minimal, one or two points and not every game but by the end of the first season his team was one of the best in their league.

Even with all the time and energy spent with other people's children Ivan made time for his own.

"I want to buy our sons a TRS-80," Ivan said one Saturday after soccer season was over.

"What's that?" Kathy asked.

"It's a Radio Shack computer. The boys are young enough to learn quickly and old enough to realize its potential.

"Do you want to go with us to buy it?" he asked.

"No," she replied. "If you think it's a good idea just take them and buy it. It's good for the three of you to be alone together sometimes."

"Do you boys realize that computers are the future for you?" he told them as they bought their machine. "These machines will become the workhorses of industry. Learn all you can now. It will be a great investment for you."

From then on Pavel and Tony spent hours programming and playing with their new computer. They programmed ping-pong and other games, which they enjoyed together and with friends.

One day a swimming friend of Kathy's said, "I would love a teen-aged girl to exercise and groom my horse, Missy. She's getting fat and lazy. I don't take the time I should with her but I can't sell her. She's a spoiled pet. Would you bring your daughter to my house to work with her?"

As a surprise, Kathy took Theresa to meet the horse.

"Where are we going, Mom?"

"Somewhere."

"Why?"

"You'll know soon enough."

Down the dirt lane Theresa saw a white German Shepherd in the horse corral. Next to horses, dogs were her favorite animals.

"Oh, Mom, that's it, isn't it? The dog. You want me to meet that dog!" she said excitedly.

The horse's owner took Theresa into the corral.

They met Pepsi, the dog, at the gate.

Then Theresa saw the horse.

"A horse!" Theresa squealed, grinning from ear to ear as she looked back at her mother in disbelief.

Quickly the girl and the horse became friends. They both were 'green', learning their roles together.

Ivan loved horses, but as an engineer he had never had time for them and besides, his work had made him live in cities. The outskirts of Columbia had been an opportune time for ponies but in Portland he had not found a property that would support horses.

He loved watching his daughter ride and groom Missy.

When she had trained Missy and worked with her in a 4-H group Theresa said they were ready for the Washington County Fair.

The day of the 4-H horse events, Ivan, Kathy, and Aleesa were there, proud parents and sister of the young equestrian.

Theresa won a blue ribbon.

Ivan said," I couldn't be prouder of you. You've worked hard. It has paid off."

As Ivan's youngsters grew people would say, "Your children are respectful."

"Your children are helpful."

"How do you keep your children so involved in school and sports?"

"Thank you," he responded. "I haven't done anything except love them and show them respect."

He didn't try to analyze it but was glad for them.

"They'll go far," he said. "They have everything they will need when they are on their own."

Tony was finishing ninth grade when he came home one Spring day and said, "Mom, Dad, one of my teachers talked to me today about a camp. It is a Fellowship of Christian Athletes' Camp in Monmouth, Oregon. It's for a full week. The teacher said that the Lion's Club has given a free endowment to a student who qualifies. The qualifications are to be a good student, to be a good athlete, and to be a non-Christian. They suggested I go. I told the teacher I had to ask you first. So do you think I can go?"

Ivan looked at his maturing son.

"Do you want to go?" he asked.

"Yes, I like camping. I think it would be fun," Tony responded.

"It would be good for you to see how the other half lives," Ivan stated. Tony went.

After camp, Ivan and Kathy picked him up in downtown Portland.

"Mom," he said after getting home when Ivan had taken Aleesa bike riding. "I accepted Christ at camp. I'm a 'born again' Christian. I'm afraid to tell Dad. I think he might be angry with me."

"Is God good?" Kathy asked.

"Yes."

"Then God will make your father happy to hear whatever you tell him. You need to be open with him. Tell him."

Upon hearing, Ivan said, "It can't hurt."

Soon afterward Kathy developed some personal problems and began searching for help. Having seen Tony's attitude change and his apparent contentment, she sought God. She came to know that without doubt He existed. Something was still missing. She didn't know what.

Attending church with Tony one Sunday in September 1976, she heard that her problem was sin, that God cannot be reached by frail human effort but Jesus Christ died to save us from our sin and to set us right with God the Father. She trusted Jesus and accepted that her debt was fully paid by Him. He is the only door to the Father.

She was thrilled with her new purpose of living, to obey God, to love Him and others as God loved her. She explained to Ivan what had happened in her heart.

"I don't understand," he said. "I feel jealous of this Jesus."

"Would you rather have me like I was without Jesus or like I am now with Him?" Kathy asked.

"No question!" he quickly responded. "The way you are now is better than before. Nonetheless, let me ask you this, How would you like it if I started believing in one of the Greek goddesses, like Venus, and told you I love her and will live to please her?"

Ivan didn't know why she didn't answer for a long time. He wasn't going to ask.

Finally, she said, "I sense a deeper love for you now than I ever did before. Everything is in richer color and all my senses seem more alive. Venus, or any other man-made god, is not the One holy Creator. Of course I would feel jealous if you followed her because it would be her physical beauty you would be seeing. The Jesus of the Bible is real and is living right now. He has sent the Holy Spirit to mankind as He promised in the Bible. Jesus is God. I know it sounds impossible but it is His spirit that is fulfilling me and giving me a new life. I'm ashamed to have lived so long and not sought Him before this. But now I am here for you, for always, just as before, only better."

He embraced her and understood that she was still his wife. He was puzzled by her "Jesus" talk.

"As long as He doesn't come between us. That's all I'm concerned about," he said.

Each Sunday Kathy went to church with Tony, her Bible under her arm. Ivan stayed home with the three children who didn't want to go.

On the rare occasions when Ivan chose to go to church with his wife he would say after the service, "What the pastor said, I already knew."

The next Mother's Day Ivan told his children, "Today we will all honor your mother by going to church with her."

Theresa began joining Kathy and Tony on Sundays.

A few years went by.

Late in 1981, after Pavel and Tony were in college and Theresa was married, Kathy went to Ivan, "I would like to sing in the church choir. It would require an hour and a half one weeknight for rehearsal and singing at both Sunday morning services. There are several day 'performances' twice a year, at Easter and Christmas. Would you mind if I committed to the choir?"

"I think it would be good for you." he replied. "You would have something mid-week to look forward to."

On choir nights with Kathy gone, Ivan caught up on work that he brought home, studied his investments for his retirement years or relaxed with music or television.

Ivan worked in his yard and vegetable garden in season on the weekends. When it was cold he had inside projects.

From late September through April he managed his men's soccer team and played a game on Sunday afternoons. Phoning players before games, getting player rosters, having cones, nets, cards, and uniforms ready, driving to and from the game, showering and dressing took up the afternoon, from one o'clock to five-thirty.

Except for Saturdays, Ivan was not able to be with his family.

In 1984 Ivan told Kathy, "I want you to take Aleesa to Bulgaria to see my family and my country. She will see the village in which I was born and Sofia where I lived. I want you to go when school is out."

Aleesa was thirteen.

"It's still a Communist country," Kathy said. "Is it safe to go?"

"It is for you," he answered. "The people might cause problems for me, so I won't go. But I want one of our children to see my homeland."

Every other day for the three weeks they were in Bulgaria Ivan called to talk with his wife.

"It is good to hear your voice," he'd say. "Can you come home in a couple of days?"

"Honey, people are planning to see us. I have the plane tickets for our return. I'll be back then."

"I want you home now."

"But this trip was expensive. You wanted us to come. We haven't yet seen your relatives in Rogozen or Malorad. Enough, Sweetheart! We'll be home later. I love you and I miss you. We'll be back soon."

"Not soon enough," he said, sounding like a small boy.

When Ivan's phone rang a week before Kathy and Aleesa were due home, he answered.

"Ivanov residence."

"Hi, Sweetie. Would you like us home tonight?" Kathy asked.

"Are you serious? Where are you?" he almost shouted. "I'll be at the airport to pick you up. Just tell me when."

"We're at JFK in New York. I changed our tickets and we'll be home at ten o'clock Portland time. I love you. I can hardly wait to see you."

"Ten o'clock, I'll be there. I love you too, Sweetie. Why are you coming home early? You've only been gone five and a half weeks. What happened to next week?"

"Nothing," she replied. "We have been gone long enough. We have much to tell you. We don't want to stay in Massachusetts and New Jersey now. Maybe next year we'll visit Mom and Dad's families. Now we want to be home!"

"What did your aunts and cousins say?"

"They were disappointed but they seemed to understand. I told them we'd make another trip especially to see them. They seemed to be Okay with that. But they are getting older and I don't want to wait too long."

"I'll see you at ten o'clock! Thanks for calling." He hung up the phone and sat smiling for a long time.

Waiting for the passengers to get off the plane was difficult. Then she was in his arms. He held her in a long embrace.

When they finally looked at each other, both faces were radiant.

"It was a wonderful trip. Thank you. I learned a lot about you while I was gone," she said. "Your people are so loving and kind. They were happy to see us, more than happy. They are very generous. Bulgaria is not like America. Even Aleesa was different while we were there. And then Austria was beautiful and Greece...there is so much I want to tell you."

"It's good having you safely home again," he answered.

They didn't sleep that night. Questions had to be answered. Answers triggered more questions and so the night wore into daylight.

Two weeks later Ivan took his wife and daughter to a resort where he had rented a large house. The rest of the family met them there. The older three children brought their spouses. Ivan and Kathy's two grandchildren, still babies, came also.

They were all gathered to celebrate Ivan and Kathy's twenty-fifth wedding anniversary. The children had contributed towards the purchase of a large silver punch bowl and tray with twelve silver cups and a ladle, to provide a perfect silver anniversary gift. To cap the event, Ivan had told his children that he wanted them to take care of all the meals for the three-day weekend so that his wife would be free from concerns about food.

Over the next twelve years life went on. There were projects at work for Ivan. He was highly esteemed and thus rewarded with promotions and salary increases.

The couple elected to live simply, to live below their means and enjoy their lives.

Little by little Ivan experienced God tugging at his heart.

Pavel also came to know Jesus as his savior.

"Dad," he said one day after accompanying Ivan and Kathy to a church function. "I have something that the Lord has told me to tell you."

"Sure," Ivan said. "Let's go home."

"No, Dad. He wants me to tell you here."

"Okay."

"God loves you, Dad," he started, continuing until the gospel of Jesus had been made clear.

"Do you want to respond?" Pavel asked.

"You did a good job, Pav," Ivan said. "Thanks."

"I hope you aren't mad but I had to."

"You did fine, son."

For a week in June for four years, Ivan enjoyed a family camp with church people. He joined a Bible study group with folks older than himself and found that intelligent people also loved Jesus, like his wife and children seemed to. He learned a little about the Bible.

"Sweetie," Kathy said one day in December, "I bought a chronological Bible that is intended to be read for fifteen minutes a day, to complete it in a year. I'm going to start on January 1. Would you be interested in doing that, too?"

"I don't have much time for reading anything other than technical journals but it sounds fine," he said, taking the book and casually thumbing through it.

"I couldn't read a day's worth in less than an hour. The meanings of the words bogs me down. These readings are too long for me."

"That's okay, I just thought you might like to."

"I would like to know what the Bible says, cover to cover," he said.

"How about if I read to you every day before work. That way we would both hear it."

"That might be a good way. Let's try it and see. If we have to stop, we'll stop."

Early next December, Ivan said, "I don't know if you would like to but I'd like to read through the Bible again next year. Now that we've almost finished the New Testament, I think the things in the Old Testament will make more sense. I forgot some things and re-reading would fill in the gaps in my understanding. I want to re-read the prophecies that I now know were fulfilled."

Trying to disguise her enthusiasm, Kathy agreed to read for another year.

Completing the second year's reading, Ivan said, "I'm glad we read all of the Bible in order. I thought it was just a series of quotes and moral stories by which people could live. I found it to be a history of people. Knowing that makes a difference to me, somehow."

Sunday school teachers, pastors, and other Christians patiently answered his many questions.

Finally Ivan realized that believing in Jesus as his personal savior was a choice he could make only in faith. All of his questions could not be answered rationally, intellectually. The basic facts were consistent in the Bible. Believing what it said about Jesus was easy.

One day he knew where the journey of his life had taken him. He had been born in Bulgaria as the subject of a good king. He was basically free in a free country. Then everything had changed. His country was no longer free and certainly, he was not. He had escaped from the oppressive government in favor of freedom. He found that after he had escaped and had been put into jails and prisons he was lacking freedom more than ever. Believing that freedom was still possible and waiting for him, he had pressed on. Arriving in America he was free to do more than he had been allowed to do elsewhere. He chose school that freed him to learn and study but he wasn't really free. He had married and had to do what was needed for his wife and family whether he had wanted to or not. Was that freedom? Inside, he was still not free. Now he had come to freedom through faith in God. This freedom allowed him to do what was right rather than to do what he wanted, to his own destruction.

He had become free to thank God. He had gone from freedom to freedom. At last he was truly free, and would remain so throughout eternity.

July 2001, Ivan (right) with grand nephew, niece, and their son at Rila Monastery.

Family in Rogozen, August 2001. Ivan is second from right in glasses.

ENDNOTES

1 *Vahn' chose*: little Ivan's (*Ee vahn's*)

2 *Ro' go zehn:* village where Ivan was born in 1939

3 *Taht' ko*: Daddy

4 *Vrah' tsah:* town thirty miles from Rogozen halfway to Sofia, capital of Bulgaria

5 *Chee'-cho*: uncle (father's brother)

6 *O ree yah' ho vo*: the county seat

7 *me keet' see*: plural for *mekitsa*: fried bread

8 *boo zah'*: a specialty drink

9 *buch' vah* : a type of large wooden wine-storage barrel used in villages.

10 *rah kee' ah* brandy made from local fruit.

11 *o cah reen' ah* : mouth instrument with flute-like sound

12 *bah la lie' kah*: guitar-like instrument

13 *guy' dah*: (g as in great): bagpipes

14 *Ho ro'*: common circle dance

15 *bah' nee tsee*: sweet, salty confections

16 *Vlah' dee*

17 *Vahn' ko, Zah brah vahn' ko:* Little Ivan, little forgetter (Vancho and Vanko are both familiar names for Ivan)

18 *Kah de' o-tee'-vash:* where are you going?

19 Axis: Bulgaria was aligned with Germany and Japan in W.W.II. Russia was with the Allies. The Russians were pushing the Germans out of Eastern Europe through Bulgaria.

20 three kilometers: about two miles

[21] *Leh' lyah*: aunt: (father's sister)

[22] *Bope*: peasant's way of saying bean soup: more culturally: *fasoul* : *fah sool'*

[23] Meet-cohs

[24] Ket-you-shee

[25] Ghee or' ghee Dee mee troff': the revered leader of Bulgarian socialism likened to George Washington

[26] *Tee' ho*: Be quiet

[27] *kahsh-kah-vahl'*: a hard, uncolored, tasty cheese, similar in flavor to Parmesan

[28] Rye' kin skee: the clan name, similar to an American family name

[29] Vassil A. Vassilev, *Bulgaria-13 Centuries of Existence* (Sofia Press; 1979), p.28.

[30] Nicene Creed submitted by St. Nicholas Orthodox Church; 2210 SW Dolph Ct; Portland, Oregon

[31] *See nee do mah' tee*: blue tomatoes: eggplants

[32] *Buke luke'*: garbage

[33] *sah bore': village bazaar day*

[34] *shkem beh' chor bah'*: tripe soup

[35] *loo kahn' kah*: sausage

[36] Mah' Moe: (different case): 'o' ending used when speaking to someone

[37] *mee lee' tsee ah*: military police

[38] *Bah' bah*: Grandmother

[39] *Boo' bah lah zee*: Bug is walking: children's game: "Bugs are walking on you!"

[40] *Neh day! Ka' ko*: Don't! Sister.

[41] *Rahs boy nik*: mischief maker

[42] *Dee ah' doe*: grandfather

[43] *Nah rode' nee*: national

[44] *Renaissance Woman in the Classroom*, By Molly Winans: Encarte On line. Encarte Concise Encyclopedia: http://encarta.msn.com/index/concise/0vol0B/014a1000.asp. Several references used.

[45] *Col' hose*: communist collective farm

[46] *Tah' teh*: Dad

[47] *creme caramel* = caramelized custard

[48] *see' reh neh*: feta cheese

49 *voo ee' nah's:* mother's sister'

50 *loo tee' ka:* hot sauce

51 The village where relatives lived near Rogozen.

52 Deuteronomy 31:6 & Hebrews 13:5 KJV Bible

53 Vahn' ko: familiar form of Ivan, similar to Vancho: denoting an older child

54 *Tee' ho de te' to me:* Quiet, my child.

55 *soak:* dilute fruit juice

56 *stu teen' kee:* pennies

57 *key'-no:* movie

58 *Harmonica:* Accordion-like instrument, with buttons on both sides rather than on only one with keys on the other.

59 *Slahd car' nee tsa:* Sweet shop

60 about thirty yards

61 *Vee' toe shah:* mountain a few miles south of the city.

62 about fifty-four yards

63 *Dee nah' moe So' fee ah:* Sofia's soccer team which Ivan and his friend supported.

64 *Leb' vah:* dollars

65 *Do veej' deh neh:* Until we meet again

66 *leh' vah :* plural for *lev :* Bulgarian currency artificially set to a dollar, then 32 *leva* was worth $32.00

67 *stu teen' key:* cen'ts

68 *vo dah':* water

69 *hleb':* bread

70 *mle' chehn shah' co lahd:* milk chocolate

71 Zlatograd: large southern city south and east of Kurdzhali

72 Ker' jah lee: (j as in jelly) South Central city 30 mi. north of where the boys wanted to cross the border

73 Ee vahn' eh: nickname for Ivan

74 *mee lee' tsee ah:* government military, the only police in Bulgaria at that time

75 Ko mo tin knee': city in NE Greece, region of Thrace

76 Xan-thi': city 60 miles due S. of Plovidiv, Bulgaria in N. Greece

77 *rahm-vai' :* light rail

78 The doctrine that there is no God.

79 Dra' ma: Town halfway between Komotini and Thessaloniki

[80] Yes, I speak Bulgarian. I am called Borko (familiar for Boris).

[81] The sah lo nik' ee: second largest Greek city, located on the eastern side of Gulf of Salonika in Northern Greece.

[82] Ivane! Kak see? = Ivan! How are you?

[83] KP = kitchen patrol, usually pealing potatoes, and cutting them.

[84] Popeto = Poe' peh toe means 'the preacher'

[85] Georgo = Ghee-or'-go

[86] Son. Literally small boy.

[87] Bo'-by = short for Borislav

[88] Chicago Loop's elevated light rail train.

[89] Ivan Ivanov = Eye'-vun Eye'-vun-off

[90] Ivan Pavlov = Ee-Vahn' Pahv-loff'

[91] Kakvo e tova = kak-vo' eh to-va' = What is that?

[92] Blagodaria = Blag-o-dahr'-ria = thank you.

[93] American College Dictionary; p. 487

[94] Kale mera -kah le meh'-rah = good morning

[95] Te kan is - Tee kahn' ees = How are you?

[96] progymnasium= pro gihm nah' sium=school in Bulgaria equivalent to high school in America.

[97] Ochi Chornia = Russian song ="Dark Eyes"